ST(P) MATHEMATICS 1B

ST(P) MATHEMATICS series

ST(P) 1A
ST(P) 1B
ST(P) 1A Teacher's Notes and Answers
ST(P) 1B Teacher's Notes and Answers

ST(P) 2A
ST(P) 2B
ST(P) 2A Teacher's Notes and Answers
ST(P) 2B Teacher's Notes and Answers

ST(P) 3A
ST(P) 3B
ST(P) 3A Teacher's Notes and Answers
ST(P) 3B Teacher's Notes and Answers

ST(P) 4A
ST(P) 4B
ST(P) 4A Teacher's Notes and Answers
ST(P) 4B Teacher's Notes and Answers

ST(P) 5A (with answers)
ST(P) 5B (with answers)

ST(P) 5C
ST(P) 5C Copy Masters
ST(P) 5C Teacher's Notes and Answers

ST(P) Resource Book

ST(P) MATHEMATICS 1B

L. Bostock, B.Sc.

S. Chandler, B.Sc.

A. Shepherd, B.Sc.

E. Smith, M.Sc.

Stanley Thornes (Publishers) Ltd

First published in 1990 by:
Stanley Thornes (Publishers) Ltd
Ellenborough House
Wellington Street
CHELTENHAM GL50 1YW
UK

98 99 00 / 10 9

British Library Cataloguing in Publication Data
ST(P) mathematics 1B
1. Mathematics
I. Bostock, L.
510

ISBN 0-7487-0143-5

Typeset by Tech-Set, Gateshead, Tyne & Wear.
Printed and bound in Great Britain at Redwood Books, Trowbridge.

CONTENTS

INTRODUCTION

This is the first book in a series designed for use in secondary schools. This book is intended for use in the first year of secondary education (year 7) and starts at the beginning of Level 4 of the National Curriculum in mathematics.

Together with books 2B and 3B, the series aims to prepare pupils to achieve about Level 6 for tests at the age of 14 plus (i.e. Key Stage 3, at the end of year 9). Books 4B and 5B continue the work necessary to achieve the intermediate levels at GCSE.

There are plenty of straightforward exercises, with questions divided into two types.

The first type, identified by plain numbers, e.g. **12.**, helps you to see if you understand the work. These questions are considered necessary for every chapter you attempt.

The second type, identified by a single underline, e.g. <u>**12.**</u>, are extra, but not harder, questions for quicker workers, for extra practice or for later revision.

Most chapters end with mixed exercises. These will help you revise what you have done, either when you have finished the chapter or at a later date.

Finally a word of advice: when you arrive at an answer, whether with the help of a calculator or not, always ask yourself 'Is my answer a reasonable one for the question that was asked?'

1 SYMMETRY

LINE SYMMETRY

These drawings are symmetrical. If they were folded along the broken line, one half would fit exactly over the other half.

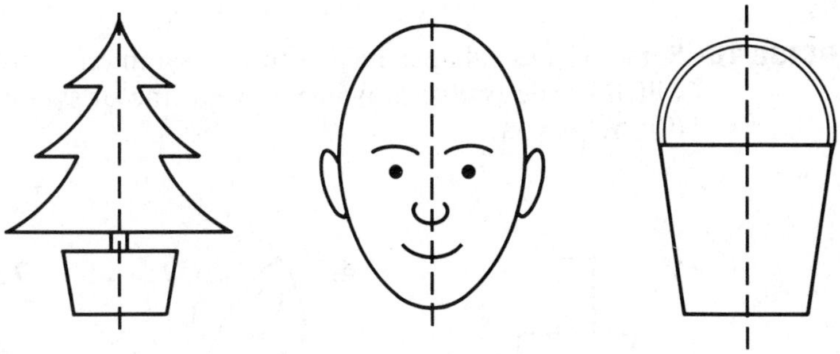

EXERCISE 1a In this exercise you can place a mirror along each dotted line to help you to answer the question. In each question state whether or not the dotted line is a line of symmetry.

1.

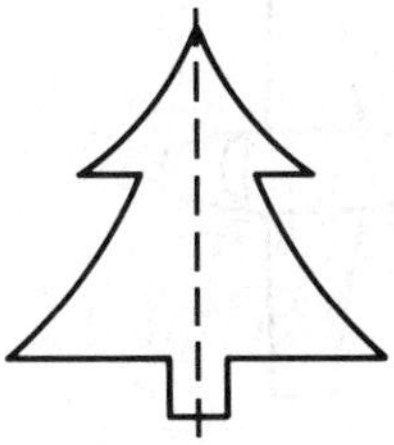

2.

3.

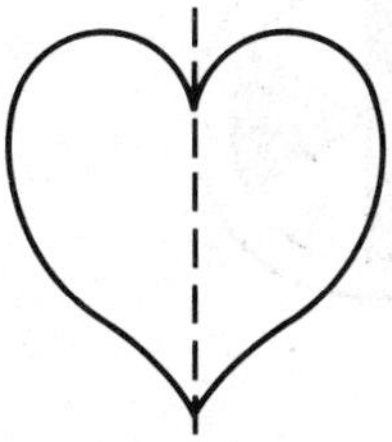

4.

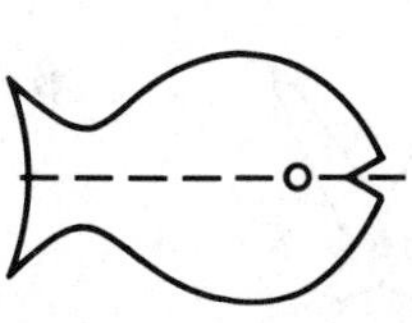

5.

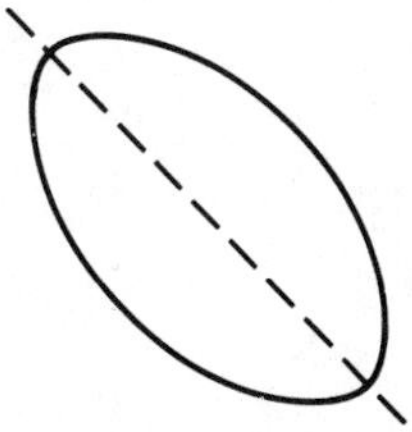

6.

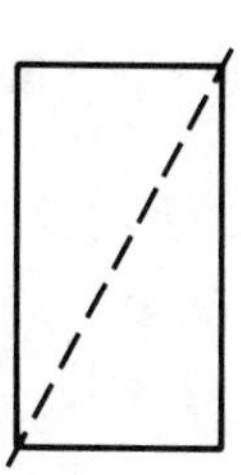

7. 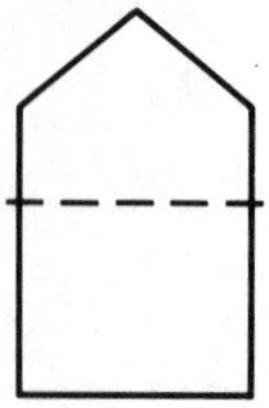 **8.** 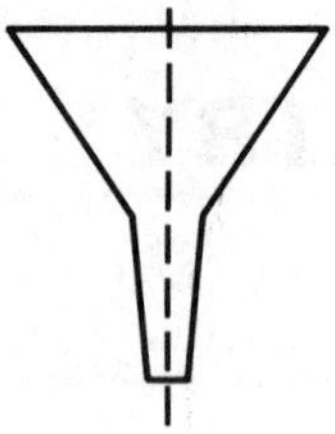 **9.** 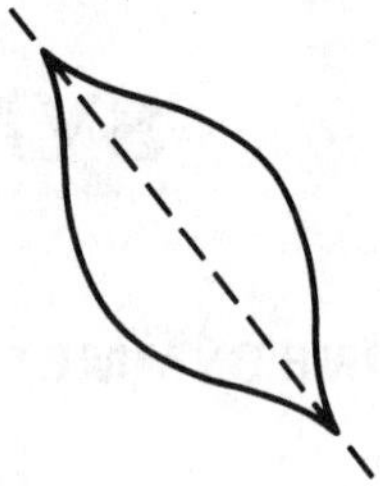

EXERCISE 1b Some of these shapes have a line of symmetry and some do not. Say which of the twelve drawings have a line of symmetry. Use a mirror if it helps you.

1. 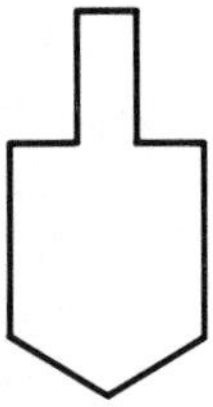 **4.**  **7.** 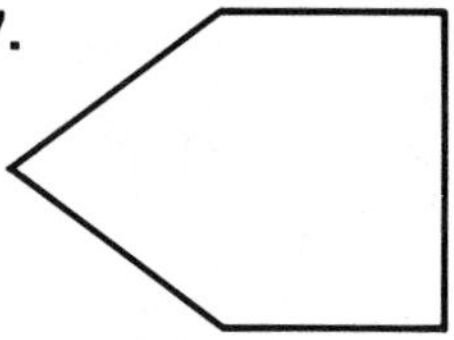

2.  **5.** 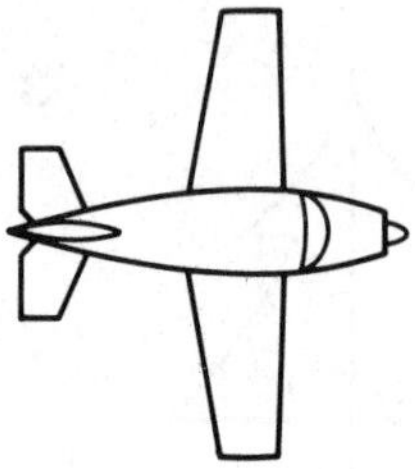 **8.** 

3. 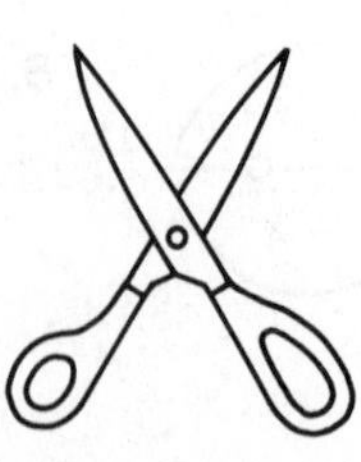 **6.**  **9.** 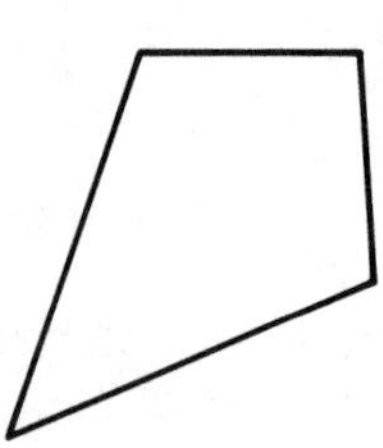

10.

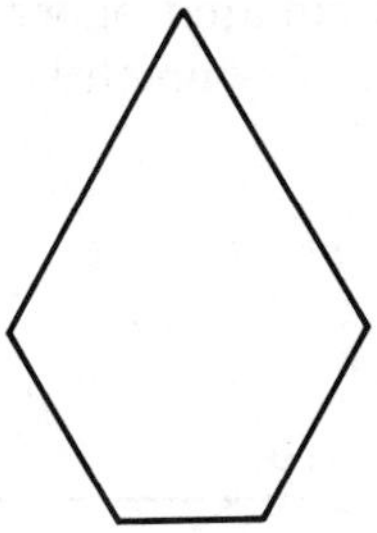

11.

12.

EXERCISE 1c **1.** Each of these shapes has one part marked with a letter and another part marked with a number. Pair off each lettered part with a numbered part so that the complete shape has a line of symmetry.
For example, A and 2 make a shape that has a line of symmetry.

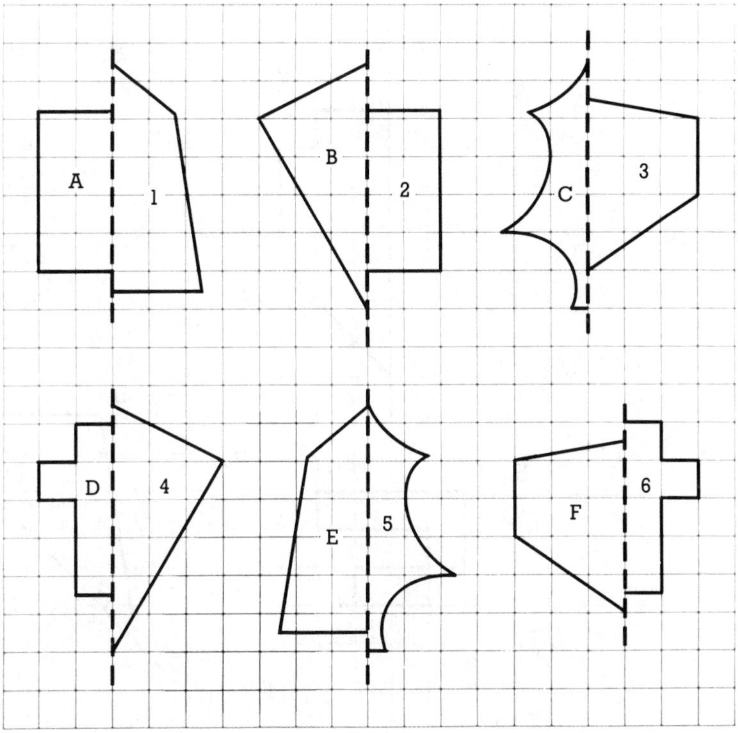

Copy the following drawings on squared paper and complete them so that the broken line is the line of symmetry.

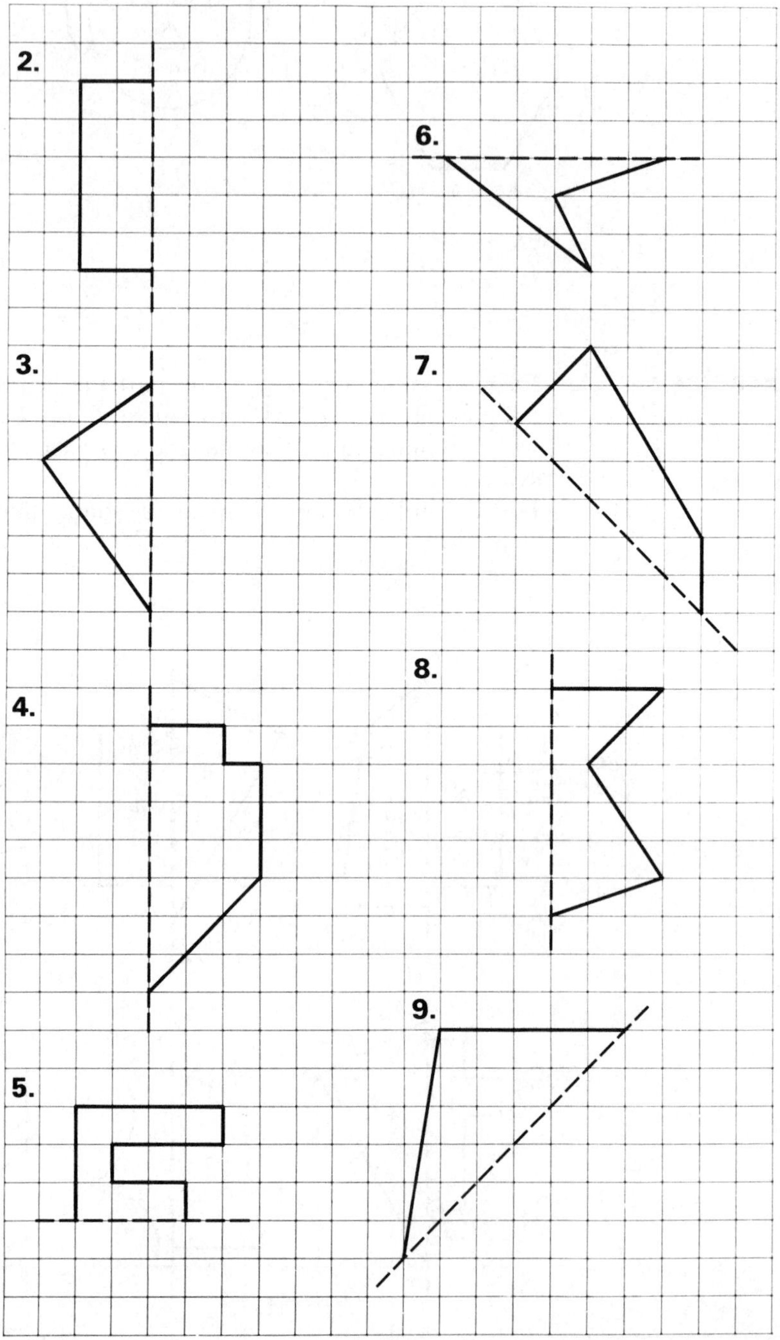

10. Copy this clock face three times.

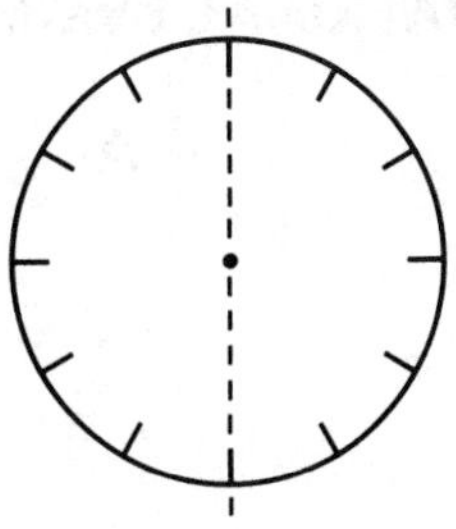

a) On the first copy, draw the hands showing a time of 10 to 2. Remember to make the minute hand longer than the hour hand. Is the dotted line a line of symmetry?

b) On your second copy, draw the hands in a position where the dotted line is a line of symmetry.

c) Is there another position of the hands where the dotted line is a line of symmetry? If so, draw it.

11. Trace and arrange these objects so that they are placed symmetrically about the vase.

12. Look at these flat shapes.

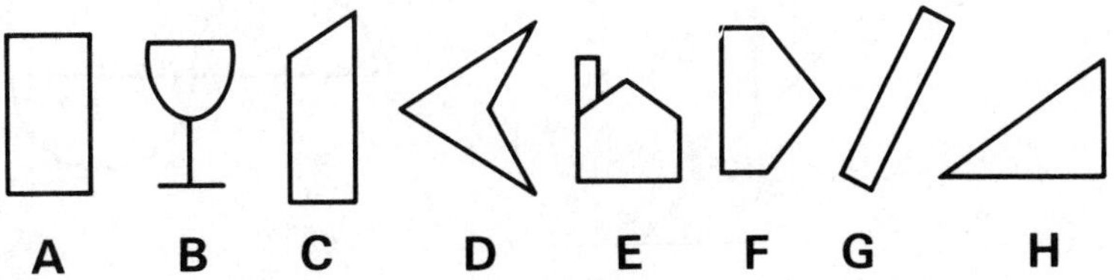

a) Name those that have line symmetry.

b) Name those that do not have line symmetry.

ROTATIONAL SYMMETRY

A

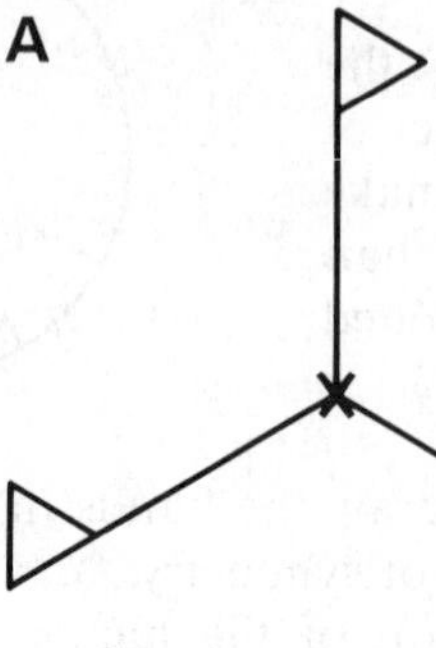

B

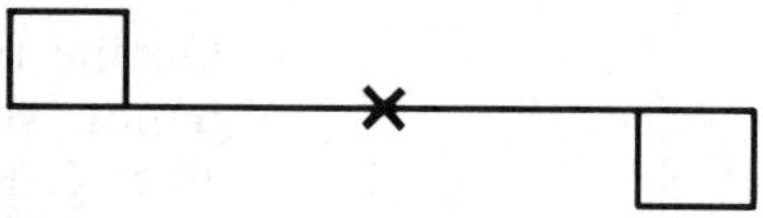

D

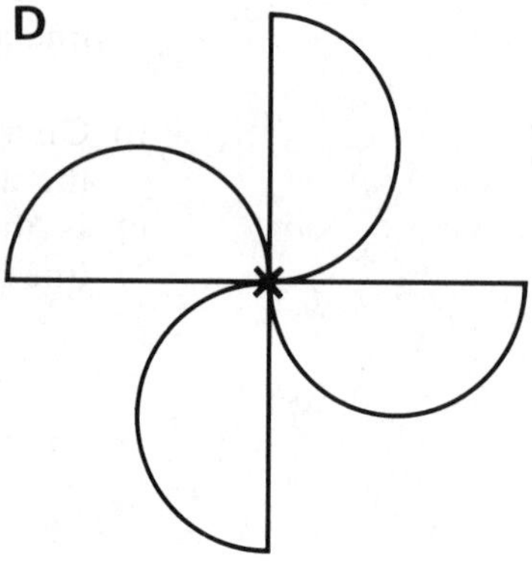

C

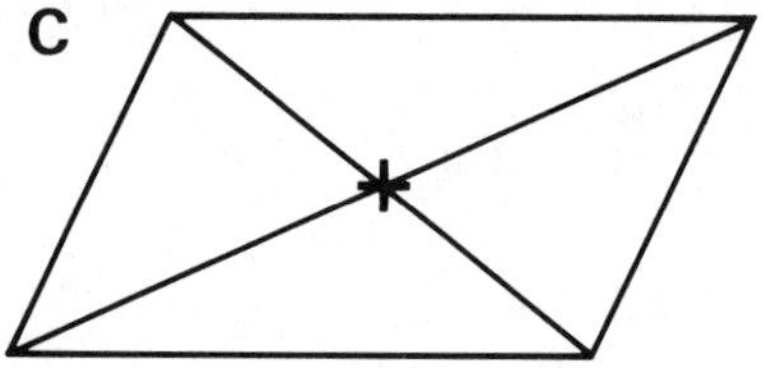

These shapes have a different type of symmetry. None of them has a line of symmetry. However, each can be turned, or rotated, about a centre point (marked with a **×**) and still look the same.

A can be in three different positions and still look the same.
B and C can each be in two different positions and still look the same.
D can be in four different positions and still look the same.

You can test these statements if you lay a piece of tracing paper over each shape, trace the shape and turn the tracing paper about the cross until it fits over the shape again.

EXERCISE 1d Use tracing paper to decide which of the following shapes have rotational symmetry.

1.

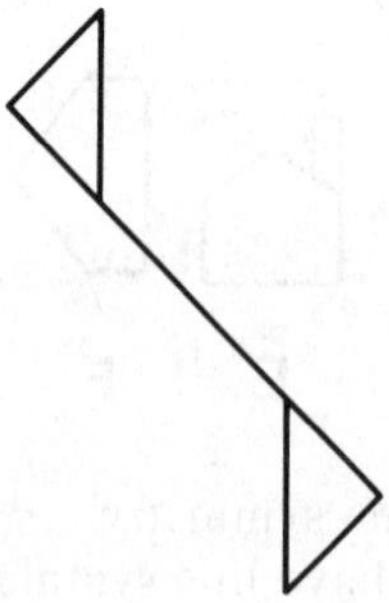

2.

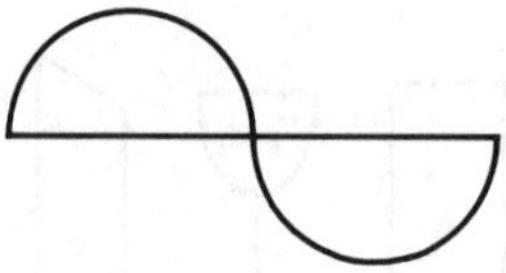

3.

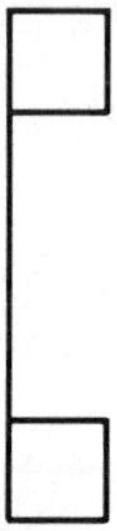

4.  **6.**  **8.** 

5. 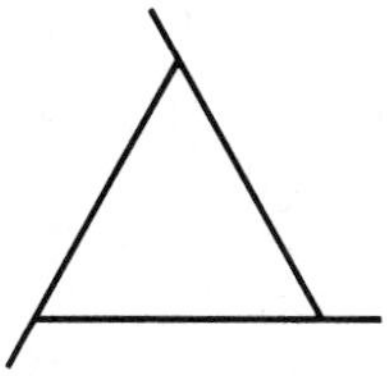 **7.** 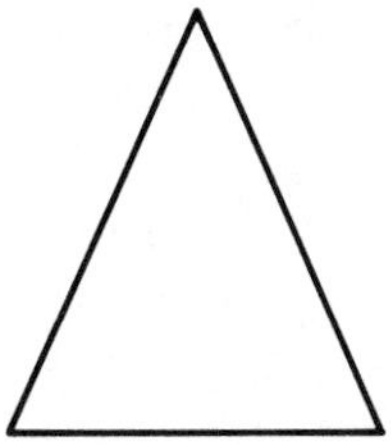 **9.** 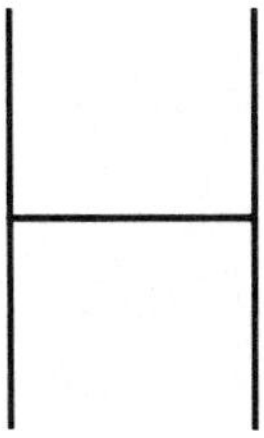

10. Draw four letters of this alphabet that have rotational symmetry.

A B C D E F G H I J K L M N O P Q R S T U V W X Y Z

11. Draw two letters of the alphabet that do *not* have rotational symmetry.

You will have noticed that some shapes have both line symmetry and rotational symmetry.

12. Which of the following shapes have rotational symmetry but do *not* have line symmetry?

a)  b) 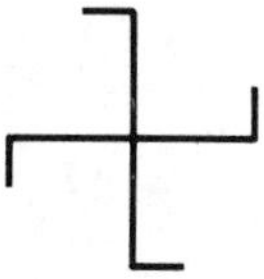 c)  d) 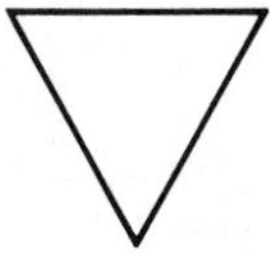

13. Which of the following shapes have *both* line symmetry *and* rotational symmetry?

a) 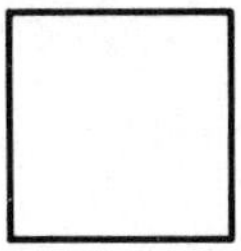 b)  c)  d) 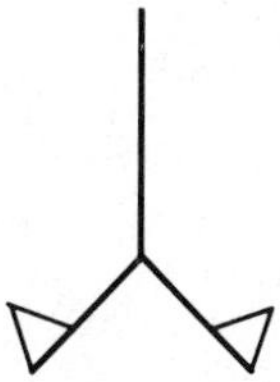

14. Which of the following shapes have line symmetry but do *not* have rotational symmetry?

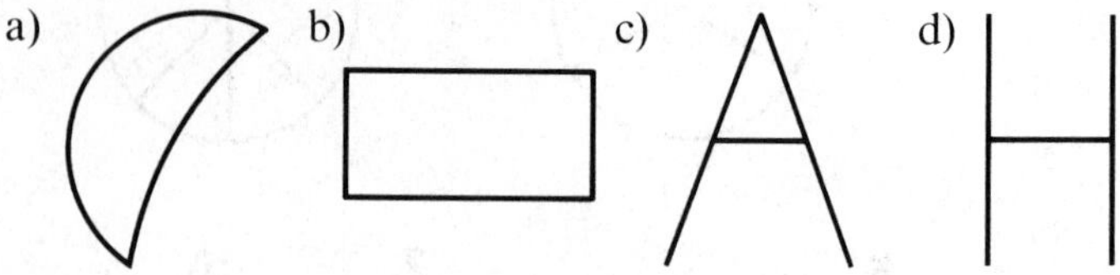

2 WHOLE NUMBERS 1

WHOLE NUMBERS

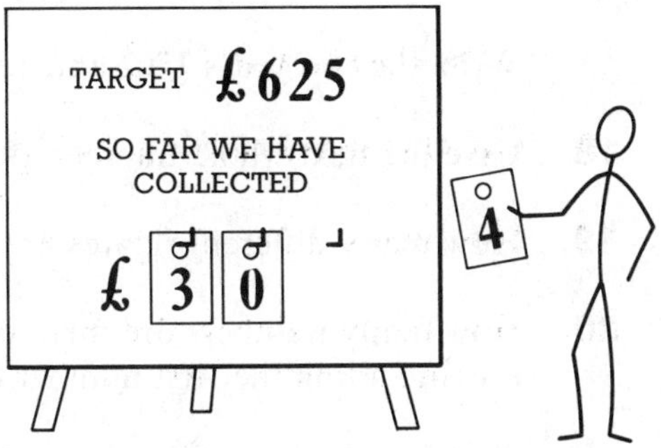

625 is a *whole number*. It is made up of three *figures*, 6, 2 and 5. The *number* 304 contains three figures, i.e. 3, 0 and 4.

Numbers can be written or spoken in words, which say how many thousands, how many hundreds etc., there are in the number. For example, 1948 is "one thousand, nine hundred and forty-eight".

Note however that when we mean *the year* 1948 we say "nineteen forty-eight".

EXERCISE 2a Write the following numbers in figures.

1. Thirty-eight

2. Eighteen

3. Two hundred and sixty-one

4. Four hundred and twenty

5. Four hundred and two

6. Seventy-two

7. Four hundred and thirty-six

8. Nine hundred and seventy

Write the following numbers in words.

9. 56

10. 112

11. 607

12. 310

13. 304

14. 276

15. 79

16. 131

17.

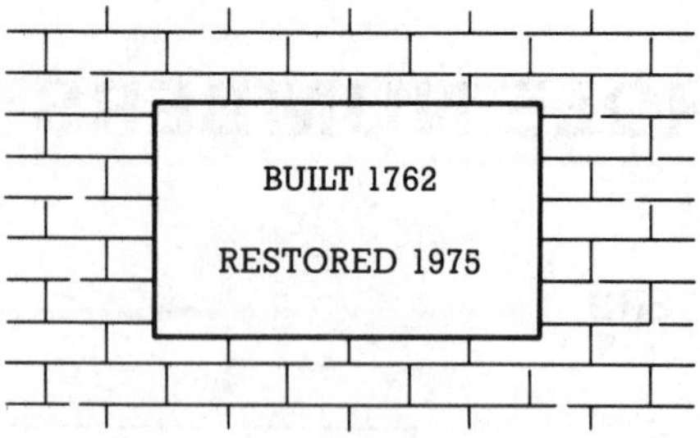

Write the two years 1762 and 1975 in words.

18. Give the next whole number after 399.

19. How many different figures are used for writing numbers?

20. How many numbers are there from 8 to 15 inclusive?
(i.e. including the first number 8 and the last number 15.)

21. If you write down the numbers 1 to 15 inclusive, how many *figures* have you written?

22. "Five thousand people signed the petition in support of saving the open grassy space."
Write down the number of signatures in figures.

23. "A crowd of four thousand attended the match."
Write the number in the news headline above, in figures.

PLACE VALUE

For three hundred and forty-two we write 342.
For three hundred and twenty-four we write 324.
The same figures are used but they are in different *places*.
In 342, the 2 means 2 units or 2 "ones". The 4 means 4 "tens", or forty.

We can write a number with figures under place headings,

		Hundreds	Tens	Units
e.g.	416 can be arranged as	4	1	6
and	103 can be arranged as	1	0	3

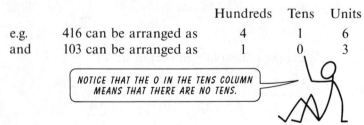

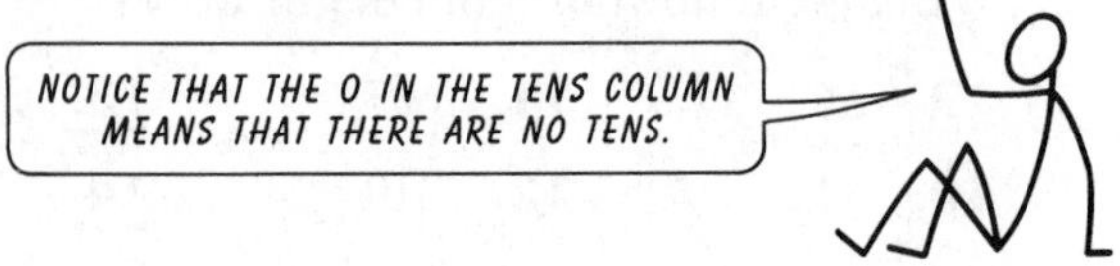

NOTICE THAT THE 0 IN THE TENS COLUMN MEANS THAT THERE ARE NO TENS.

EXERCISE 2b

1. What is the meaning of the 5 in each of the following numbers?

a) 15 b) 57 c) 1523 d) 5621

2. Write down the numbers 67 and 782 putting the figures under place headings.

3. Write down, in figures, the numbers given below.

	Thousands	Hundreds	Tens	Units
a)		3	6	2
b)	9		4	3
c)			7	

4. Write down, in words, the numbers given in Question 3.

5. a) What is the value of the first 8 in 828?
b) What is the value of the second 8 in 828?

Write twenty-five thousand in figures.

	Thousands	Hundreds	Tens	Units
2	5	0	0	0

THIS FIGURE OVERFLOWS INTO THE NEXT COLUMN.

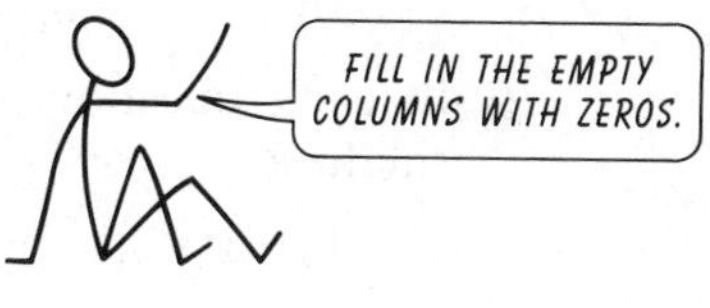

FILL IN THE EMPTY COLUMNS WITH ZEROS.

The number is 25 000.

6. Write the following numbers in figures.

a) Two thousand and forty-one
b) Four thousand, three hundred and forty
c) Nineteen thousand and twenty-four
d) Thirty thousand and six

7. Write the following numbers in words.

a) 4024 b) 14 600

8. Write the numbers 42 000 and 12 007 in words.

9.

You have to read this headline aloud. Write down in words what you will say.

SIZES OF NUMBERS

EXERCISE 2c

Put the numbers 302, 230, and 320 in size order, starting with the smallest.

230, 302, 320

LOOK AT THE HUNDREDS FIGURES FIRST, THEN THE TENS.

In each question, put the numbers in size order, starting with the smallest.

1. 403, 431, 43

2. 812, 281, 821

3. 101, 99, 909

4. 85, 56, 519

5. Which is the biggest, 654, 499 or 436?

6. Give the number that comes next after 349.

7.

a) Write down all the different two and three figure numbers that can be made using two or three of these cards.

b) Put the numbers that you found in (a) in order of size, smallest first.

ADDITION

You should know the pairs of numbers that add up to 10.
For example,

$$4 + 6 = 10 \quad \text{and} \quad 1 + 9 = 10$$

Then it is easier to add numbers that come to more than 10,

e.g. $4 + 9 = 4 + 6 + 3 = 10 + 3 = 13$

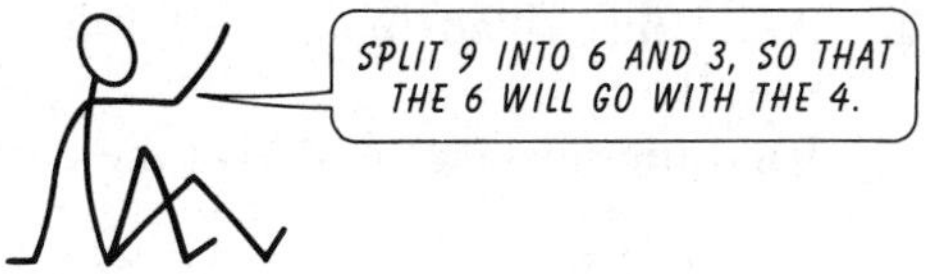

SPLIT 9 INTO 6 AND 3, SO THAT THE 6 WILL GO WITH THE 4.

EXERCISE 2d **1.** Write down all the number pairs that add up to 10.

Work out, in your head

2. $4 + 7$ **4.** $2 + 9$ **6.** $6 + 7$ **8.** $3 + 9$

3. $5 + 8$ **5.** $9 + 9$ **7.** $8 + 3$ **9.** $4 + 8$

10. Copy and complete the following addition table.

+	0	1	2	3	4	5	6	7	8	9
0							6			
1										
2				5						
3										
4										
5										
6										
7										
8										
9			11							18

CHECK THAT YOU AGREE WITH THE NUMBERS ALREADY IN THE TABLE.

11. Anna bought 9 freesias at one flower shop and 7 more at another shop. How many freesias did she buy altogether?

12. What is the total score on each target?

a)

b)

c)

13. Anna has filled in an addition table but she has made two mistakes.
Find the mistakes and give the correct numbers.

+	2	5	7	9
4	6	8	11	13
6	8	11	13	16

MORE ADDITION

EXERCISE 2e Always look at your answer to make sure that it is sensible.
If you add 23 and 72 and get 75, you can see that you must have made a mistake.

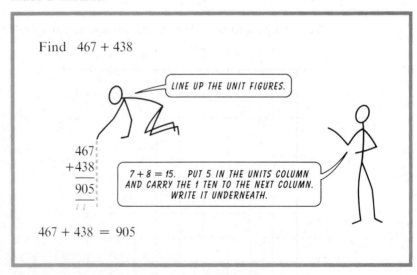

Find 467 + 438

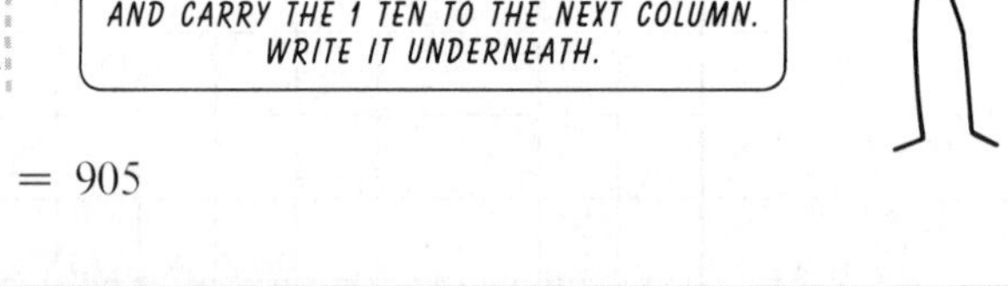

LINE UP THE UNIT FIGURES.
7 + 8 = 15. PUT 5 IN THE UNITS COLUMN AND CARRY THE 1 TEN TO THE NEXT COLUMN. WRITE IT UNDERNEATH.

$$\begin{array}{r} 467 \\ +438 \\ \hline 905 \\ \hline {\scriptstyle 1\,1} \end{array}$$

467 + 438 = 905

Copy and complete the following calculations.

1. $\begin{array}{r} 24 \\ +17 \\ \hline \\ \hline \end{array}$ **2.** $\begin{array}{r} 37 \\ +45 \\ \hline \\ \hline \end{array}$ **3.** $\begin{array}{r} 46 \\ +27 \\ \hline \\ \hline \end{array}$ **4.** $\begin{array}{r} 58 \\ +28 \\ \hline \\ \hline \end{array}$

Write each of the following additions in the same way as in the previous questions and find the answer.

5. 23 + 46 **6.** 58 + 123 **7.** 432 + 126 **8.** 342 + 89

Work out, in your head

9. 34 + 51 **10.** 23 + 6 **11.** 37 + 47 **12.** 18 + 19

13. Jan spent 25 p on coffee and 18 p on biscuits. What did she spend altogether?

14.

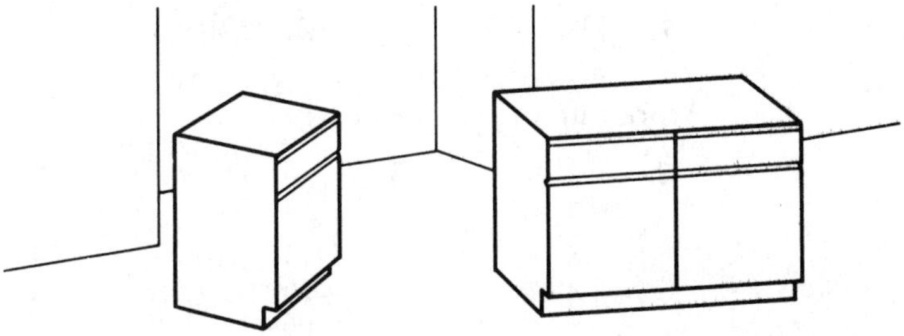

One kitchen unit is 42 cm wide and a second is 86 cm wide. Will they fit side by side in a space 130 cm wide?

Find

15. $\begin{array}{r} 345 \\ +124 \\ \hline \\ \hline \end{array}$ **16.** $\begin{array}{r} 812 \\ +181 \\ \hline \\ \hline \end{array}$ **17.** $\begin{array}{r} 429 \\ +391 \\ \hline \\ \hline \end{array}$ **18.** $\begin{array}{r} 648 \\ +277 \\ \hline \\ \hline \end{array}$

Write each of these additions in the same way as in the previous questions and find the answer.

19. 123 + 368 **20.** 413 + 473 **21.** 365 + 278

22. Dave's snooker cue was 145 cm long. He added an extension which was 48 cm long. How long was the extended cue?

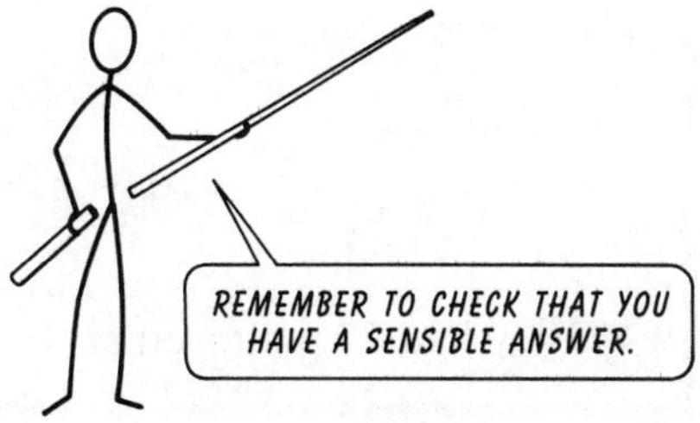

REMEMBER TO CHECK THAT YOU HAVE A SENSIBLE ANSWER.

23. a) Are the answers to 45 + 4 and 4 + 45 the same?
b) Are the answers to 31 + 24 and 24 + 31 the same?
c) Does the order of the numbers matter?

24. Add 100 to each of the following numbers.
a) 643 b) 59 c) 7

ADDING THREE OR MORE NUMBERS

EXERCISE 2f Work out, in your head

1. 4 + 6 + 7 **2.** 5 + 9 + 5 **3.** 11 + 5 + 3

Work out, in your head

4.	5.	6.	7.
3	6	9	3
7	7	6	9
8	3	4	7
+4	+10	+8	+1
—	—	—	—

Copy and complete

8.	9.	10.
123	303	403
67	45	89
+ 21	+ 13	+111
—	—	—

Find

11. 45 + 35 + 23 **12.** 72 + 23 + 54 **13.** 34 + 23 + 34

Mary, Ann and Ahmed pooled their money. Mary had 21 p, Ann had 37 p and Ahmed had 19 p. How much money did they have altogether?

$$\begin{array}{r} 21 \\ 37 \\ +19 \\ \hline 77 \\ \hline \end{array}$$

They had 77 p altogether.

14.

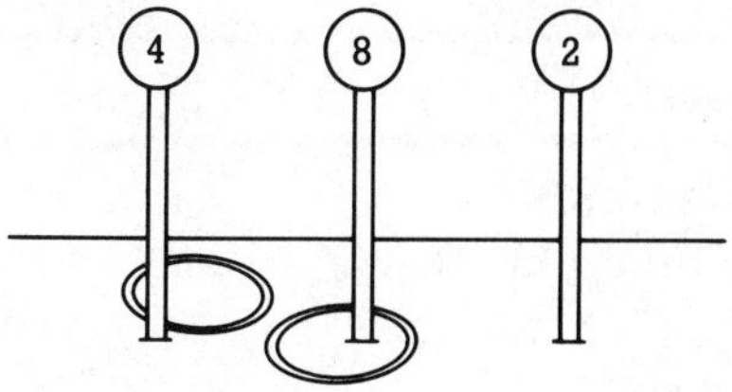

A sideshow at a fete has three posts over which rings are thrown.

a) Jason puts one ring over each pole. What is his score?

b) Pam scores two 8s and a miss. Is her score better than Jason's?

c) What is the highest possible score with three rings?

15.

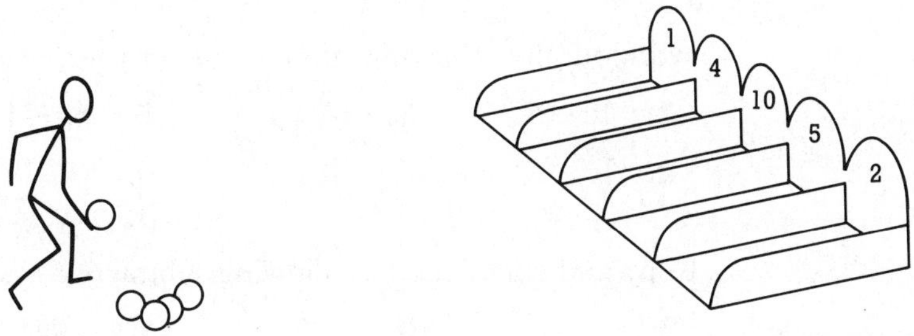

a) Jason manages to roll one ball into each alley. What is his score?

b) Pam gets three balls into the alley marked 5 and one into the alley marked 4. What is her score?

16.

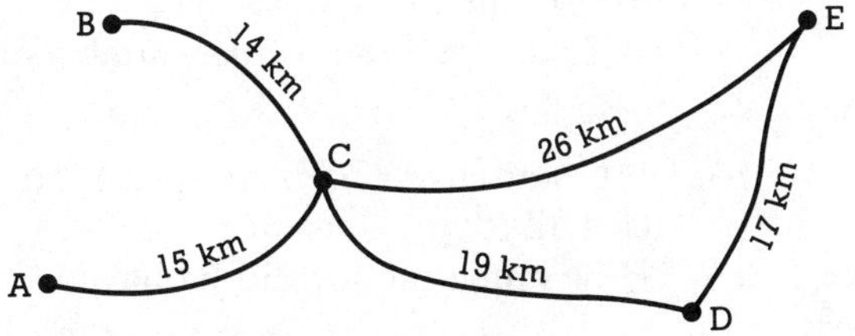

a) How far is it from A to E, going by the direct route via C?

b) How far is it from B to D, going by the direct route via C?

c) How far is it from A to E going via C and D?

17. A bus starts from the bus station with 23 passengers. At the next three stops it picks up 5, 13 and 9 passengers respectively. If no one has got off, how many passengers are there on the bus after the third stop?

SUBTRACTION

EXERCISE 2g

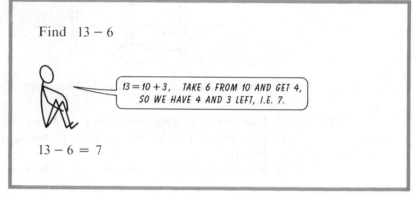

Find $13 - 6$

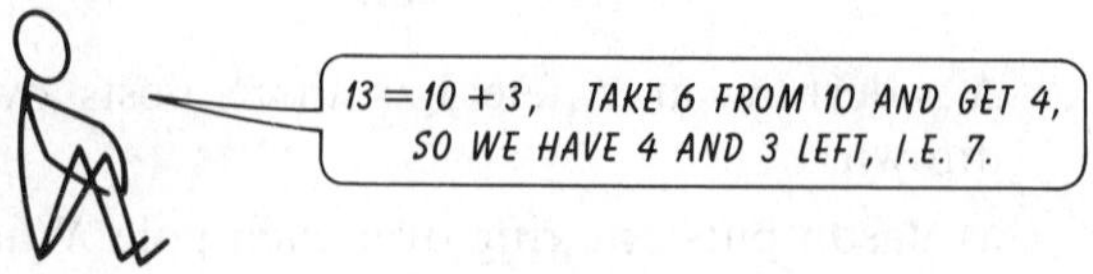
13 = 10 + 3, TAKE 6 FROM 10 AND GET 4,
SO WE HAVE 4 AND 3 LEFT, I.E. 7.

$13 - 6 = 7$

Work out the following subtractions in your head.

1. $10 - 5$ **3.** $10 - 1$ **5.** $11 - 4$ **7.** $17 - 9$

2. $10 - 7$ **4.** $10 - 3$ **6.** $14 - 8$ **8.** $13 - 5$

Copy and complete the following subtractions.

9. $\begin{array}{r} 24 \\ -\ 3 \\ \hline \\ \hline \end{array}$ **10.** $\begin{array}{r} 32 \\ -11 \\ \hline \\ \hline \end{array}$ **11.** $\begin{array}{r} 76 \\ -51 \\ \hline \\ \hline \end{array}$ **12.** $\begin{array}{r} 45 \\ -32 \\ \hline \\ \hline \end{array}$

13. a) Are the answers to $12 - 9$ and $9 - 12$ the same?
b) Are the answers to $34 - 11$ and $11 - 34$ the same?
c) Does the order of the numbers matter?

14. Ian was given 65 p to spend. He bought a magazine which cost 32 p.
How much money did he have left?

MORE SUBTRACTION

In the next exercise, the second units figure (the one to be subtracted) is bigger than the first units figure, so you can "borrow" ten from the next column.
There are two methods of subtraction. The one called "decomposition" is more popular.

EXERCISE 2h

Find 45 − 27

USE 1 TEN FROM THE NEXT COLUMN, THEN TAKE 7 FROM 15.
IF 1 TEN IS USED FROM THE 4, THEN 3 TENS ARE LEFT. TAKE 2 FROM 3.

$$\begin{array}{r} {}^{3}\not{4}{}^{1}5 \\ -27 \\ \hline 18 \end{array}$$

45 − 27 = 18

Copy and complete the following subtractions.

1. $\begin{array}{r} 42 \\ -23 \\ \hline \end{array}$ **2.** $\begin{array}{r} 64 \\ -37 \\ \hline \end{array}$ **3.** $\begin{array}{r} 41 \\ -35 \\ \hline \end{array}$ **4.** $\begin{array}{r} 34 \\ -19 \\ \hline \end{array}$

Write each of the following subtractions in the same way as in the previous questions and find the answers.

5. 23 − 9 **6.** 67 − 34 **7.** 86 − 28 **8.** 134 − 56

9. 72 − 3 **11.** 48 − 19 **13.** 62 − 58 **15.** 86 − 59

10. 121 − 29 **12.** 36 − 18 **14.** 174 − 15 **16.** 31 − 27

A piece of wood is 92 cm long. If 19 cm is cut from it, how long is the piece that is left?

Length left = (92 − 19) cm
= 73 cm

$$\begin{array}{r} {}^{8}\not{9}{}^{1}2 \\ -19 \\ \hline 73 \end{array}$$

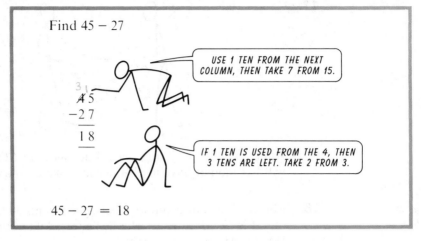

17.

Anne wants to buy this scarf, but has only 62 p. How much will her mother have to give her to make up the difference?

18. Martin thinks of a number between 10 and 30. Susan guesses that it is 27. Martin says she has guessed 9 too high. What is Martin's number?

19. When a bus carrying 21 passengers arrives at a stop, 7 passengers get off and 13 get on. How many passengers are there on the bus when the bus moves off?

20. Steve and Sarah are washing up. There are 82 plates and so far they have dealt with 56 of them. How many more are there to do?

21. Len picked 92 plums but had to throw away 25 of them. How many plums did he have left?

MIXED EXERCISES

EXERCISE 2i

1. What is the place value of 5 in 352?

2. Put the numbers 808, 89, 880, 98 in order of size with the smallest first.

3. Find the value of a) $9 + 7 + 11$ b) $72 - 14$.

4. Copy the following set of numbers. Put + or − in each space so that the calculation is correct.

$$6 \square 5 \square 4 \square 3 \square 2 = 6$$

5.

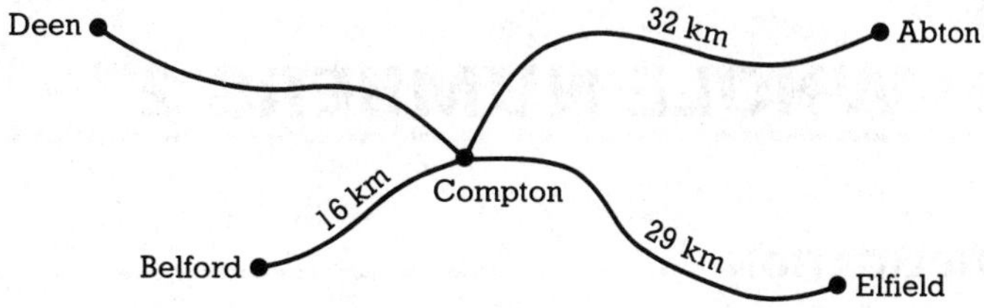

a) Dave drives from Abton to Belford via Compton. How far does he drive?

b) Sally drives 56 km from Deen to Elfield. How far is it from Deen to Compton?

EXERCISE 2j

1. What are the place values of the two 3s in 303? What is the difference between them?

2. Mr Jepson brought 62 pieces of paper to the lesson but only 39 pieces were used.
How many were left?

3. Give the next three numbers after 97.

4. Which is the bigger, four hundred and sixteen or four hundred and sixty?

5. What is the total score?

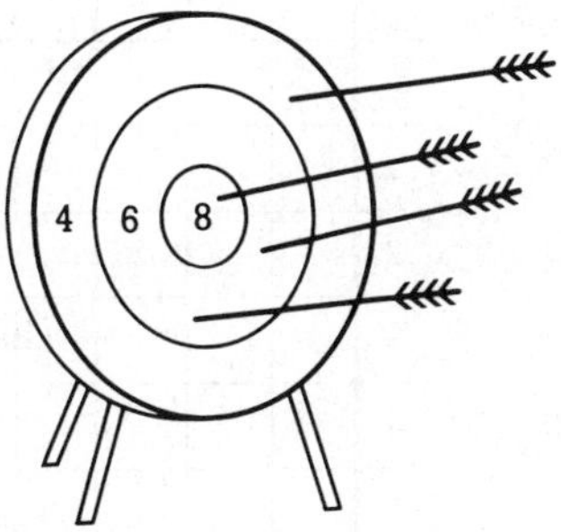

3 WHOLE NUMBERS 2

MULTIPLICATION

You need to know your multiplication tables. Question 4 of the next exercise gives you a chance to check how easily you can recall them.

EXERCISE 3a **1.** Jonathan bought 6 packs of pens, each holding 8 pens. How many pens did he get?

2.

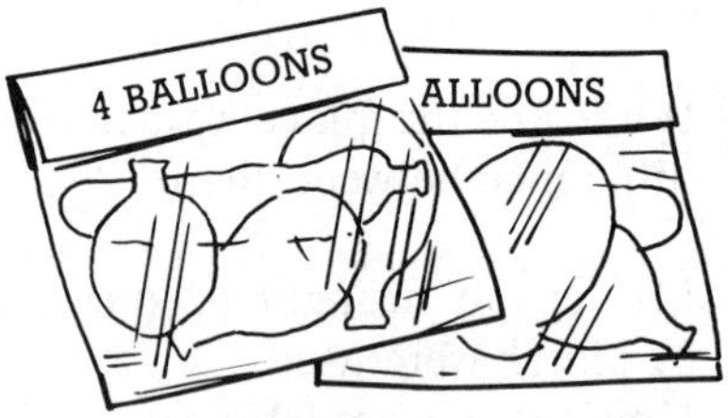

For a party, Stella bought 8 of these packets. How many balloons did she get?

3. Oranges come in bags of 5. How many oranges are there in 9 bags?

4. Copy and complete the following multiplication table.

×	0	1	2	3	4	5	6	7	8	9
0				0						
1										
2							12			
3										
4										
5										
6										
7										
8										
9			18							

5. Write down, without looking at the table, the answers to the following multiplications.

a) 4×7 b) 7×3 c) 9×2 d) 3×6

Now make up your own questions and test yourself on your knowledge of the number facts.

6.

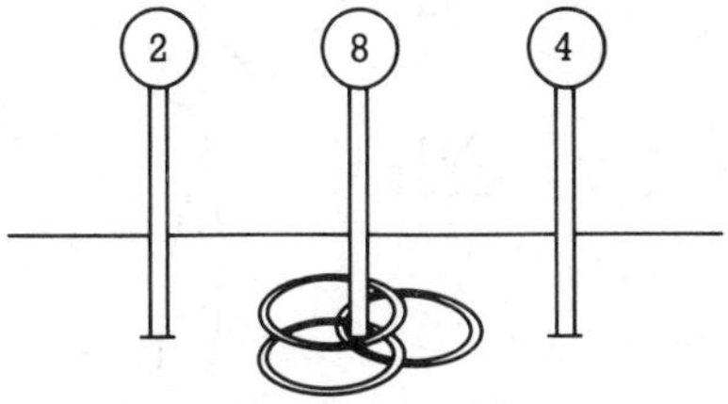

a) At the fete, Dave threw 3 rings over the middle post. What was his score?

b) Winston managed to get 5 rings over the right-hand post. What was his score?

7. a)

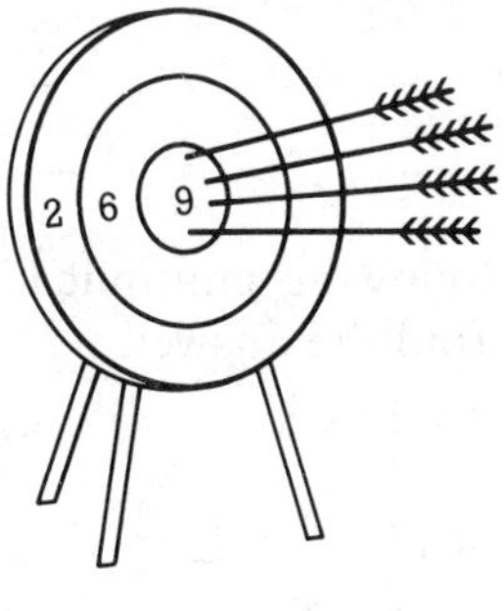

b)

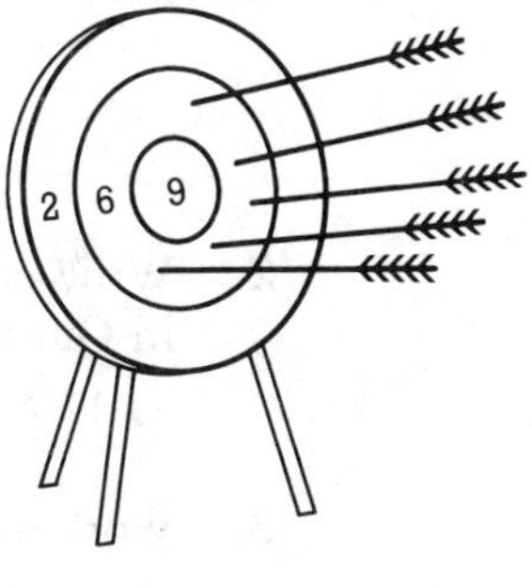

What are the two total scores?

8. David had to write about 60 words on the subject of *pets*. He found that he had used 9 words per line and had written 7 lines.
How many words had he written? Had he written enough words?

9. Rashida always makes sure that she swims 8 lengths each week. How many lengths does she swim in 5 weeks?

MORE MULTIPLICATION

EXERCISE 3b

Find 34×6

$$\begin{array}{r} 34 \\ \times\ \ 6 \\ \hline 204 \\ \hline 2 \end{array}$$

TO START, FIND 4×6, I.E. 24. WRITE DOWN 4 AND CARRY 2 TO THE TENS COLUMN.

$34 \times 6 = 204$

1. Copy and complete the following multiplications.

a) $\begin{array}{r} 15 \\ \times\ 6 \\ \hline \\ \hline \end{array}$ b) $\begin{array}{r} 204 \\ \times\ \ 7 \\ \hline \\ \hline \end{array}$ c) $\begin{array}{r} 32 \\ \times\ 9 \\ \hline \\ \hline \end{array}$

2. Write each of the following multiplications in the same way as in Question 1 and find the answer.

a) 17×3 b) 17×8 c) 25×5

3. Work out, in your head

a) $2 \times 4 \times 3$ b) $6 \times 2 \times 3$ c) 16×2

4.

How much would 7 apples cost?

5. For an outing, 8 coaches have been hired. Each coach holds 43 passengers. All the coaches are full. How many passengers are there altogether?

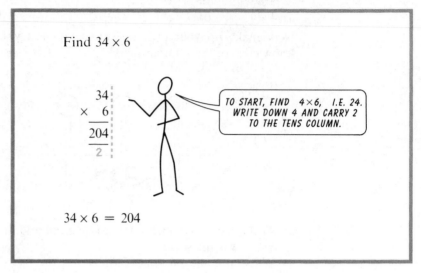

6. Eight bricks are laid end to end. Each brick measures 26 cm in length. How far do the bricks stretch?

7. a) Do 5×4 and 4×5 give the same answer?
b) Are the answers to 9×8 and 8×9 the same?
c) Do you have to be careful about the order of the numbers when doing multiplication?

DIVISION

If you know your multiplication tables, division is easy. You can think of division as the reverse of multiplication.

For example, to find $48 \div 8$ you can say, "What do I have to multiply 8 by to get 48?"

Now $8 \times 6 = 48$

so $48 \div 8 = 6$

EXERCISE 3c Find

1. $36 \div 6$ **3.** $45 \div 9$ **5.** $24 \div 3$ **7.** $18 \div 2$

2. $36 \div 9$ **4.** $32 \div 4$ **6.** $42 \div 7$ **8.** $30 \div 5$

9. Share 56 sandwiches equally amongst eight people.
How many will each person get?

10.

THAT IS £27,
PLEASE.
ADMISSION
£3

How many people are being paid for?

11. At the beginning of the school year, 72 exercise books are handed out to a group of children. Each one receives 8 exercise books.
How many are there in the group?

MORE DIVISION

EXERCISE 3d

Divide 128 by 4

$$\begin{array}{r}32\\4\overline{)128}\end{array}$$

4 INTO 12 FIRST,
THEN 4 INTO 8.

$128 \div 4 = 32$

Find

1. $82 \div 2$	**3.** $246 \div 2$	**5.** $69 \div 3$	**7.** $147 \div 7$
2. $84 \div 4$	**4.** $168 \div 8$	**6.** $186 \div 6$	**8.** $217 \div 7$

9. Divide 96 by 3.

10. How many 6s are there in 66?

11.

£4
EACH

Anthony wants to buy as many shrubs for his garden as possible. He has £128 to spend.
How many shrubs can he buy?

12. Hilary paid 306 p for 6 issues of a magazine.
What is the cost of one issue?

DIVISION WITH REMAINDERS

If we multiply whole numbers together the answer is a whole number, and the same is true of addition and subtraction.

However, if we divide one whole number by another we may not always get a whole number answer. For instance, $7 \div 2$ gives 3 with a remainder of 1 unit.
(We could also get $3\frac{1}{2}$ or 3·5 but these will be dealt with later.)

EXERCISE 3e

Eggs are packed in boxes of six. If there are 58 eggs, how many boxes will be filled and how many eggs will be left over?

$58 \div 6 = 9$, rem 4 $\quad (6 \times 9 = 54)$

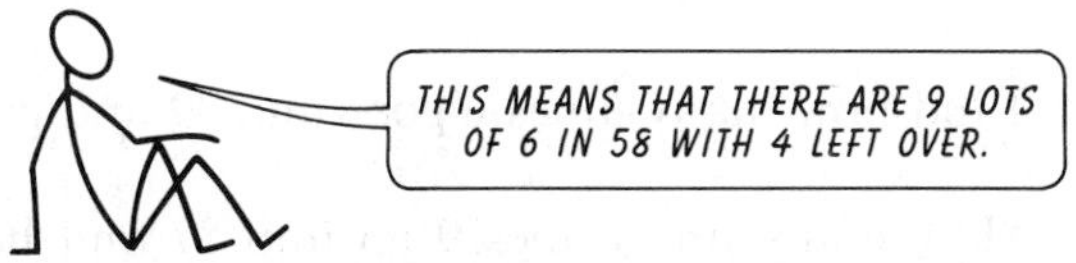

THIS MEANS THAT THERE ARE 9 LOTS OF 6 IN 58 WITH 4 LEFT OVER.

The eggs will fill 9 boxes with 4 eggs left over.

1. Share 38 chocolates equally amongst 5 people.
How many chocolates do they each get and how many are left over?

2. There are 62 numbers, written with 9 numbers per line.
How many complete lines are there, and how many numbers are there in the last, incomplete, line?

3. In a classroom, 32 desks are to be arranged in complete rows, with 5 to the row.
How many rows are there, and how many desks will have to be left at the front of the classroom?

4.

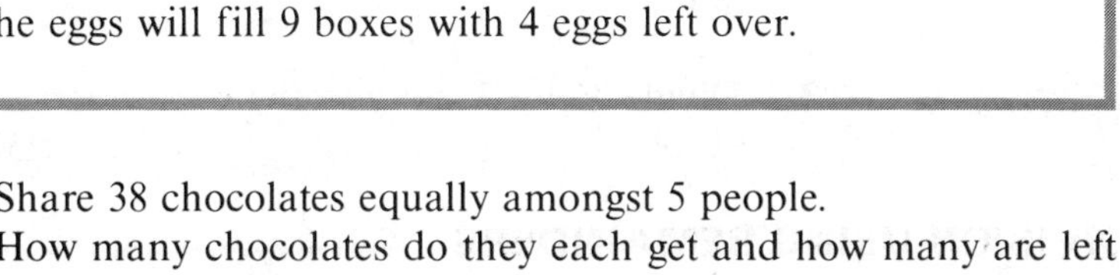

I have 47 seedlings and 6 pots. I want to plant as many of the seedlings as possible but with the same number in each pot.
How many do I put in each pot and how many seedlings are left over?

What is the remainder when 17 is divided by 3?

$17 \div 3 = 5$, rem 2 $\quad (3 \times 5 = 15)$

So the remainder is 2.

Find the remainder in each of the following calculations.

5. $50 \div 6$ **7.** $19 \div 2$ **9.** $58 \div 7$

6. $28 \div 3$ **8.** $71 \div 8$ **10.** $43 \div 5$

11. Find how many times 6 goes into 39 and give the remainder.

12. How many times does 9 go into 87 and how many units are left over?

13. Divide 36 by 7 and give the remainder.

DIVISION USING REMAINDERS

To divide 79 by 3 we need to use remainders.

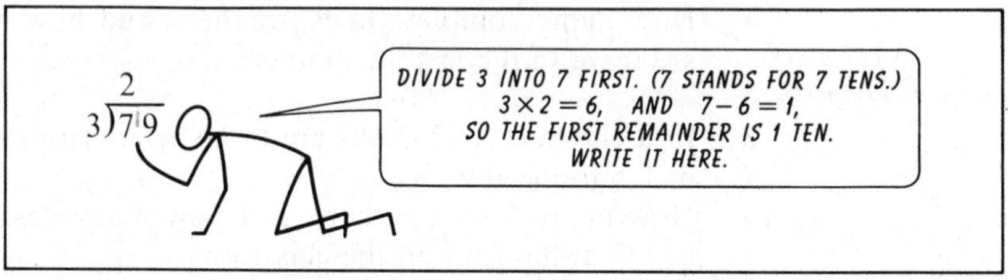
2
3)7¹9
DIVIDE 3 INTO 7 FIRST. (7 STANDS FOR 7 TENS.)
3 × 2 = 6, AND 7 − 6 = 1,
SO THE FIRST REMAINDER IS 1 TEN.
WRITE IT HERE.

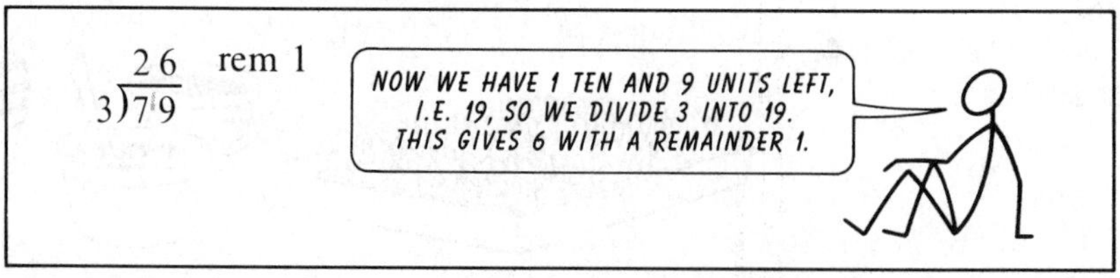
26 rem 1
3)7¹9
NOW WE HAVE 1 TEN AND 9 UNITS LEFT,
I.E. 19, SO WE DIVIDE 3 INTO 19.
THIS GIVES 6 WITH A REMAINDER 1.

SO 79 ÷ 3 = 26, REMAINDER 1.

EXERCISE 3f

Find how many times 6 goes into 74 and give the remainder.

$$\begin{array}{r} 1\,2 \quad \text{rem } 2 \\ 6\overline{)7^{1}4} \end{array}$$

6 GOES INTO 7 ONCE, AND THE FIRST REMAINDER IS 1. THEN 6 GOES INTO 14 TWICE.

$74 \div 6 = 12$, remainder 2

1. Find how many times 5 goes into 93 and give the remainder.

2. Divide 67 by 4, giving a whole number answer and the remainder.

3. When 59 is divided by 6, what is the whole number answer? What is the remainder?

4. Miriam has 118 p and buys as many ballpoint pens as she can at 9 p each.
How many pens does she buy and how much money has she left over?

5. Mrs Lim has collected 92 balls of wool to knit jerseys for Oxfam. Each jersey takes 7 balls.
How many jerseys can she knit and how much wool has she left over?

6. Dave has collected 88 cornflakes packet tokens so that he can send off for a collection of booklets on space travel.
Each booklet requires 5 tokens. How many booklets can he get and how many tokens will he have left over?

7. There are 60 chairs in the school hall. To clear the hall for a volley-ball match, the chairs have to be put in the store room in stacks of 8. How many full stacks will there be? How many chairs will be left over?

8. Students attending a special lecture are asked to fill the rows of chairs starting at the front. There are 7 chairs in each row. If 67 students attend, how many rows will be filled? How many students will there be in the last row?

MULTIPLICATION BY TENS

Ten matchsticks, each 3 cm long, are laid end to end.

If we count up we find that the length of the line is 30 cm, so

$$3 \times 10 = 30$$

When we multiply by ten, the number of units becomes the number of tens.

In the same way, the number of tens becomes the number of hundreds.

For example, 6×10 i.e. 6 units $\times$ 10, becomes 6 tens i.e. 60, and $63 \times 10 = 630$.

Hundreds	Tens	Units	
	6	3	$\times 10$
6	3	0	

Notice that the figures move one place to the left.

Similarly in $48 \times 1000 = 48\,000$ the 48 has moved three places to the left and zeros have filled the gaps left. If you think of moving the figures when multiplying by tens it will help when you start to use decimals.

EXERCISE 3g

Calculate

a) 4×10 b) 42×10 c) 420×100

a) $4 \times 10 = 40$

b) $42 \times 10 = 420$

c) $420 \times 100 = 42\,000$

Find

1. 7×10 **3.** 6×100 **5.** 32×10 **7.** 16×100

2. 10×8 **4.** 90×100 **6.** 47×1000 **8.** 220×10

9. A sewing-thread maker supplies thread in boxes of 100 reels. One shop orders 80 boxes. How many reels should the shop receive?

10. Stamps come in sheets of 200. How many stamps are there in 10 sheets?

11.

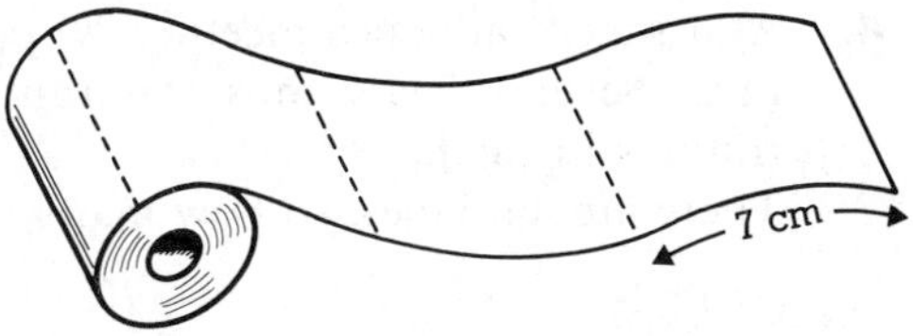

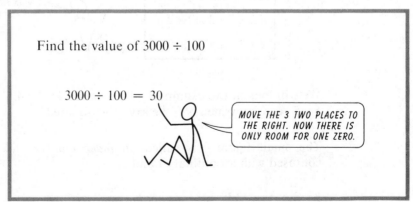

Labels come in a tear-off strip and each label is 7 cm long. How long is a strip of 1000 labels?

DIVISION BY TENS

Because division is the reverse of multiplication, we carry out the opposite process and move the figures to the right.

Hundreds	Tens	Units	
4	0	0	÷ 10
	4	0	

EXERCISE 3h

Find the value of 3000 ÷ 100

3000 ÷ 100 = 30

MOVE THE 3 TWO PLACES TO THE RIGHT. NOW THERE IS ONLY ROOM FOR ONE ZERO.

1. Divide each of the following numbers by 10.

a) 70 b) 400 c) 6000

2. Divide each of the following numbers by 100.

a) 800 b) 9000 c) 5400

3. Exercise books are packed in tens. A class needs 300 books at the beginning of term.
How many packets must be ordered?

4. At a school athletics meeting, 80 people enter for the 100 metre race. Several heats must be run, with the same number of runners in each.
There are ten lanes, so how many heats are there?

INDEX NUMBERS

Scientists sometimes have to deal with numbers like

$$2 \times 2 \times 2 \times 2 \times 2 \times 2$$

so they use a shorter way of writing them.

$2 \times 2 \times 2 \times 2 \times 2 \times 2$
$\times 2 \times 2 \times 2 \times 2 \times 2 \times$
$2 \times 2 \times 2$

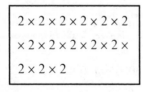

We will look at two examples, 5×5 and $4 \times 4 \times 4$.
5×5 can be written 5^2. We say "five squared".

The small figure ^{2} is called an *index number* and must not be confused with an ordinary number,

i.e. 5^2 is *not the same* as 5×2

$4 \times 4 \times 4$ can be written as 4^3 because there are three 4s to be multiplied together. We say "four cubed".

EXERCISE 3i

> Write 6×6 in index form.
>
> $6 \times 6 = 6^2$

Write each of the following numbers in index form.

1. 3×3

2. 8×8

3. $2 \times 2 \times 2$

4. $9 \times 9 \times 9$

5. 4×4

6. $10 \times 10 \times 10$

> Find the value of a) 5^2 b) 4^3
>
> a) $5^2 = 5 \times 5$
> $= 25$
>
> b) $4^3 = 4 \times 4 \times 4$
> $= 16 \times 4$
> $= 64$

Find the value of

7. 2×2

8. $2 \times 2 \times 2$

9. $3 \times 3 \times 3$

10. 4×4

11. 4^2

12. 2^2

13. 3^3

14. 6^2

15. 7^3

16. 10^2

17. 8^2

18. 5^3

19. Find the value of "three squared".

20. Find the value of "two cubed".

EXERCISE 3j

1. Which statement is correct?
a) $6^2 = 12$ b) $6^2 = 36$

2. Which statement is correct?
a) $4 \times 4 = 4 \times 2$ b) $4 \times 4 = 4^2$

3. Give the value of the following numbers
a) 9×2 b) 9×9 c) 9^2

4. "Three cubed is equal to nine".
Is this statement true or false?
If it is false, write a correct version.

5. James has 2^3 apples and David has 3^2 apples.
Which of the two has the greater number of apples?

6. Find the missing number.

$$\square^2 = 81$$

7. When a number is squared, the result is 64.
What is the number?

8. The square of a number is 121. Use your calculator to find the number.

MIXED EXERCISE

EXERCISE 3k

1. Find 54×2, $54 - 2$, $54 + 2$ and $54 \div 2$.

2. Is the value of 34×6 the same as the value of 6×34?

3. Cake boxes will hold 10 cakes each. How many boxes are needed for

a) 600 cakes b) 3000 cakes?

4.

Lettuces are planted in rows of 8. How many rows are needed for 104 lettuces?

5. Which is the bigger, 7×8 or 9×6?

6. What is the cost of 9 notebooks at 75 p each?

7. Find the value of 7^2.

4 FRACTIONS

THE MEANING OF FRACTIONS

Imagine cutting this length of wood into two equal pieces.

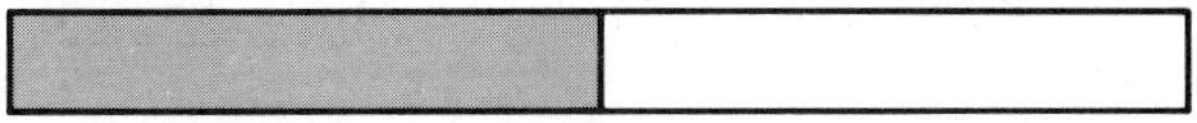

Each piece is one half of the whole length of wood. One half is a fraction. We write it $\frac{1}{2}$.

If we cut the length of wood into four equal pieces, each piece is one quarter of the whole length of wood. We write this $\frac{1}{4}$.

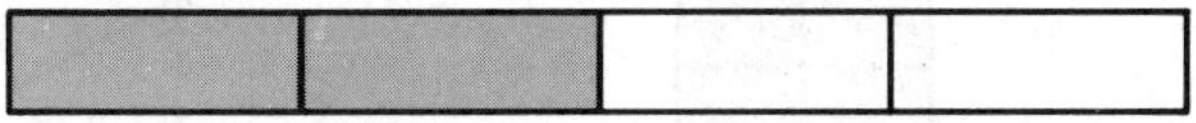

We can see that two quarters, i.e. $\frac{2}{4}$, is the same as $\frac{1}{2}$. Similarly if we cut the length of wood into six equal pieces we can see that three sixths, i.e. $\frac{3}{6}$, is the same as $\frac{1}{2}$.

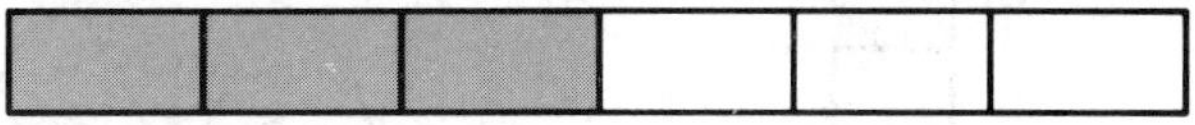

EXERCISE 4a

Write down the fraction that is shaded.

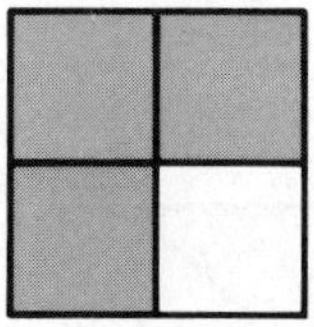

The fraction shaded is $\frac{3}{4}$

In each of the following sketches, write down the fraction of the shape that is shaded.

1.

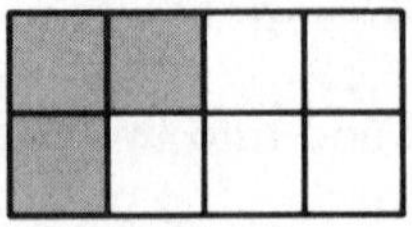

2.

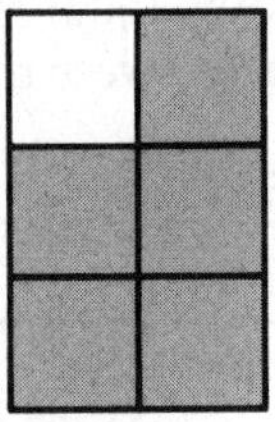

3.

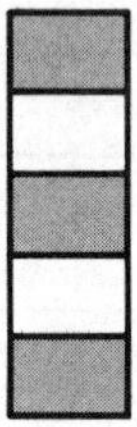

4.

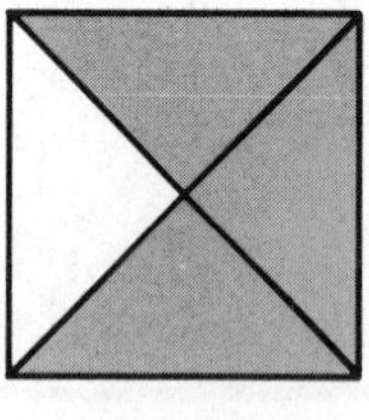

5.

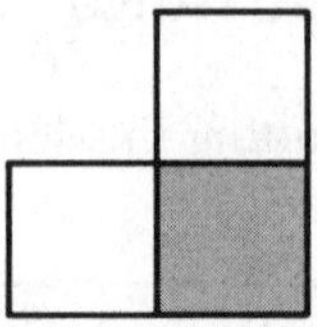

6.

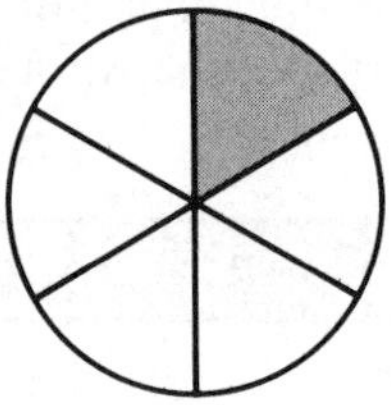

7.

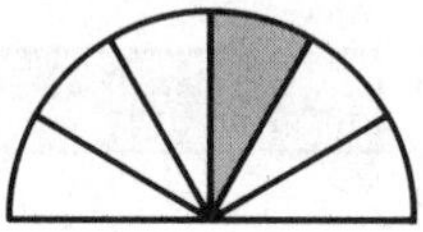

8.

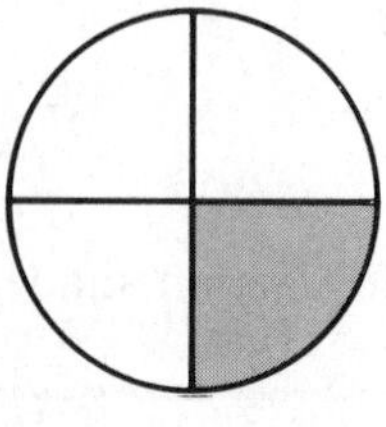

9.

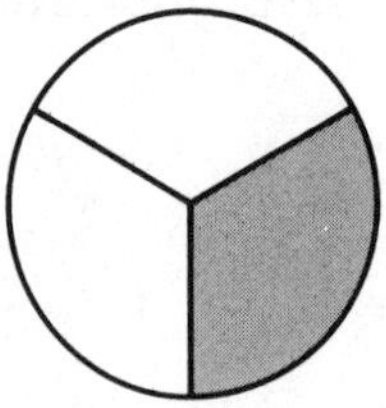

10.

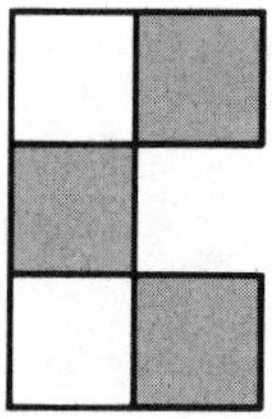

11.

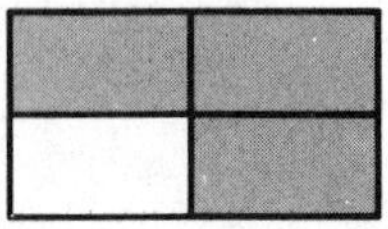

12.

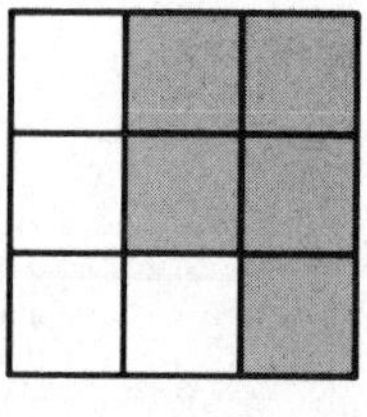

FRACTIONS OF A QUANTITY

There are 16 sweets in the bag.
To find half of these Ann must separate them into two equal piles.

The number of sweets in each pile is the number of 2s in 16,

so $\frac{1}{2}$ of 16 $= 16 \div 2$

$= 8$

EXERCISE 4b

Find $\frac{1}{2}$ of 40

$\frac{1}{2}$ of 40 $= 20$

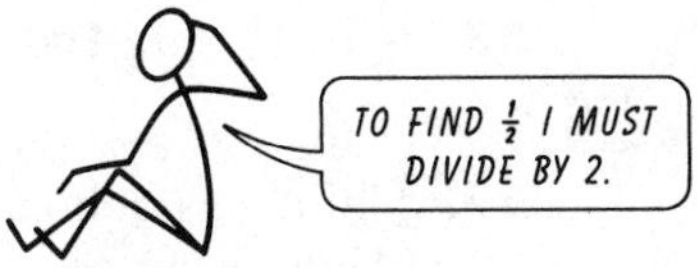

Find

1. $\frac{1}{2}$ of 10 **3.** $\frac{1}{2}$ of 60 **5.** $\frac{1}{2}$ of 108 **7.** $\frac{1}{2}$ of 58

2. $\frac{1}{2}$ of 8 **4.** $\frac{1}{2}$ of 72 **6.** $\frac{1}{2}$ of 246 **8.** $\frac{1}{2}$ of 134

Find $\frac{1}{4}$ of 16

TO FIND $\frac{1}{4}$ I MUST DIVIDE BY 4.

$\frac{1}{4}$ of 16 = 4

Find

9. $\frac{1}{4}$ of 20 **10.** $\frac{1}{4}$ of 60 **11.** $\frac{1}{4}$ of 120 **12.** $\frac{1}{4}$ of 148

Find $\frac{3}{4}$ of 28

TO FIND $\frac{3}{4}$, FIRST FIND $\frac{1}{4}$ OF 28 AND THEN MULTIPLY THE ANSWER BY 3.

$\frac{1}{4}$ of 28 = 7

So $\frac{3}{4}$ of 28 = 3×7

= 21

Find

13. $\frac{3}{4}$ of 12 **14.** $\frac{3}{4}$ of 32 **15.** $\frac{3}{4}$ of 48 **16.** $\frac{3}{4}$ of 72

17. John has a box of 12 pencils. He gives half of them to Sue.
How many does Sue get?
How many does John still have?

18. Mrs Smith has 24 eggs. She uses $\frac{1}{4}$ of them.
How many eggs does she use?
How many does she have left?

19. Lee Ann has 44 records. She gives $\frac{3}{4}$ of them to Sally.
How many does Sally get?
How many does Lee Ann keep?

20. Jean has a packet of 20 ginger biscuits. She gives $\frac{1}{2}$ of them to Yuzo and $\frac{1}{4}$ of them to Joyce. The rest she keeps.

a) How many biscuits does Yuzo get?
b) How many biscuits does Joyce get?
c) How many biscuits does Jean keep?

EQUIVALENT FRACTIONS

We saw at the beginning of the chapter that $\frac{1}{2}$ of the length of wood was exactly the same as $\frac{2}{4}$ of the length and also exactly the same as $\frac{3}{6}$ of it.

We say that $\frac{1}{2}$, $\frac{2}{4}$ and $\frac{3}{6}$ are *equivalent fractions.*

Now $\frac{1}{2} = \frac{1 \times 2}{2 \times 2} = \frac{2}{4}$ and $\frac{1}{2} = \frac{1 \times 3}{2 \times 3} = \frac{3}{6}$

All we have to do to find the equivalent fractions is to multiply the top and bottom by the same number.

For example,

$$\frac{1}{3} = \frac{1 \times 5}{3 \times 5} = \frac{5}{15}$$

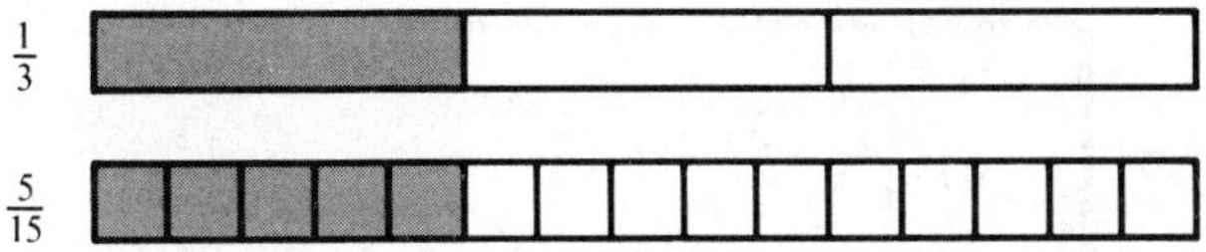

EXERCISE 4c In Questions 1 to 6 copy the diagrams onto squared paper and shade them to show that

1. $\frac{1}{3} = \frac{2}{6}$

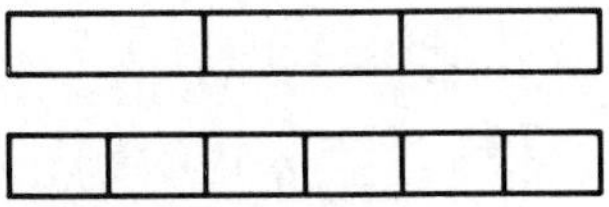

4. $\frac{5}{10} = \frac{1}{2}$

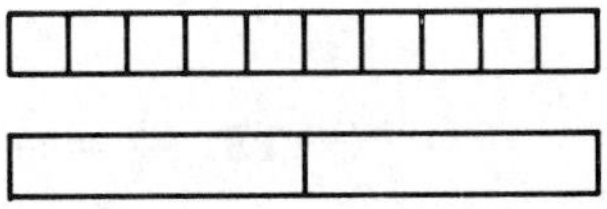

2. $\frac{1}{4} = \frac{2}{8}$

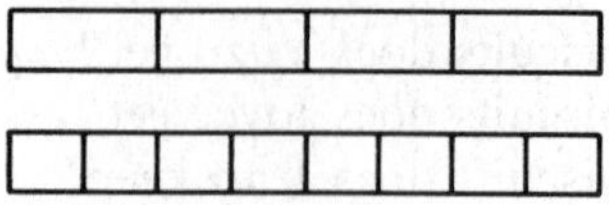

5. $\frac{9}{12} = \frac{3}{4}$

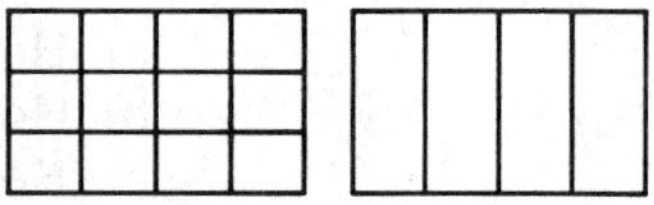

3. $\frac{2}{3} = \frac{8}{12}$

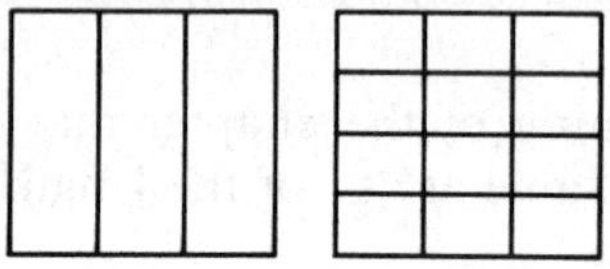

6. $\frac{12}{20} = \frac{3}{5}$

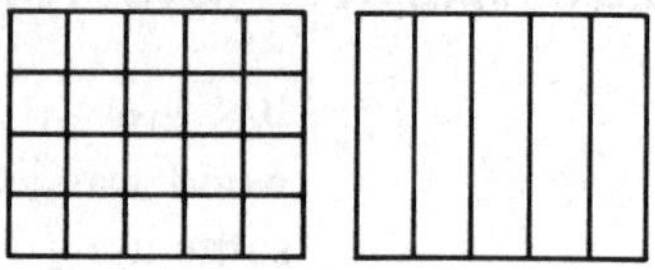

In Questions 7 to 12 draw diagrams similar to those used in Questions 1 to 6 to show that

7. $\frac{1}{5} = \frac{2}{10}$ **9.** $\frac{6}{12} = \frac{1}{2}$ **11.** $\frac{3}{5} = \frac{9}{15}$

8. $\frac{3}{4} = \frac{6}{8}$ **10.** $\frac{6}{9} = \frac{2}{3}$ **12.** $\frac{15}{20} = \frac{3}{4}$

In Questions 13 to 21 fill in the missing numbers to make equivalent fractions.

a) $\frac{1}{4} = \frac{3}{\ }$ b) $\frac{1}{4} = \frac{\ }{20}$

a) $\frac{1}{4} = \frac{1 \times 3}{4 \times 3} = \frac{3}{12}$ b) $\frac{1}{4} = \frac{1 \times 5}{4 \times 5} = \frac{5}{20}$

13. $\frac{1}{3} = \frac{2}{\ }$ **14.** $\frac{2}{3} = \frac{\ }{6}$ **15.** $\frac{1}{2} = \frac{5}{\ }$

16. $\frac{3}{4} = \frac{9}{}$

17. $\frac{2}{5} = \frac{}{20}$

18. $\frac{5}{12} = \frac{}{48}$

19. $\frac{3}{8} = \frac{}{16}$

20. $\frac{4}{5} = \frac{20}{}$

21. $\frac{2}{7} = \frac{10}{}$

SIMPLIFYING FRACTIONS

Just before Exercise 4c we saw that

$$\frac{1}{3} = \frac{1 \times 5}{3 \times 5} = \frac{5}{15}$$

Looking at this the other way round.

$$\frac{5}{15} = \frac{\not{5} \times 1}{\not{5} \times 3} = \frac{1}{3}$$

We say we have *cancelled* the 5s.

Another way of looking at it is to say "What number will divide exactly into the top and the bottom?" You may need to do this several times.

EXERCISE 4d

Simplify $\frac{8}{10}$

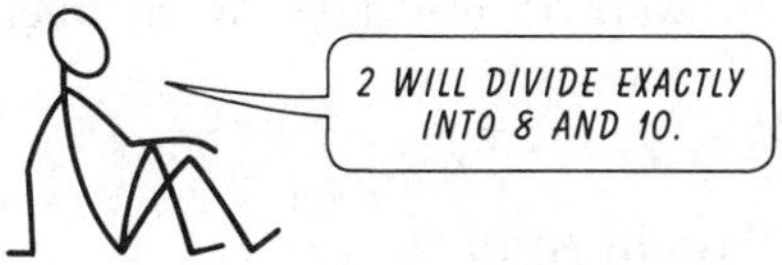
2 WILL DIVIDE EXACTLY INTO 8 AND 10.

$$\frac{8}{10} = \frac{4}{5}$$

Simplify the following fractions

1. $\frac{3}{6}$

2. $\frac{2}{12}$

3. $\frac{3}{9}$

4. $\frac{2}{8}$

5. $\frac{6}{8}$

6. $\frac{9}{12}$

7. $\frac{4}{10}$

8. $\frac{10}{12}$

Simplify $\frac{12}{18}$

$$\frac{12}{18} = \frac{6}{9}$$

$$\frac{6}{9} = \frac{2}{3}$$

$$\therefore \quad \frac{12}{18} = \frac{2}{3}$$

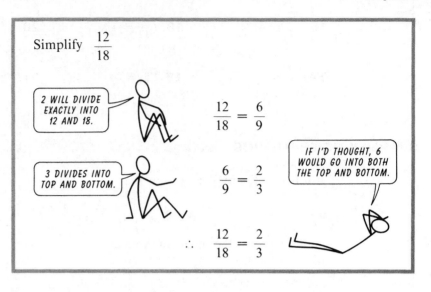

Simplify the following fractions

9. $\frac{8}{12}$ **11.** $\frac{9}{18}$ **13.** $\frac{8}{24}$ **15.** $\frac{6}{36}$

10. $\frac{12}{16}$ **12.** $\frac{20}{24}$ **14.** $\frac{16}{20}$ **16.** $\frac{8}{28}$

ONE QUANTITY AS A FRACTION OF ANOTHER

EXERCISE 4e

Last April there were 15 wet days. What fraction of April was wet?

There are 30 days in April

15 wet days $= \frac{15}{30}$ of April

$= \frac{3}{6}$ of April

$= \frac{1}{2}$ of April

1. Mrs. Cook bought 12 cooking apples. Six of them were bad. What fraction of the apples were bad?

2. In a class of 26 pupils, 13 of them are girls.
What fraction of the class are girls?

3. In class 1B there are 7 boys and 21 girls.
a) How many pupils are there in the class?
b) What fraction of the class are girls?
c) What fraction of the class are boys?

4. In a car park, 36 out of the 72 cars were made in the United Kingdom.
What fraction is this?

5. Fourteen out of the 56 oranges in a box are bad.
a) What fraction of the oranges are bad?
b) How many good oranges are there?
c) What fraction of the oranges are good?

In Questions 6 to 11 write the first quantity as a fraction of the second quantity.

6. 25 p; 50 p

7. 15 minutes; 30 minutes

8. £12; £16

9. 14 p; 56 p

10. 15 cm; 60 cm

11. £63; £84

Write 45 minutes as a fraction of 1 hour.

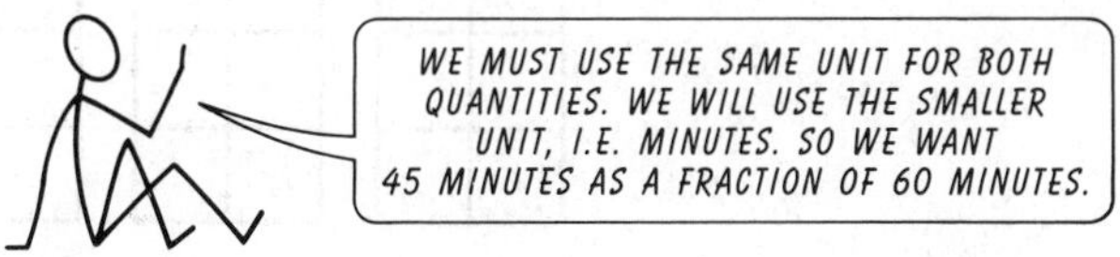

WE MUST USE THE SAME UNIT FOR BOTH QUANTITIES. WE WILL USE THE SMALLER UNIT, I.E. MINUTES. SO WE WANT 45 MINUTES AS A FRACTION OF 60 MINUTES.

$$45 \text{ minutes} = \frac{45}{60} \text{ of 1 hour}$$

$$= \frac{3}{4} \text{ of 1 hour}$$

In Questions 12 to 27 write the first quantity as a fraction of the second quantity.

12. 30 seconds; 1 minute

13. 50 p; £1

14. 150 p; £2

15. 75 p; £1

16. 30 seconds; 2 minutes

17. 135 minutes; 3 hours

18. 50 p; £2

19. 68 p; £1.36

20. 40 seconds; 1 minute

21. 15 p; 45 p

22. 375 p; £5

23. 60 p; £1.80

24. £1.50; £2

25. 30 seconds; 3 minutes

26. 40 p; £1

27. $1\frac{1}{2}$ hours; 6 hours

MIXED NUMBERS

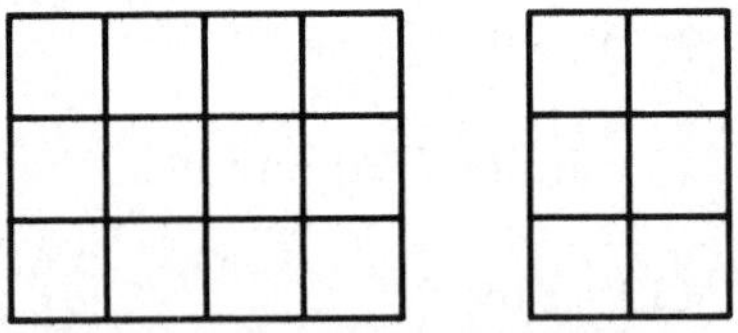

Steve has one and a half bars of milk chocolate.
We write this as $1\frac{1}{2}$ bars; $1\frac{1}{2}$ is called a *mixed number.*

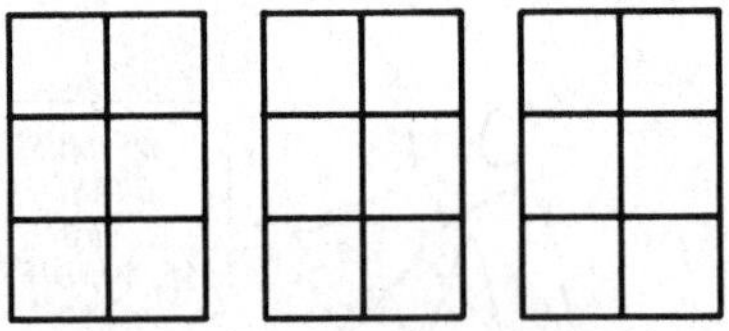

If Steve broke the large bar in half he would have three half bars. We write this as $\frac{3}{2}$ bars; $\frac{3}{2}$ is called an *improper fraction* because the top number is bigger than the bottom number.

Since the amount of chocolate Steve has is unchanged,

$$\frac{3}{2} = 1\frac{1}{2}$$

EXERCISE 4f In Questions 1 to 12 change the improper fractions into mixed numbers.

Write $\frac{12}{5}$ as a mixed number.

$$\frac{12}{5} = \frac{10+2}{5}$$

$$= \frac{10}{5} + \frac{2}{5}$$

$$= 2 + \frac{2}{5}$$

$$= 2\frac{2}{5}$$

1. $\frac{7}{2}$

2. $\frac{9}{2}$

3. $\frac{5}{4}$

4. $\frac{9}{4}$

5. $\frac{7}{4}$

6. $\frac{13}{4}$

7. $\frac{11}{5}$

8. $\frac{19}{7}$

9. $\frac{27}{5}$

10. $\frac{25}{8}$

11. $\frac{14}{3}$

12. $\frac{32}{7}$

5 INTRODUCING ANGLES

TURNING

When the hand of a clock starts at 12 and moves round until it stops at 12 again, it has made one complete turn.

One complete turn is called a revolution.

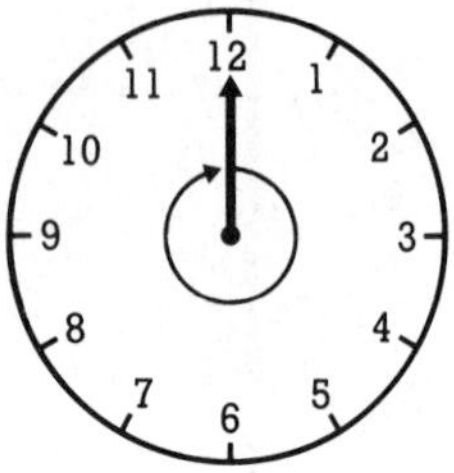

EXERCISE 5a

a) The hand of a clock goes from 12 to 6. What fraction of a revolution has it turned through?

b) The hand of a clock starts at 2 and moves round to 11. What fraction of a revolution has it turned through?

a)

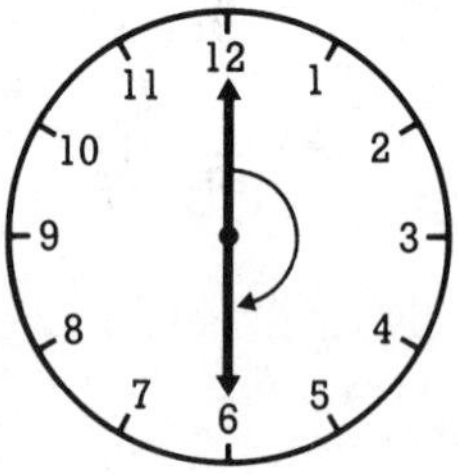

It has turned through $\frac{1}{2}$ of a revolution.

b)

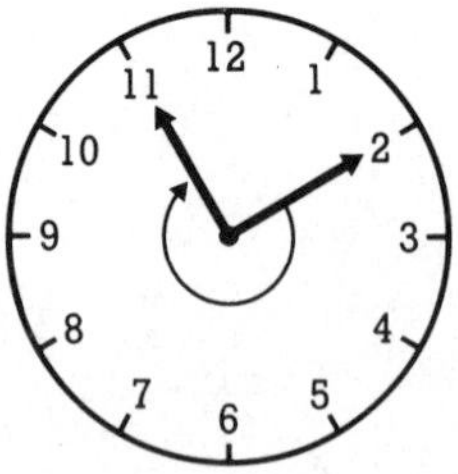

It has turned through $\frac{3}{4}$ of a revolution.

State what fraction of a revolution the hand of a clock turns through when it goes from

1. 3 to 9

2. 4 to 7

3. 4 to 10

4. 9 to 6

5. 5 to 8

6. 7 to 10

7. 11 to 5

8. 2 to 5

9. 8 to 11

10. 6 to 3

11. 1 to 7

12. 1 to 10

13. 5 to 2

14. 10 to 4

15. 12 to 9

Where does the hand of a clock stop if it starts at 3 and turns through $\frac{1}{4}$ of a revolution?

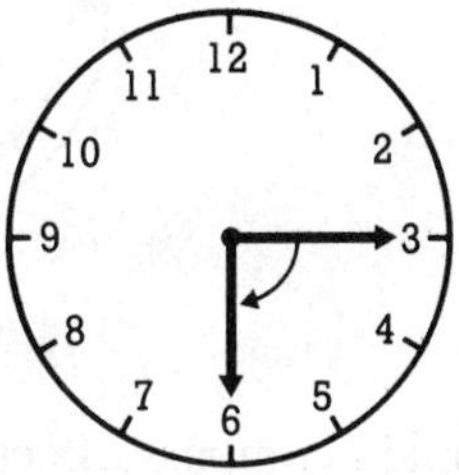

It stops at 6.

State where the hand of a clock stops if

16. it starts at 12 and turns through $\frac{1}{4}$ of a revolution

17. it starts at 3 and turns through $\frac{1}{2}$ of a revolution

18. it starts at 6 and turns through $\frac{1}{4}$ of a revolution

19. it starts at 2 and turns through $\frac{1}{2}$ of a revolution

20. it starts at 3 and turns through $\frac{3}{4}$ of a revolution

21. it starts at 5 and turns through $\frac{1}{4}$ of a revolution

22. it starts at 10 and turns through $\frac{1}{2}$ of a revolution

23. it starts at 9 and turns through $\frac{3}{4}$ of a revolution

24. it starts at 8 and turns through $\frac{1}{4}$ of a revolution

25. it starts at 7 and turns through $\frac{1}{2}$ of a revolution.

BEARINGS

People, such as explorers and scouts, use a *compass* to find the right direction.

The four main compass directions are north (N), south (S), east (E) and west (W).

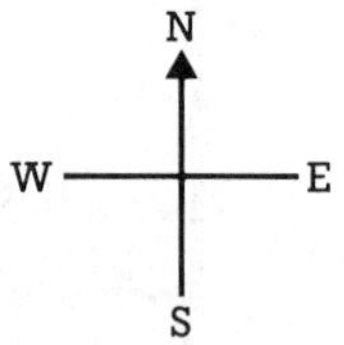

Thomas stands facing north. If he turns clockwise through quarter of a revolution, in what direction will he be facing?

THIS IS THE WAY A CLOCK HAND GOES ROUND, SO THIS WAY IS CLOCKWISE.
N
E

He will face east.

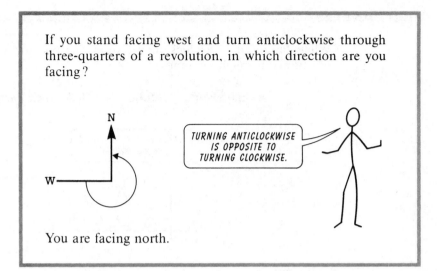

If you stand facing west and turn anticlockwise through three-quarters of a revolution, in which direction are you facing?

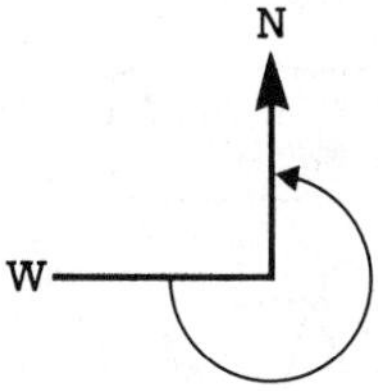
N
W

TURNING ANTICLOCKWISE IS OPPOSITE TO TURNING CLOCKWISE.

You are facing north.

EXERCISE 5b

1. If you stand facing east and turn anticlockwise through $\frac{3}{4}$ of a revolution, in which direction are you facing?

2. If you stand facing south and turn clockwise through $\frac{1}{4}$ of a revolution, in which direction are you facing?

3. If you stand facing north and turn, in either direction, through a complete revolution, in which direction are you facing?

4. If you stand facing west and turn through $\frac{1}{2}$ a revolution, in which direction are you facing? Does it matter whether you turn clockwise or anticlockwise?

5. If you stand facing south and turn through $1\frac{1}{2}$ revolutions, in which direction are you facing?

6. If you stand facing west and turn clockwise to face south what part of a revolution have you turned through?

7. If you stand facing north and turn clockwise to face west how much of a revolution have you turned through?

8. If you stand facing east and turn to face west what part of a revolution have you turned through?

RIGHT ANGLES

When the hand of a clock moves from one position to another, it has turned through an angle.

A quarter of a revolution is called a *right angle*.

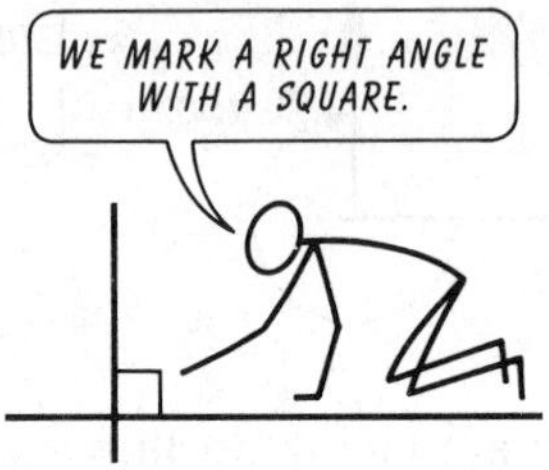

EXERCISE 5c

How many right angles does the hand of a clock turn through if it starts at 12 and stops at 6?

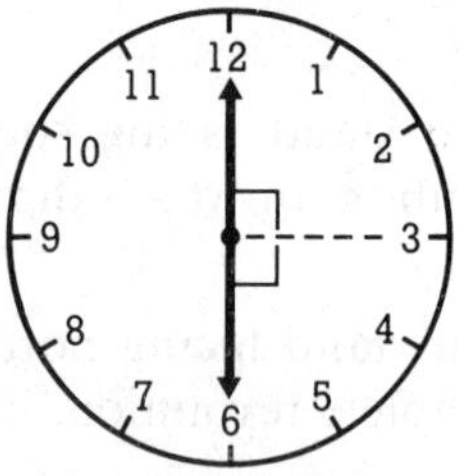

It has turned through 2 right angles.

Half a revolution is 2 right angles.

State how many right angles the hand of a clock turns through if

1. it starts at 6 and stops at 9

2. it starts at 1 and stops at 7

3. it starts at 4 and stops at 10

4. it starts at 11 and stops at 2

5. it starts at 12 and stops at 9.

State how many right angles you turn through if

6. you start facing north and turn clockwise to the east

7. you start facing south and turn anticlockwise to the west

8. you start facing east and turn to the west

9. you start facing north and turn to the south

10. you start facing west and turn anticlockwise to the south.

Where does the hand of a clock stop if it starts at 1 and turns through 3 right angles?

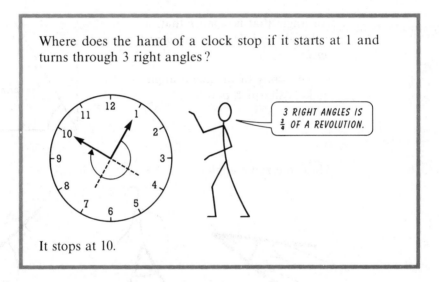

It stops at 10.

Say where the hand of a clock stops if

11. it starts at 1 and turns through 2 right angles

12. it starts at 6 and turns through 1 right angle

13. it starts at 12 and turns through 3 right angles

14. it starts at 8 and turns through 2 right angles

15. it starts at 11 and turns through 1 right angle.

Give the direction in which you will be facing if you obey the following instructions.

16. Start facing east and turn clockwise through 3 right angles.

17. Start facing north and turn anticlockwise through 1 right angle.

18. Start facing north and turn clockwise through 1 right angle.

19. Start facing west and turn through 2 right angles.

ACUTE ANGLES

An angle that is *smaller* than a right angle is called an *acute angle*,

i.e. the *arms* of an acute angle make a sharpish point.

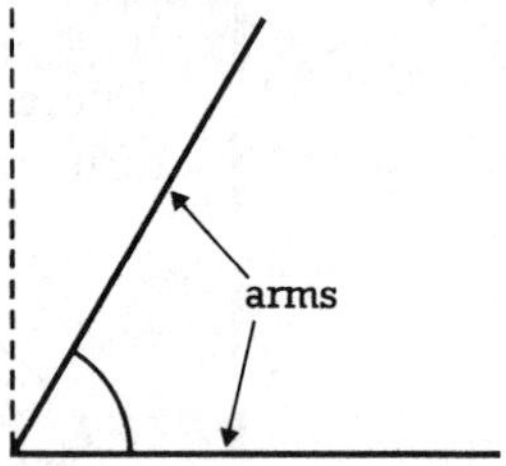

These are acute angles.

OBTUSE ANGLES

If an angle is bigger than 1 right angle but less than 2 right angles it is called an *obtuse angle*.

These are obtuse angles.

REFLEX ANGLES

Reflex angles are larger than two right angles. They look like this

EXERCISE 5d Each angle is either acute, obtuse, reflex or a right angle. Give the name of each angle.

1. 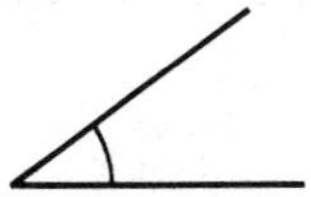

4. 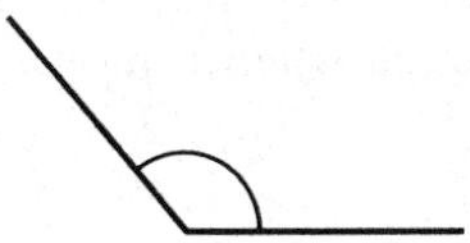

7. 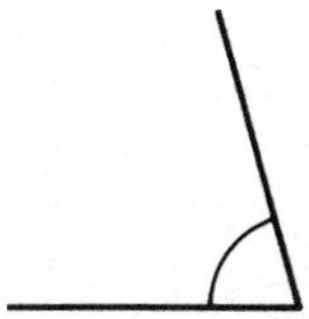

2. 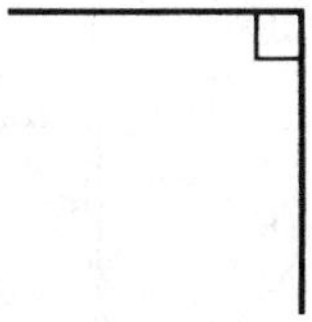

5. 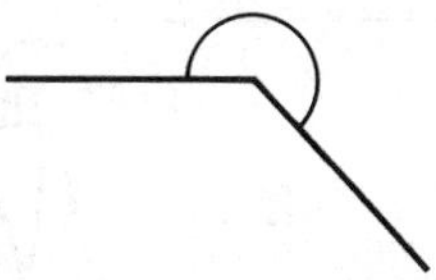

8. 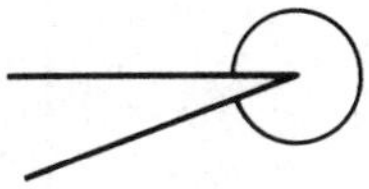

3. 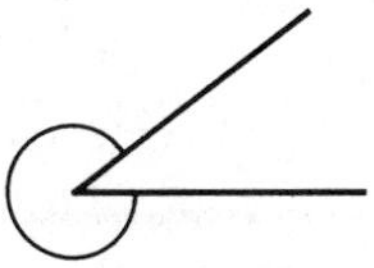

6. 

9. 

DEGREES

One complete revolution is divided into 360 parts. Each part is called a *degree*.

360 degrees is written 360°

EXERCISE 5e How many degrees are there in

1. half a revolution

2. three right angles

3. one right angle

4. quarter of a revolution?

How many right angles correspond to

5. 270°

6. 180°

7. 360°?

How many degrees has the hand of a clock turned through when it moves from 3 to 6?

It has turned through 90°.

How many degrees does the hand of a clock turn through when it goes from

8. 12 to 6

9. 1 to 4

10. 5 to 8

11. 3 to 9

12. 12 to 9

13. 5 to 2

14. 2 to 8

15. 4 to 10

16. 11 to 5?

How many degrees have I turned through if I turn anticlockwise from facing east to facing south?

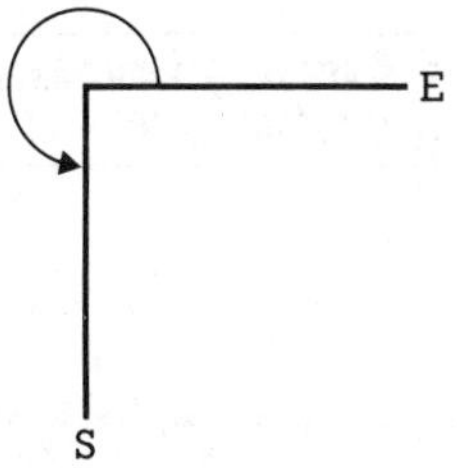

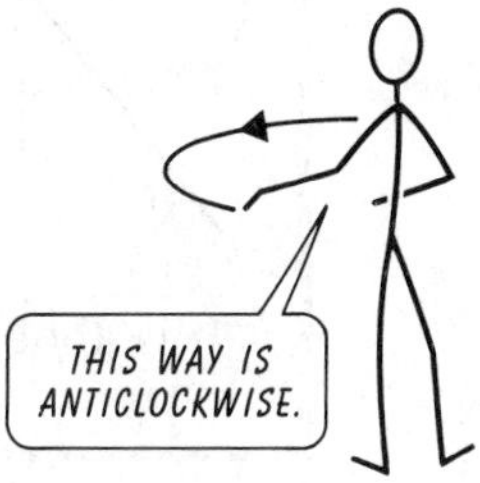

I have turned through 270°.

How many degrees have I turned through if

17. I turn clockwise from north to east

18. I turn anticlockwise from south to north

19. I turn clockwise from west to north

20. I turn from east to west?

ESTIMATING ANGLES

When a revolution is divided into six equal parts, each angle is 60°.

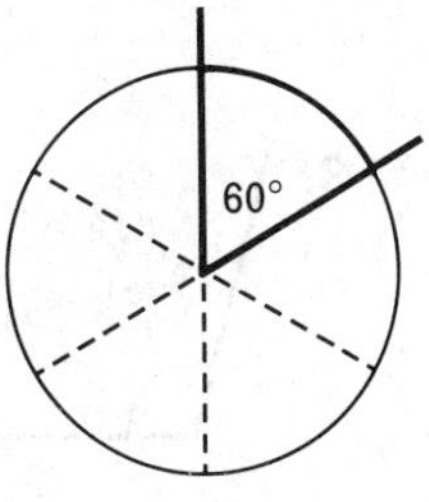

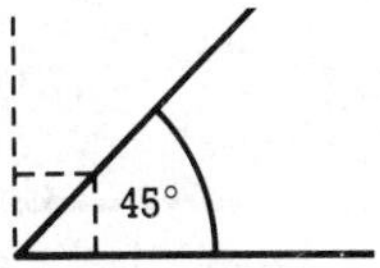

Half of a right angle is 45°.

These two angles are useful if we have to estimate the size of an angle.

EXERCISE 5f

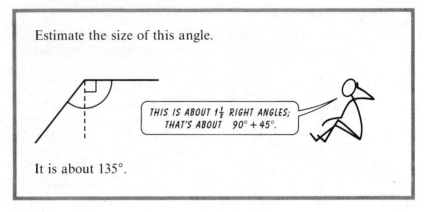

Estimate the size of this angle.

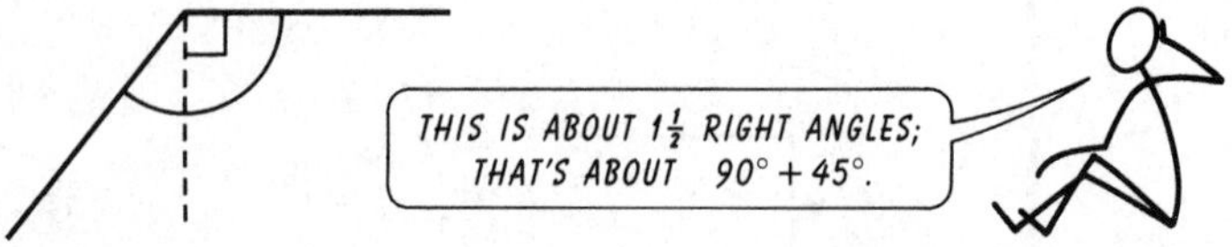

THIS IS ABOUT $1\frac{1}{2}$ RIGHT ANGLES;
THAT'S ABOUT $90° + 45°$.

It is about 135°.

Estimate the size of each angle.

1. 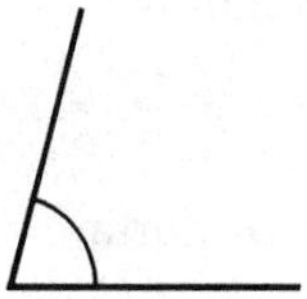

4. 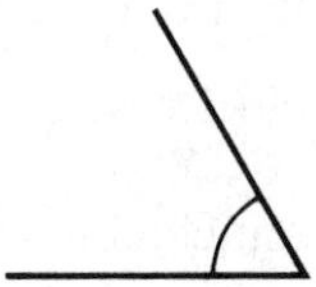

7. 

2. 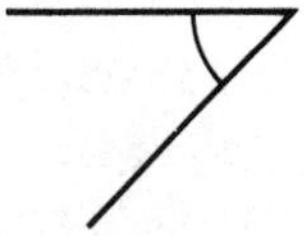

5. 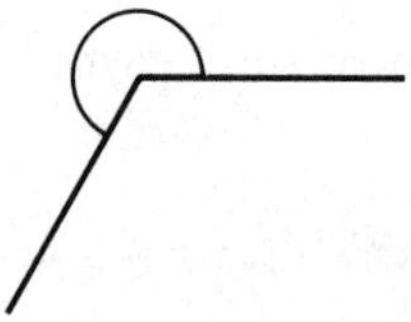

8. 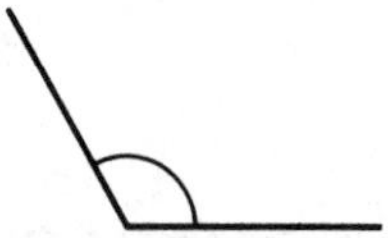

3. 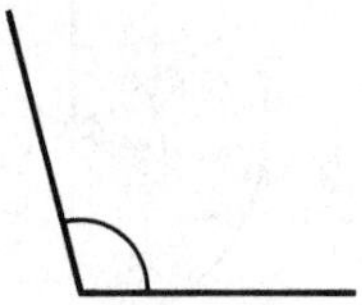

6. 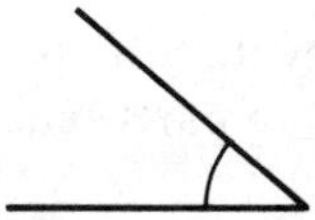

9. 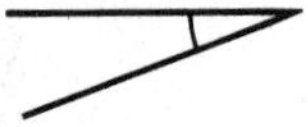

MIXED EXERCISE

EXERCISE 5g

1. What fraction of a revolution does the hand of a clock turn through when it moves from
   a) 1 to 10 b) 11 to 5?

2. If I face west and turn through 1 right angle, in what direction am I then facing if

a) I turn anticlockwise b) I turn clockwise?

3. How many right angles are there between the east and west directions?

4. How many degrees are there between the north and south directions?

5. How many degrees are there in

a) three right angles b) quarter of a revolution?

6. What fraction of a revolution corresponds to

a) 180° b) 90° c) 270°?

7. How many degrees have I turned through if I start facing west and turn

a) clockwise to the south b) anticlockwise to the north?

8. Say whether each of these statements is true or false;

a) 65° is an acute angle
b) half a right angle is 45°
c) 90° is half a revolution
d) 170° is a reflex angle.

9. Say whether each of these angles is acute, obtuse or reflex.

a)
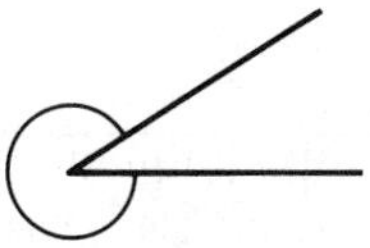
b)
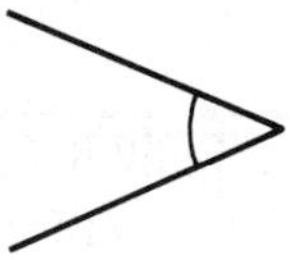
c)
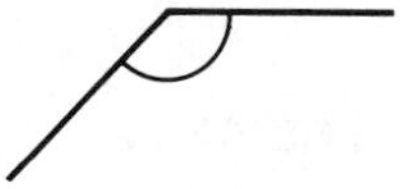

10. Estimate each of these angles.

a)
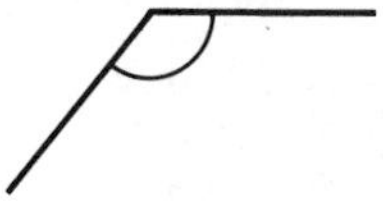
b)
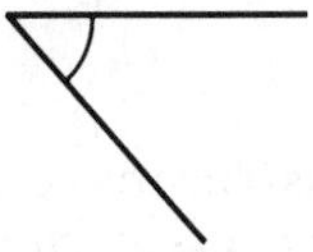
c)
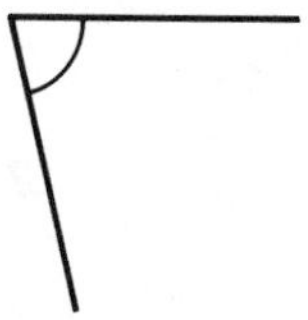

6 WHOLE NUMBERS 3

WHOLE NUMBER APPROXIMATIONS

We often want only a rough idea of the size of a number, rather than the exact number.

For example, to say in a news broadcast that "Five thousand, eight hundred and sixty-two pounds were stolen in a bank raid" is too complicated. "About six thousand pounds" would be clearer.

We need to be able to give numbers perhaps to the nearest ten or to the nearest hundred, or, as in the case above, to the nearest thousand.

EXERCISE 6a

1.

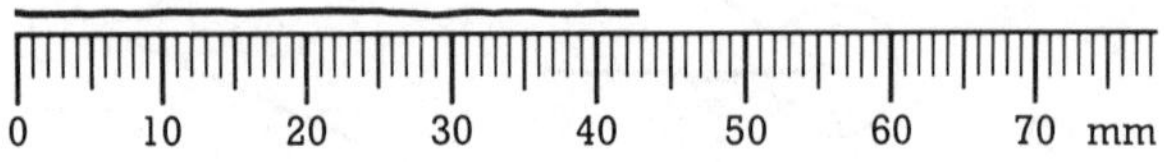

a) Is the length of this string nearer to 40 mm or to 50 mm?
b) How did you decide?

2. This instrument is used by estate agents to measure rooms.

a) Is the number on the display nearer to 600 or to 700?
b) Which figure did you look at to help you decide?

3.

a) What is the weight shown, to the nearest hundred kg?
b) Which figure did you look at to help you decide?

a) Give 390 to the nearest hundred.
b) Give 42 to the nearest ten.

a) 390 to the nearest hundred is 400.

IT IS NEARER TO 400 THAN TO 300.

b) 42 to the nearest ten is 40.

4. "£410 was collected in aid of the local hospital."
To the nearest hundred pounds, how much was collected?

5. 8700 people were counted through the turnstiles at a match.
How many is this to the nearest thousand?

6. In a jumbo matchbox there are 640 matches.
To the nearest hundred, how many matches are there?

7. Give the following numbers to the nearest ten.
a) 82 b) 94 c) 47 d) 67

8. Give the following numbers to the nearest hundred.
a) 430 b) 190 c) 660 d) 240

a) Give 65 to the nearest ten.
b) Give 8500 to the nearest thousand.

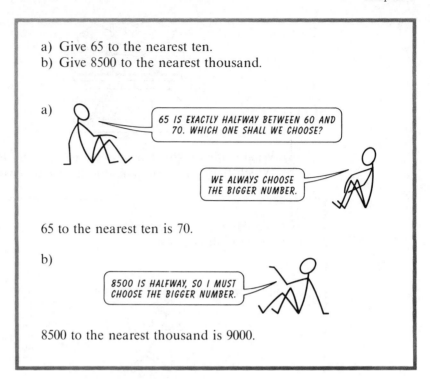

a)

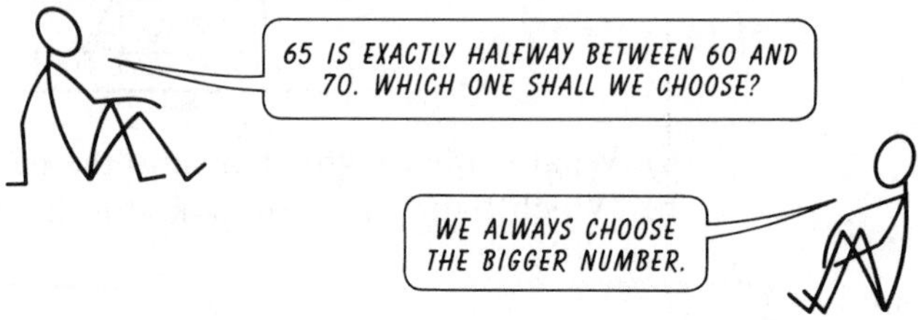

65 IS EXACTLY HALFWAY BETWEEN 60 AND 70. WHICH ONE SHALL WE CHOOSE?
WE ALWAYS CHOOSE THE BIGGER NUMBER.

65 to the nearest ten is 70.

b)

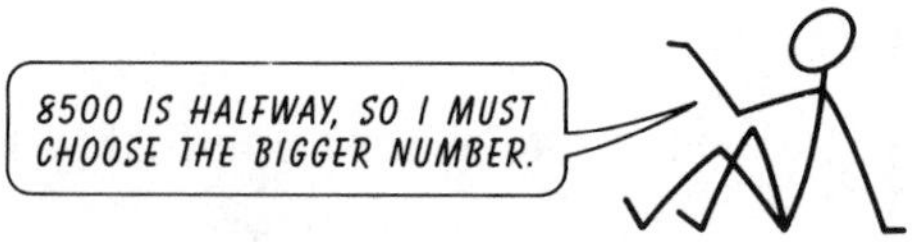

8500 IS HALFWAY, SO I MUST CHOOSE THE BIGGER NUMBER.

8500 to the nearest thousand is 9000.

9. Give each number to the nearest ten.
a) 75 b) 25 c) 95

10. Give each number to the nearest hundred.
a) 650 b) 450 c) 150

11. Round each number to as simple a number as possible.
a) 87 b) 140 c) 4500 d) 32

12. Gavin is doing a rough check around the class to find out how much charity money has been collected so far. Bena has collected 78 p.
To the nearest 10 p, how much should she tell Gavin she has collected?

13. Class 2B collected 370 buttons and 220 marbles to sell on their stall at the school fête.
When Elena reported to the fête committee, she gave each of these numbers to the nearest hundred.
What numbers did she report?

MORE COMPLICATED NUMBERS

When giving a simple approximation for, say, 470, we look at the size of the *second* figure.

If it is 5 or over, we give the bigger of the two round numbers, i.e. 500 rather than 400.

We do the same with a number like 586. We look at the 8, which is over 5. So 586 to the nearest hundred is 600.

EXERCISE 6b

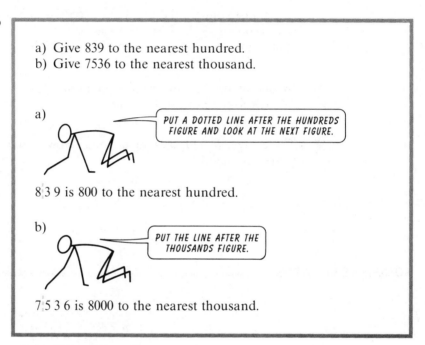

a) Give 839 to the nearest hundred.
b) Give 7536 to the nearest thousand.

a)

PUT A DOTTED LINE AFTER THE HUNDREDS FIGURE AND LOOK AT THE NEXT FIGURE.

8 3 9 is 800 to the nearest hundred.

b)

PUT THE LINE AFTER THE THOUSANDS FIGURE.

7 5 3 6 is 8000 to the nearest thousand.

1. Give each number to the nearest hundred.

a) 476 b) 129 c) 354

2. Give each number to the nearest thousand.

a) 7234 b) 3756 c) 1523

3. Daniel has collected 382 stamps.
What is the round number he tells his friends, to give them a rough idea of the size of his collection?

4. A crowd of 4292 attended a cricket match.
What round number should a reporter use?

5.

A botanist counted the number of seeds in this sunflower head and recorded 1972.
Round this to as simple a number as possible.

6. In one of the school libraries there are 4257 books. Give this number to the nearest thousand.

7. There are 378 tadpoles in a pond. How many is this to the nearest hundred?

ROUGH ESTIMATES

We can use round numbers to check that answers to calculations are sensible.

67 can be rounded to 70 and 52 rounds to 50.
70 + 50 = 120, so £1.79 is not likely to be right.

Get into the habit of checking answers. It will save you a great deal of trouble.

EXERCISE 6c

Add 77 and 24

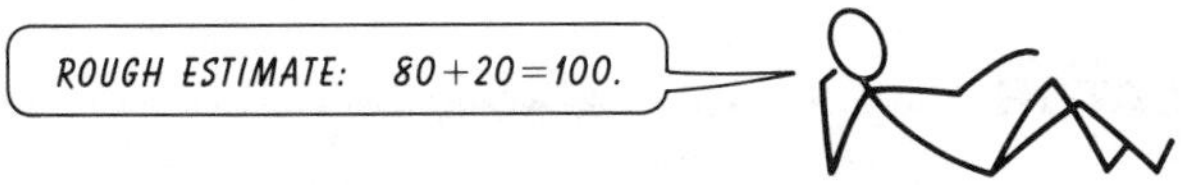
ROUGH ESTIMATE: 80+20=100.

$$\begin{array}{r} 77 \\ +\ 24 \\ \hline 101 \\ \hline \end{array}$$

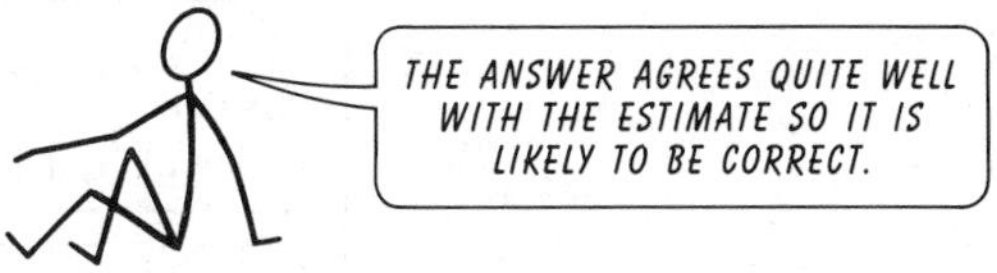
THE ANSWER AGREES QUITE WELL WITH THE ESTIMATE SO IT IS LIKELY TO BE CORRECT.

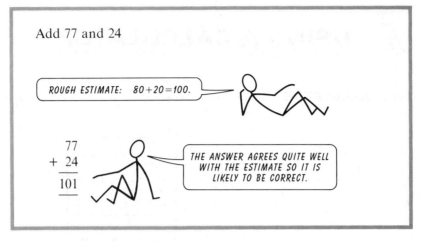

In each of the following calculations, find a rough answer, then work out the accurate answer.

1. $23 + 49$

2. $780 - 190$

3. $92 - 48$

4. $602 + 819$

In Questions 5 to 8, some of the given answers are wrong. Find which are likely to be wrong by working out rough answers.

5. $76 + 29 = 105$

6. $57 - 29 = 48$

7. $320 + 272 = 992$

8. $412 - 231 = 181$

9. Keith had a piece of wood 112 cm long. He worked out that if he cut 48 cm off, there would be 84 cm left.
Find a rough answer to the calculation. Is Keith likely to be right?

10. Jenny bought a magazine costing 98 p and a pen costing 27 p.
a) Roughly how much was the bill?
b) What was the actual bill? Does this answer agree with (a)?

11. Mr and Mrs Askew bought a sofa for £221 and a chair for £102. They were told that the total cost was £423.
Is this likely to be right?

7 USING A CALCULATOR

THE CALCULATOR

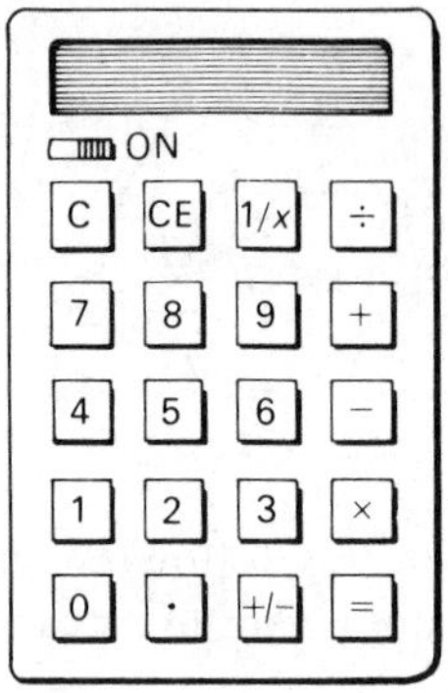

Start with simple calculations which you can check easily.
To find the value of 5×8, press the keys

[5] [×] [8] [=]

After you have pressed the [=] button, the calculator displays the answer, i.e. 40.

EXERCISE 7a

Find 12×48

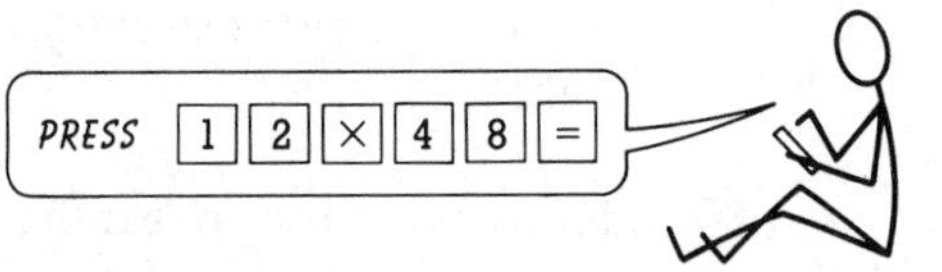

$12 \times 48 = 576$

In each question from 1 to 6, use your calculator to find the answer. The numbers are all very easy so you should be able to check the answer in your head.

1. $4 + 6 + 2$

2. 2×6

3. $9 - 5$

4. 8×2

5. $15 \div 3$

6. $31 + 7$

7. Make up three simple calculations of your own and use your calculator to work them out.

In each question from 8 to 11,

a) work out the answer *without* using a calculator,

b) work out the answer using a calculator.

Do your answers agree?

8. 3×22 ([3] [×] [2] [2] [=])

9. $78 + 14$ **10.** $52 - 14$ **11.** $52 \div 4$

12.

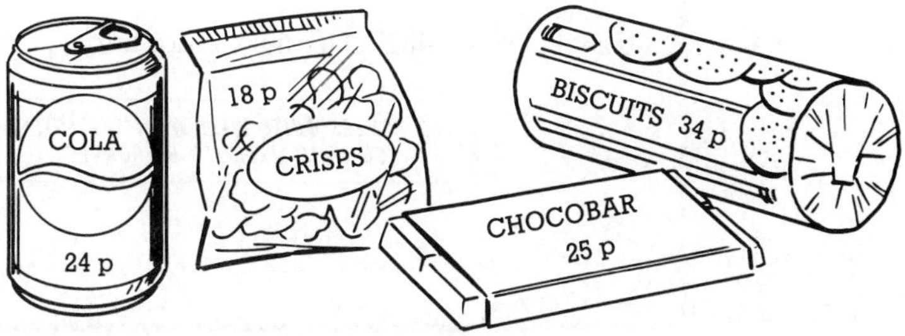

a) Lisa wants to buy 12 cans of cola. She has £2 to spend. What is the total cost of the colas? Does she have enough money?
b) Daniel buys one of each item. What is the total cost?
c) Adrian buys 6 bags of crisps. What is the cost?
d) Ali starts with 62 p and buys a Chocobar. How much money has he left?

13. Use a calculator to find

a) 2^3
b) 11^2
c) 3^3
d) 7^2

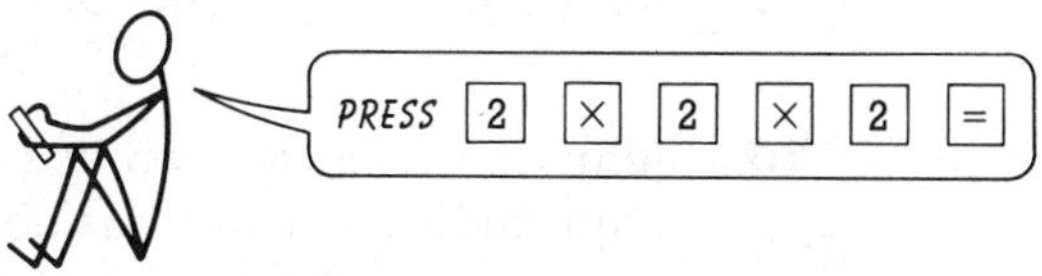

14. Four charity collectors reported that they had 72 p, 97 p, 65 p and 31 p.
How much had they collected altogether?

15. Philip buys two pens at 14 p each, a notebook at 75 p, and a magazine at 48 p.
What is his total bill?

CHECKING ANSWERS

EXERCISE 7b

Find a rough estimate for 323 + 159 and then use your calculator to find the exact answer.

$$323 \approx 300$$

$$159 \approx 200$$

≈ MEANS "IS ROUGHLY EQUAL TO".

$$323 + 159 \approx 300 + 200$$

$$= 500$$

$323 + 159 = 482$ (using a calculator)

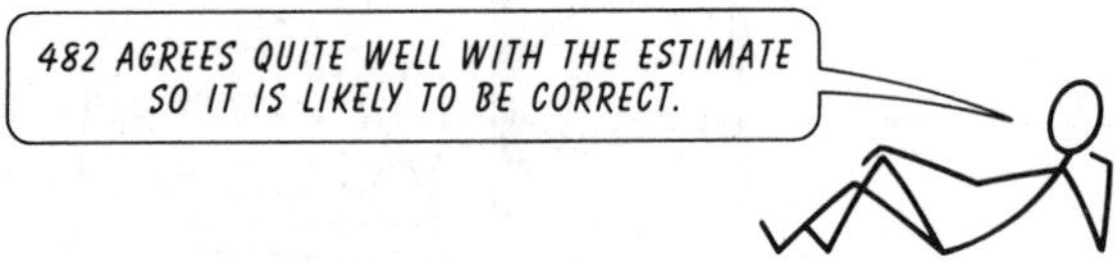

482 AGREES QUITE WELL WITH THE ESTIMATE SO IT IS LIKELY TO BE CORRECT.

For each question from 1 to 9,

a) find a rough estimate of the answer
b) work out the answer using a calculator.

Do your answers agree fairly well?

1. 47 + 32	**4.** 58 + 89	**7.** 431 + 198
2. 78 − 19	**5.** 93 − 71	**8.** 411 − 222
3. 102 + 287	**6.** 38 + 39	**9.** 278 + 432

10. John and Gita each worked out a rough answer to 670 + 987. John said the answer was about 1400 and Gita said 2000.

a) Do you agree with either of them? If not, what is *your* rough answer?
b) Use your calculator to work out the real answer.

11. On a school outing, 49 pupils were on one coach and 52 on the second.

a) Roughly, how many pupils were there on the outing?
b) Use your calculator to find the real number of pupils.

MIXED EXERCISE

EXERCISE 7c Questions 1 to 4 test your ability to work out the answers without a calculator. Check each one afterwards using your calculator.

1. 45×9

2. $128 \div 8$

3. $57 - 39$

4. $3 + 6 + 11 + 8$

Questions 5 to 12 test your ability to use a calculator to work with bigger numbers.

Find

5. 42×51

6. $182 + 54$

7. $45 + 63 + 14$

8. $93 - 78$

9. 909×4

10. 18×21

11. $288 \div 12$

12. $745 - 23$

13. A newcomer to a group was asked his name. On his calculator he pressed [3] [1] [7] [5] [3] [7] and then showed the others the display upside down. What *was* his name?

14. The answer to one of the following calculations is wrong. Find it and correct it.

a) $42 - 16 = 26$ b) $37 + 88 = 115$ c) $38 \times 6 = 228$

15. On a broken-down calculator, only the keys [2], [3], [4], [×], [+] and [=] can be used.
The calculator won't work if you press more than five times in a calculation, so [3] [+] [3] [+] [3] [=] won't give an answer.

We can get 25 using [2] [2] [+] [3] [=]

Write down four other numbers you can get as answers.
Make sure you write down the complete calculation each time so that it can be checked (e.g. $22 + 3 = 25$).

16. Do you need practice in writing 3? Then write down the answer to $12345679 \times 3 \times 9$
Now try $12345679 \times 4 \times 9$
Try other possibilities.

17. Magic squares.

In each square, each row, each column and each diagonal should add up to the same number.

Example

10	11	6
5	9	13
12	7	8

27

This number is given below the first two squares but you can find out for yourself what the number under the third square should be.
Copy and complete each square.

4		
3		7

15

	7	
8		4

21

2	11	5
7		10

EXERCISE 7d Find the answers to Questions 1 to 4 without using a calculator.

1. 231 + 69

2. 231 − 69

3. 34 + 25 + 15

4. 45 × 6

Now use a calculator to check your answers.

5. How many days are there in 15 weeks?

6. Find the sum of eighty-six, thirty-seven and forty-two.

7. Write down a two-figure number, for example 26
Reverse the figures 62
Take the smaller number from the larger 62 − 26 = 36
Add the figures together 3 + 6 = 9
If the result is a two-figure number, add its figures together.

Try this with a number of your own choice.

Now try another number.

Try it with a three-figure number.

What do you notice about the final answers?

8. Cross-number: copy and complete this puzzle.

Across

1. $48 + 37$
4. $142 - 6$
5. 15×4
6. $280 + 73 + 56$

Down

2. 51×100
3. 23×7
5. $92 - 28$

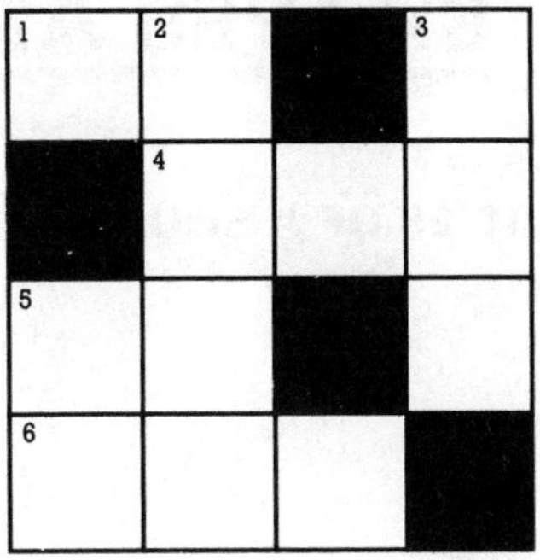

8 SHAPES AND TESSELLATIONS

PROPERTIES OF A SQUARE

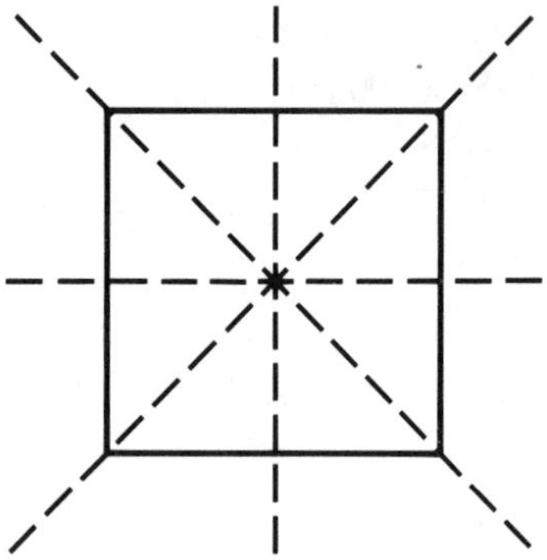

The four sides of a square are equal.
The angle at each corner of a square is a right angle.

If the diagram is folded along any one of the broken lines, each half fits exactly over the other half.

A square has four lines of symmetry.

This is a square.

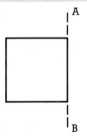

If we take AB as a line of symmetry and draw a new shape, this is the figure we get.

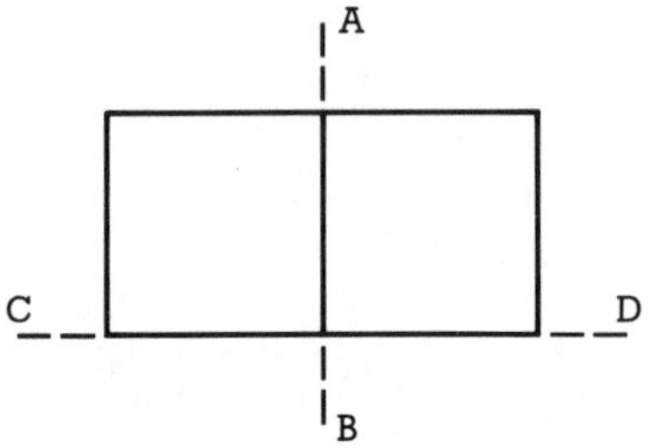

If we now draw a new figure with CD as a line of symmetry, we get this shape.

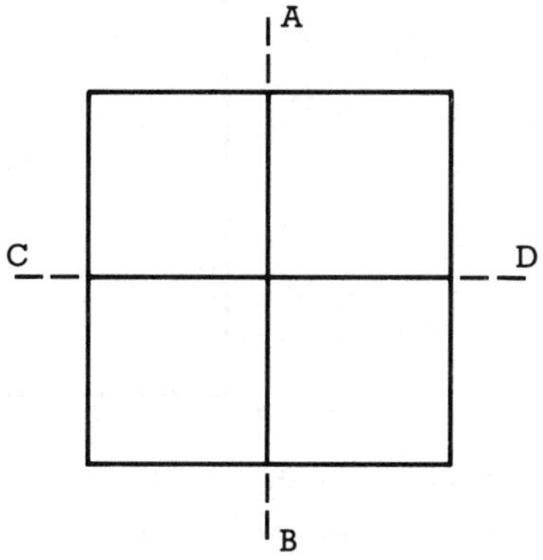

We now have four squares that fit together with no spaces between them.

TILING PATTERNS

We can continue adding squares to the diagram above to make a tiling pattern.

For example

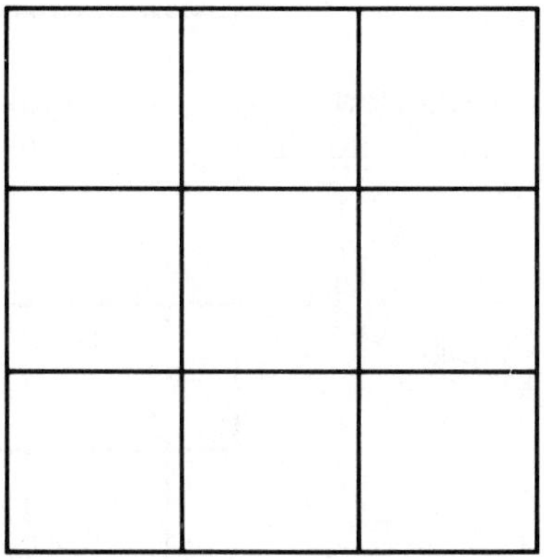

If a shape can be used to lay out a tiling pattern *without spaces*, we say that the shape *tessellates*.

A square tessellates.

EXERCISE 8a Use a dot grid paper for this exercise.

1.

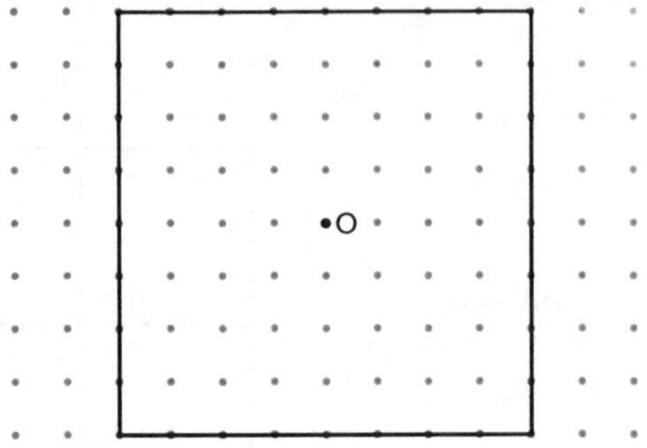

Draw a square of side 8 cm. Mark the centre of the square O.

Draw a line through O that is a line of symmetry and is at right angles to two of the sides.

Draw another line through O that is a line of symmetry at right angles to the other two sides of the square. The lines of symmetry divide the square into 4 smaller squares.

2.

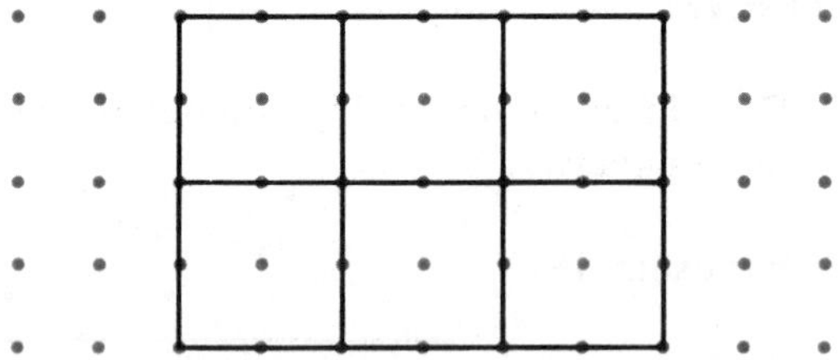

Sheila started laying square tiles on the kitchen floor. Copy her pattern and show the position of another 6 tiles.

3.

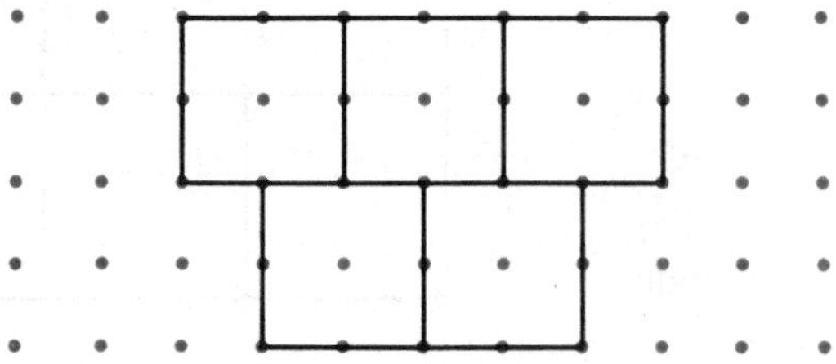

Jim started laying tiles on the bathroom floor. Here are the positions of the first 5 tiles he laid. Continue this pattern showing how he could lay a further five tiles.

4.

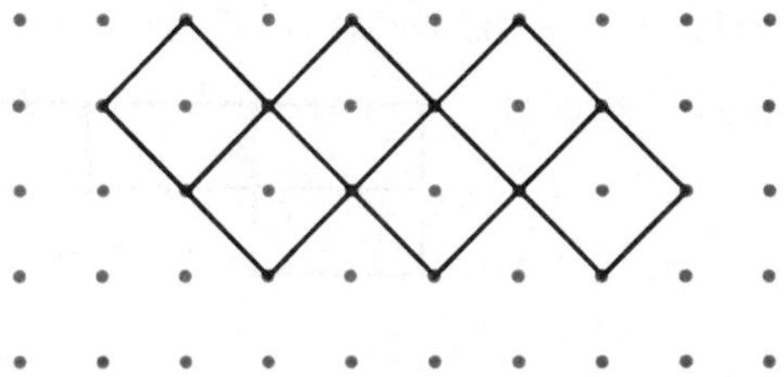

Phil started laying tiles like this. Copy this pattern onto dotted paper. Show the position of another 6 tiles.

5. Can you think of another way of laying square tiles so that there are no spaces between them ? Draw a sketch to show your arrangement.

PROPERTIES OF A RECTANGLE

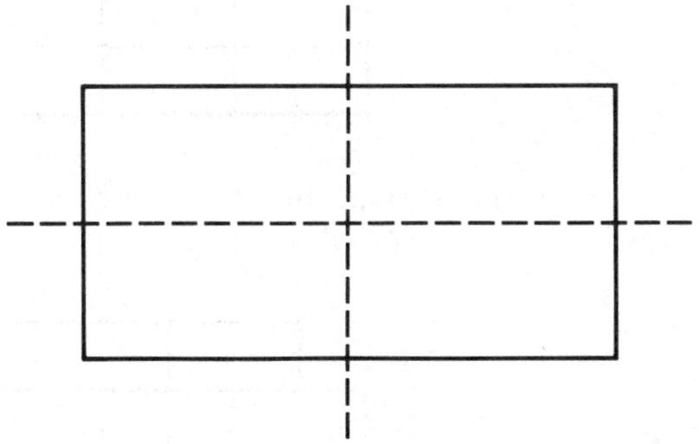

The opposite sides of a rectangle are equal. Every angle in a rectangle is 90°.

If the diagram is folded along either of the broken lines, each half fits exactly over the other half.

A rectangle has two lines of symmetry.

The two lines of symmetry divide the rectangle into 4 identical smaller rectangles.

Rectangles tessellate.

Note that, in general, a rectangle is different from a square. Two adjacent sides in a rectangle are normally different in length. When they are the same length, the rectangle is special and is called a square.

EXERCISE 8b

1.

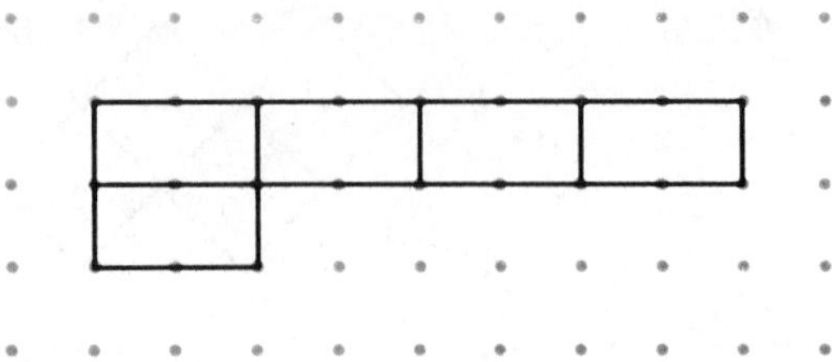

Scott lays 5 rectangular tiles like this.
Show the positions in which Scott can lay another 6 tiles keeping the same pattern.

2. Vernon builds a brick wall like this

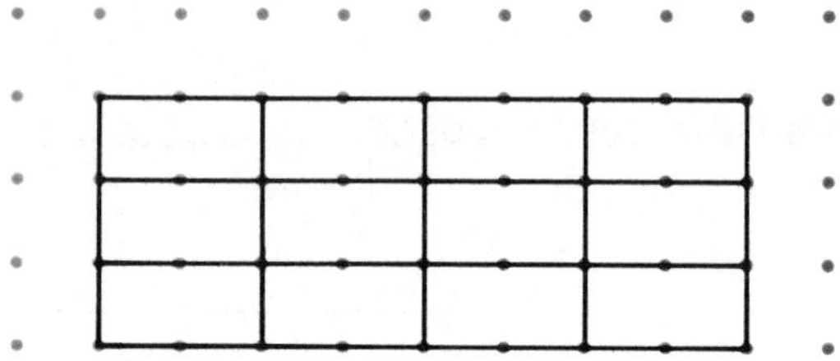

while Morgan builds it like this

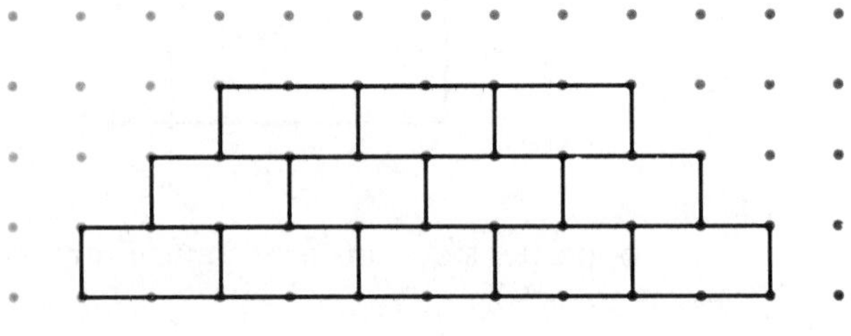

Copy each pattern and show the positions of another 6 bricks.
Which wall do you think is the stronger?
Why?

3. The first 3 bricks of Joan's wall look like this

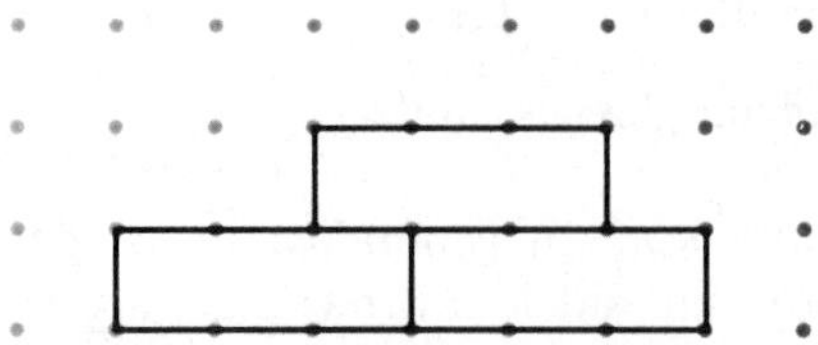

Keeping this pattern, show the positions of another 6 bricks.

4. Les lays tiles in his porch. The first 8 look like this. Continue this pattern and show how he can lay another 8 tiles.

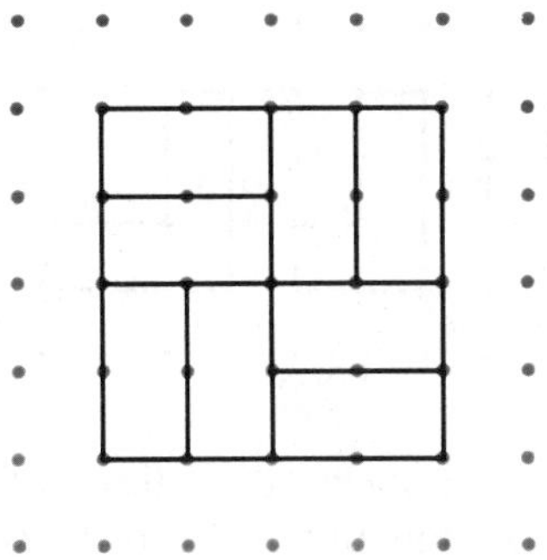

5. Use rectangular tiles like those shown below to give three different tiling patterns to cover an area without leaving any spaces in between.

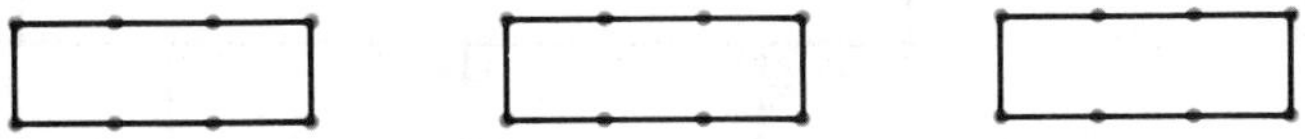

6. This is an unusual tile but it can be used for tiling.

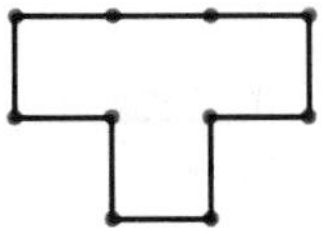

This is one way of using these tiles

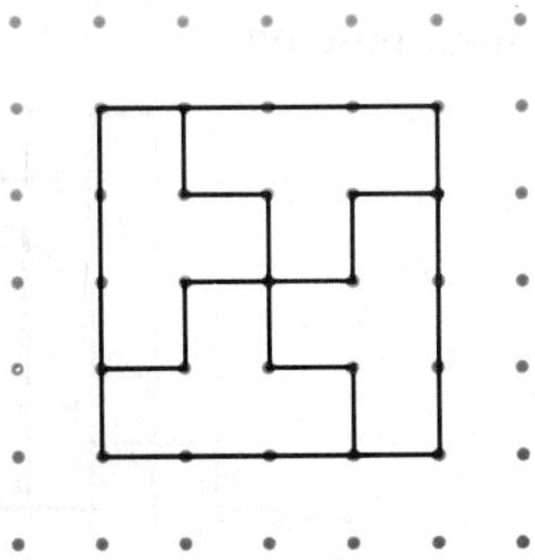

Using tiles like this, draw, if possible, some other patterns that could be used to cover a kitchen floor.

7. Here are some more unusual tiles.
Use dot grid paper to see if you can find a way of tiling a floor with them.

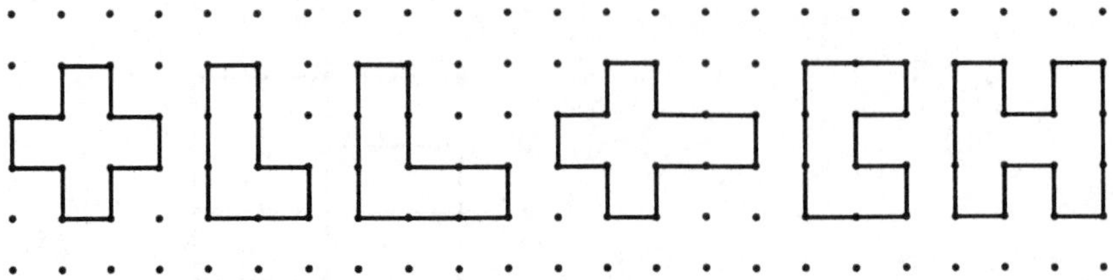

8. Tina starts tiling the bathroom floor. Rajiv spots 3 tiles that she has put down in the wrong place.
Draw the layout again putting those tiles in the correct positions. Show the positions of another 3 tiles.

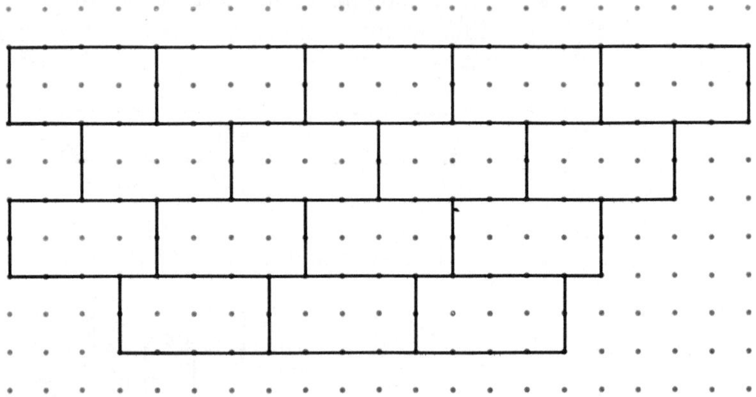

9. One of these tiles spoils the pattern. Which one?
Draw the layout again with this tile in a correct position.
Show positions for another five tiles.

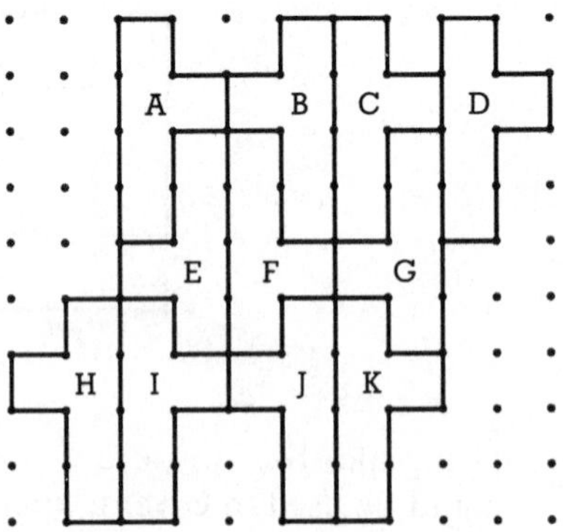

10. Shapes made up of 5 small squares, like those in Question 9, are called *pentominoes*. Here are another two pentominoes.

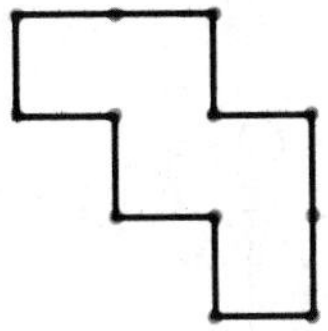

and

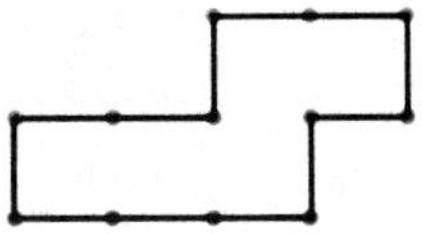

Can you find some more? There are 12 altogether.
How many of them can be used for tiling a wall?

9 PERCENTAGES

"per cent" means "out of 100".
The symbol we use for "per cent" is %.

So 60% means 60 out of 100 and we write 60 out of 100 as $\frac{60}{100}$

Hence $$60\% = \frac{60}{100}$$

EXERCISE 9a

Write 40 out of 100 as a percentage.

40 out of 100 = 40%

Write each of these marks as a percentage.

1. 20 out of 100
2. 35 out of 100
3. 66 out of 100
4. 50 out of 100
5. 72 out of 100
6. 81 out of 100
7. 90 out of 100
8. 28 out of 100
9. 100 out of 100

Write $\frac{75}{100}$ as a percentage.

$$\frac{75}{100} = 75\%$$

Write as a percentage

10. $\frac{37}{100}$	**13.** $\frac{83}{100}$	**16.** $\frac{14}{100}$	**19.** $\frac{54}{100}$
11. $\frac{45}{100}$	**14.** $\frac{99}{100}$	**17.** $\frac{69}{100}$	**20.** $\frac{28}{100}$
12. $\frac{10}{100}$	**15.** $\frac{8}{100}$	**18.** $\frac{1}{100}$	**21.** $\frac{100}{100}$

$50\% = 50 \text{ out of } 100 = \frac{1}{2}$

EXERCISE 9b

Shade 50% of this shape.

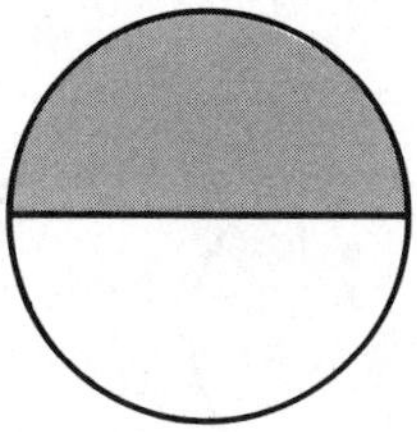

$50\% = \frac{1}{2}$

Copy and shade 50% of each of these shapes.

1. 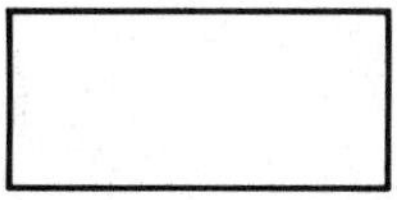 **2.** 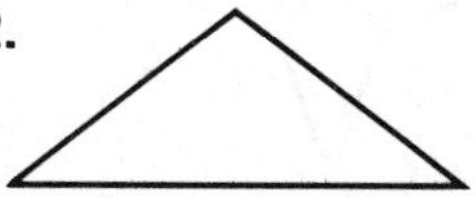 **3.** 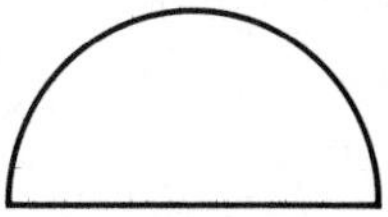

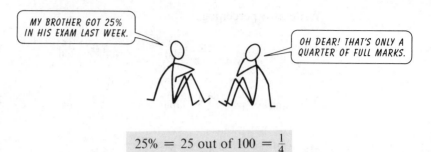

$$25\% = 25 \text{ out of } 100 = \frac{1}{4}$$

Shade 25% of this shape.

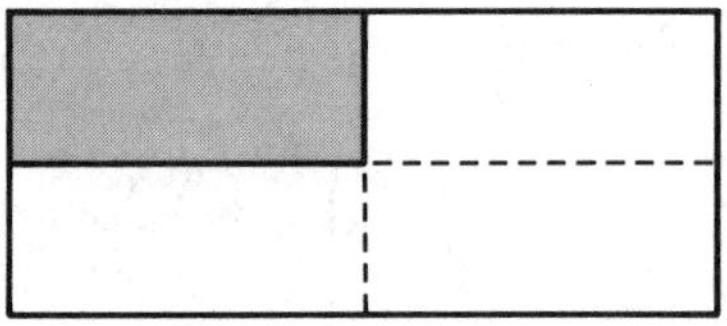

$$25\% = \frac{1}{4}$$

Copy and shade 25% of each of these shapes.

4.

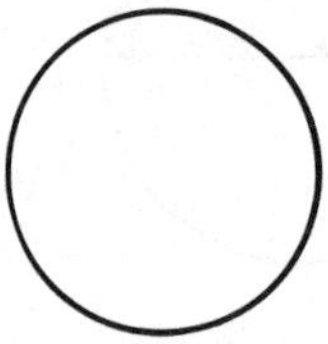

6.

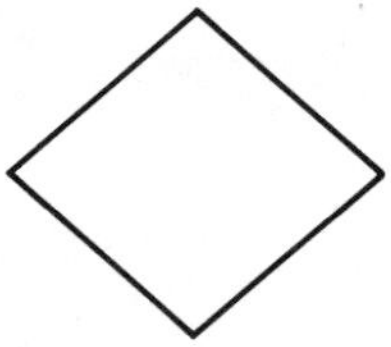

8.

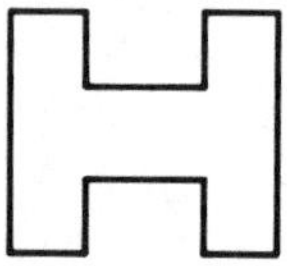

5.

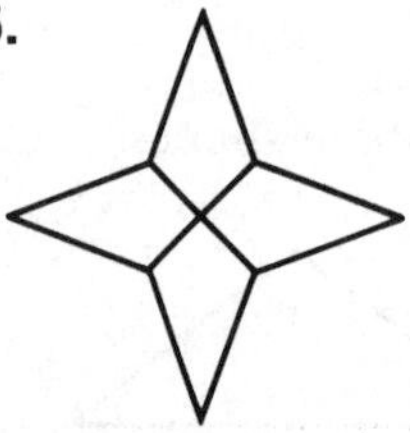

7.

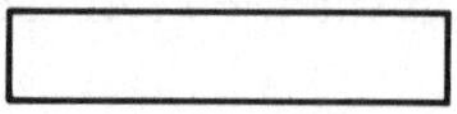

9.

If 25% is $\frac{1}{4}$ then 75% must be $\frac{3}{4}$.

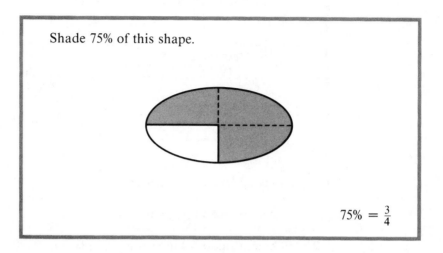

Shade 75% of this shape.

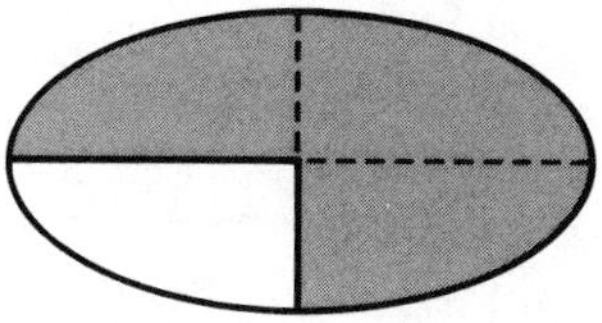

$75\% = \frac{3}{4}$

Copy and shade 75% of each shape.

10. 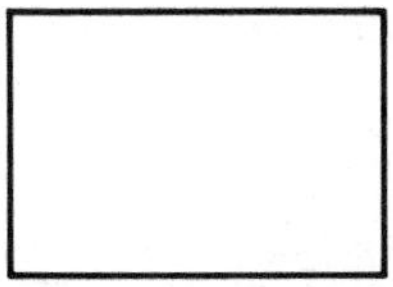 **11.** 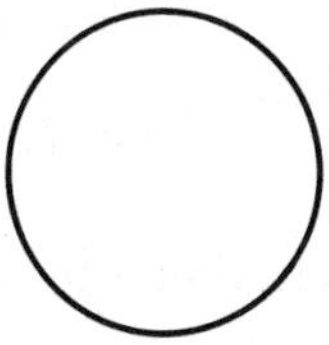 **12.** 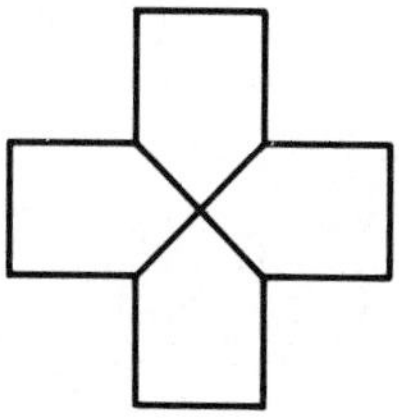

QUANTITIES AS PERCENTAGES

6 toffees is $\frac{1}{2}$ of 12 toffees so it is 50%.

EXERCISE 9c

Complete this sentence

2 books out of 8 books is . . . %

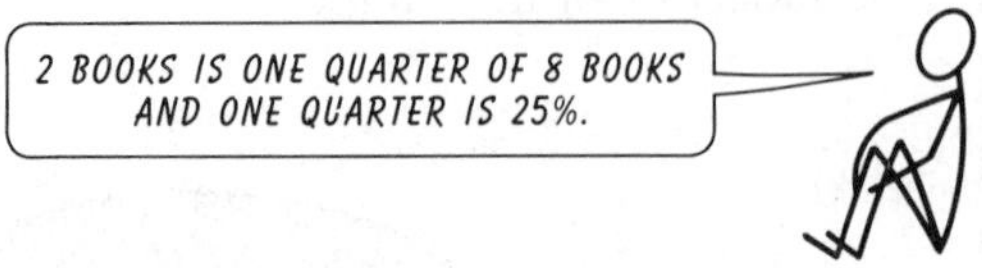
2 BOOKS IS ONE QUARTER OF 8 BOOKS AND ONE QUARTER IS 25%.

2 books out of 8 books is 25%

Copy and complete each sentence.

1. 7 pages out of 14 pages is _____%

2. 10 houses out of 40 houses is _____%

3. 6 pens out of 12 pens is _____%

4. 3 pens out of 12 pens is _____%

5. £100 out of £200 is _____%

6. 12 children out of 48 children is _____%

7. 5 p out of 10 p is _____%

8. 20 marks out of 40 is _____%

Complete this sentence

25% of £8 is £ . . .

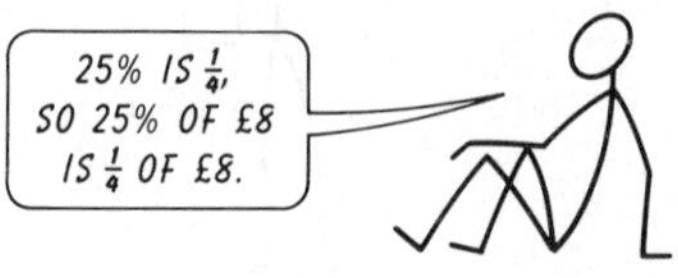
25% IS $\frac{1}{4}$,
SO 25% OF £8
IS $\frac{1}{4}$ OF £8.

25% of £8 is £2

Copy and complete each sentence.

9. 50% of 12 miles is ____ miles.

10. 50% of £40 is £____.

11. 25% of 20 children is ____ children.

12. 50% of 14 days is ____ days.

13. 25% of 80 miles is ____ miles.

14. 50% of 12 hours is ____ hours.

15. 25% of 8 bags of crisps is ____ bags of crisps.

Ann has 8 pencils but only 2 of them are sharp. What percentage of Ann's pencils are sharp?

$\frac{1}{4}$ of the pencils are sharp and $\frac{1}{4}$ is 25%.
So 25% of the pencils are sharp.

16. Richard's notebook has 30 pages and he has filled 15 of them. What percentage of the notebook has he filled?

17. Mrs Kahn made 24 mince pies and gave her children 6 of them.
What percentage of the pies did the children get?

18. Alan set out on a ten-mile hike but he gave up after five miles. What percentage of the hike had he done?

19. Four apples out of a bag of sixteen apples are bad.
What is the percentage of bad apples?

20. There are 20 slices in a new sliced loaf. When 5 slices have been eaten

a) what percentage of the loaf has been eaten?
b) what percentage of the loaf is left?

21. Debbie has 32 LPs and 25% of them are by rock groups. How many records by rock groups does she have?

22. Fifty per cent of the houses in Dell Avenue have a garage. If Dell Avenue has 32 houses, how many of them have a garage?

23. The Robinson family went on a sixteen-day camping holiday but unfortunately 25% of the time it was cold and wet.

a) How many cold and rainy days did they have?
b) What percentage of their holiday was dry?

MIXED EXERCISE

EXERCISE 9d

1. Write as a percentage

a) 72 out of 100 b) 98 out of 100 c) 9 out of 100

2. Write as a percentage

a) $\frac{51}{100}$ b) $\frac{3}{100}$ c) $\frac{26}{100}$

3. Copy and complete each sentence with a fraction.

a) 50% is b) 25% is c) 75% is

4. Copy each diagram and shade the percentage given.

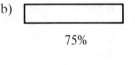

a)
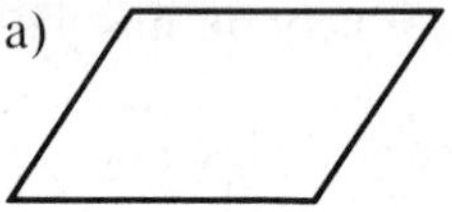
25%

b)

75%

c)
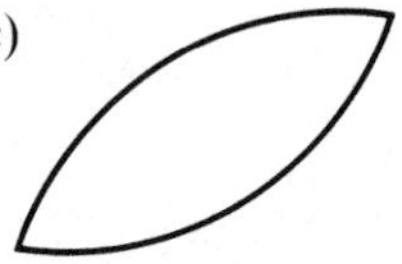
100%

Copy and complete each sentence.

5. 6 miles out of a journey of 12 miles is ... %.

6. 2 days out of an 8-day holiday is ... %.

7. 50% of £90 is £...

8. 25% of 36 biscuits is ... biscuits.

9. David's fence is 48 metres long. When he has painted 24 metres, what percentage of the fence has he painted?

10. Carol and Jill are given a box of 20 chocolates. Carol eats 5 chocolates and Jill eats 10.

a) What percentage of the chocolates does Carol eat?
b) What percentage does Jill eat?
c) What percentage of the chocolates are left?

10 STATISTICS

COLLECTING INFORMATION

Statistics is the subject that tries to make sense of large collections of information in the form of numbers. The number of items of information can run into millions as, for instance, when the ages of everyone in the UK are being considered. To learn how to handle such very large collections, we start with smaller ones.

We must start by collecting some information.

EXERCISE 10a Copy this form onto a card and then fill it in with the information asked for.

1. Name ....
2. Date of birth: Day ... Month ... Year ...
3. Height (cm) ....
4. Shoe size (continental) ....
5. Hand span (cm) ....
6. Number of brothers and sisters ....
7. Favourite colour: ring one of these
   red blue green yellow pink purple black white
8. Pets that you have at home: ring one or more of these
   cat dog hamster mouse gerbil
   fish rabbit other none

A DATABASE

The completed cards for the whole class can now be collected together. This collection of cards is a *database*.

If we want to work on one set of information, we can go through the database (looking at every card) and write down everything under that set. For example, we can extract the number of brothers and sisters of each member of the class.

MAKING A FREQUENCY TABLE

This is a list of the number of brothers and sisters of the thirty pupils in a class. Each figure represents the number of brothers and sisters of one member of the class.

0	1	1	3	0	1	2	1	0	1
1	3	1	0	1	2	3	1	1	0
1	0	2	0	1	1	1	2	4	1

To make sense of the numbers that we have collected we need to put them into order. One way of doing this is to make a *frequency table.*

The *frequency* tells us how many times the same answer was given. There are five different possible answers in our list: 0, 1, 2, 3, and 4.

We start by making a table like the one below.
Then we work down the columns in the list, making a tally mark, I, in the tally column of the table next to the appropriate item every time it occurs.

<table>
<tr><th>Number of brothers and sisters</th><th>Tally</th><th>Frequency</th></tr>
<tr><td>0</td><td>\||||</td><td></td></tr>
<tr><td>1</td><td>|||||||</td><td></td></tr>
<tr><td>2</td><td>|</td><td></td></tr>
<tr><td>3</td><td>||</td><td></td></tr>
<tr><td>4</td><td></td><td></td></tr>
<tr><td></td><td>Total</td><td></td></tr>
</table>

Next we count up the tally marks and write the total in the frequency column.

Lastly, we total the frequency column to check that the total number of items recorded in the table is the same as the number of items in the list.

EXERCISE 10b **1.** The table on page 87 is incomplete. Copy the table without the tally marks.
Now make the tally marks afresh from the original information and write the totals in the frequency table.

2. A box contains bags of crisps. Some are plain salted (S), some are salt and vinegar (V), some are cheese and onion (C) and some are prawn cocktail (P). They are taken out of the box and the flavour of each bag is written down in a list.

P	S	S	V	C	S	P	P	S
S	P	V	S	C	C	P	V	S
P	S	V	C	C	C	V	P	V
V	S	S	C	S	S	P	S	S

Make a frequency table for this list like the one in Question 1.

3. This is a list of the favourite colours of some five-year-olds, chosen from red (R), green (G), blue (B), yellow (Y) and pink (P).

R	R	P	Y	R	Y	P	G	R	B	R
P	Y	Y	R	B	Y	R	R	R	Y	Y
R	Y	B	G	Y	R	P	P	R	R	Y
Y	R	R	R	P	Y	Y	B	Y	G	R

Make a frequency table for this list.

4. This is a list of the shoe sizes of a group of five-year-olds.

26	25	27	25	23	26	24	24	27	24	25
24	23	25	24	24	23	26	23	24	25	25
23	24	25	25	24	23	24	26	25	24	23
22	24	23	27	23	25	24	24	25	23	24

Make a frequency table for this list.

5. Use the class database that was made in Exercise 10a for this question.

a) Make a list of the *month* of birth of each member of the class, and then make a frequency table for the list.

b) Make a list of the number of brothers and sisters of each member of the class and then make a frequency table for the list.

MAKING A BAR CHART

A bar chart shows frequencies very clearly.

This bar chart uses the frequency table in Question 1 on page 88 and shows the frequencies of the numbers of brothers and sisters of the pupils in a class.

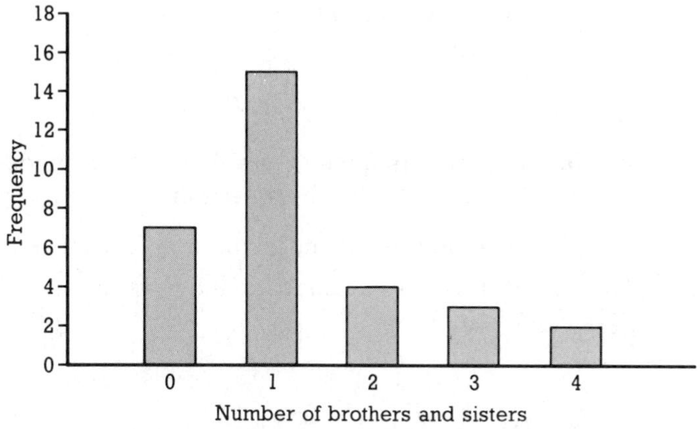

Notice that the vertical axis is used for frequency. The different kinds of item are on the horizontal axis.

Notice also that the bars are all the same width. It does not matter what width you choose to make the bars, provided that all bars are the same width. In this diagram there is a space between the bars, but the bars can touch if we want them to.

EXERCISE 10c **1.** Peter and Rachel did a survey of the types of vehicle passing the school gate one lunch hour and produced the following frequency table.

Type of vehicle	Bicycle	Motorbike	Car	Lorry
Frequency	4	10	25	16

a) How many vehicles passed the school gate altogether?

b) Which was the most common type of vehicle?

c) Draw a bar chart to show the information.

2. This frequency table shows the results of a survey into childrens' opinions about the quality of school dinners.

Opinion	Very good	Good	Satisfactory	Poor	Very poor
Frequency	2	12	20	10	8

a) How many people were asked their opinion on school dinners?

b) Draw a bar chart to show the information in the frequency table.

3. Use the frequency table that you made for Question 2 in Exercise 10b for this question.

a) Which is the most common flavour of crisp in the box?

b) Draw a bar chart to show the information in the frequency table.

4. Use the frequency table that you made for Question 3 of Exercise 10b for this question.

a) Which was the most commonly chosen colour?

b) Draw a bar chart to show the information in the frequency table.

5. Use the frequency table that you made for Question 4 of Exercise 10b.
Draw a bar chart to show the information in the frequency table.

USING BAR CHARTS

Bar charts can come in other forms. Sometimes the bars are lines. Sometimes the bars are horizontal.
When you look at a bar chart to find information from it, always read the labels on the axes carefully.

EXERCISE 10d

Use the bar chart to answer the following questions.

a) What was the most popular pet?
b) How many children had a dog as a pet?

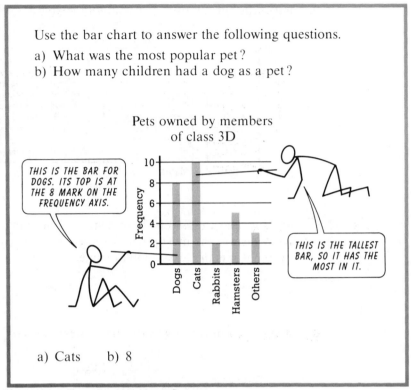

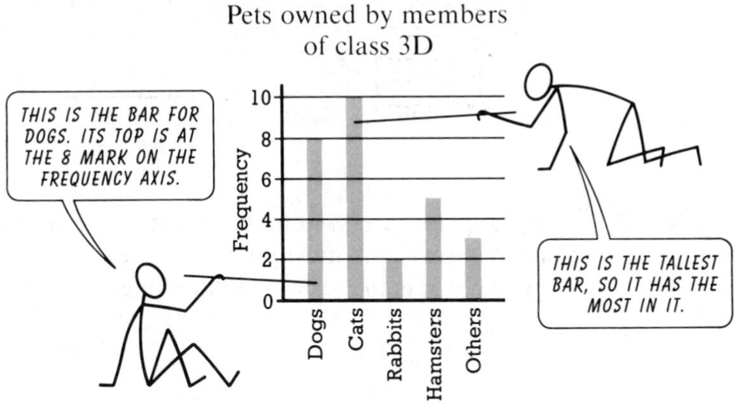

a) Cats b) 8

1. Marks in a maths test.

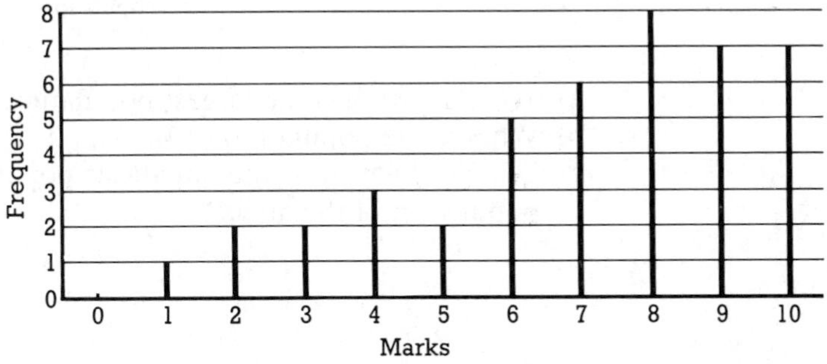

a) How many pupils got a mark of 8?

b) What was the lowest mark and how many pupils got it?

c) What was the most common mark?

2. Favourite subject from the school timetable.

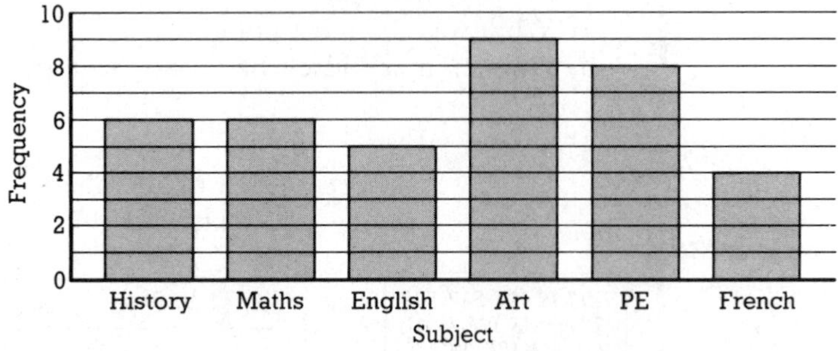

a) How many children chose history as their favourite subject?
b) What was the most popular subject?
c) What was the least popular subject?

3. Population in five towns (to the nearest thousand).

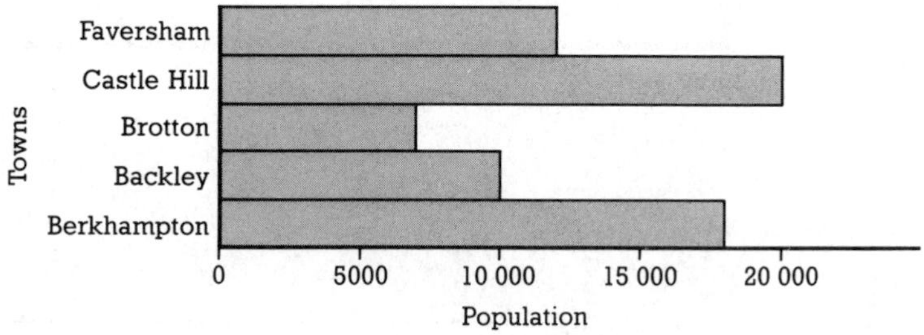

a) Which town has the largest population?
b) What is the population of Backley?
c) Which town has the smallest population? What is the population of this town?

11 DECIMALS 1

TENTHS

This bolt is being measured on a ruler marked in inches and tenths of an inch.

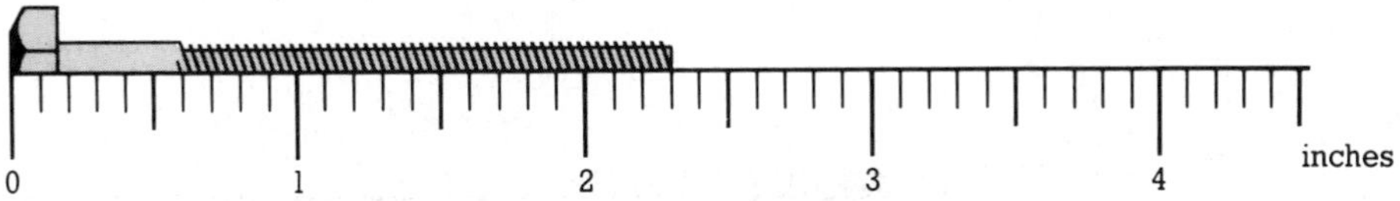

The length of the bolt is 2 inches and 3 tenths of an inch.

EXERCISE 11a Copy this table and complete it by writing down the length of each bolt.

	Inches	Tenths of an inch
1.		
2.		
3.		
4.		
5.		
6.		
7.		

1.

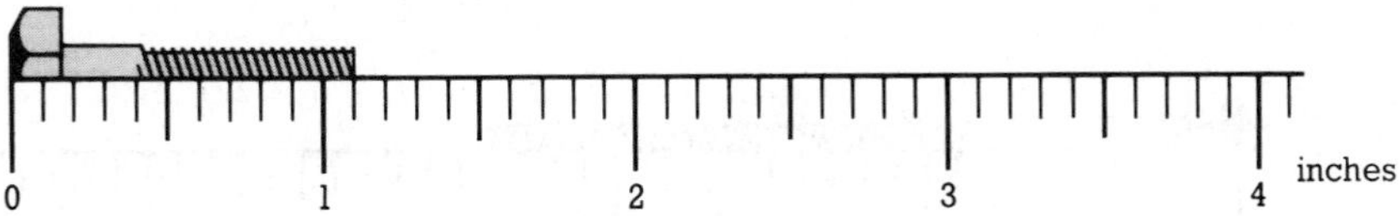

2.

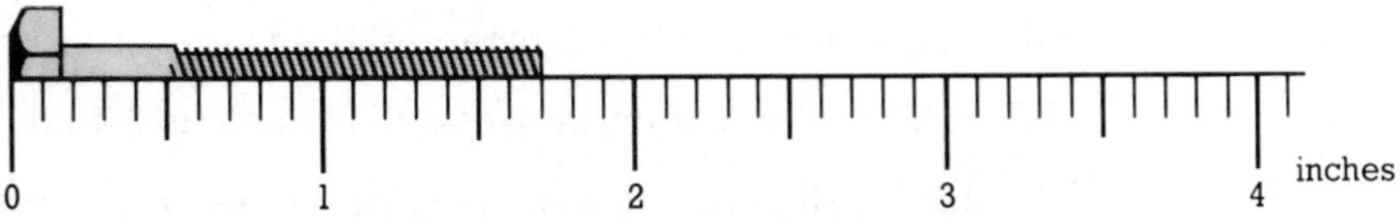

3.

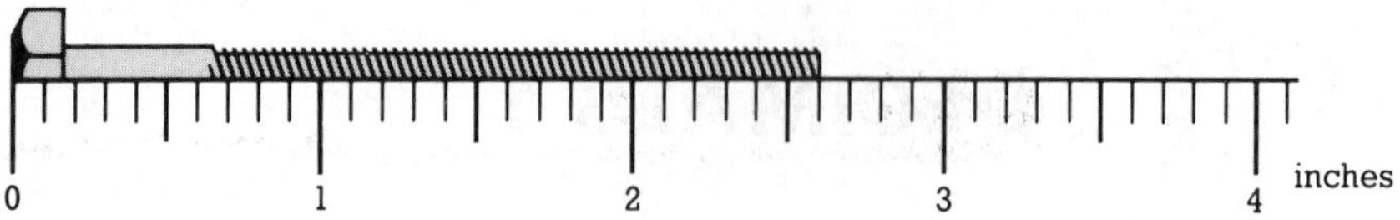

4.

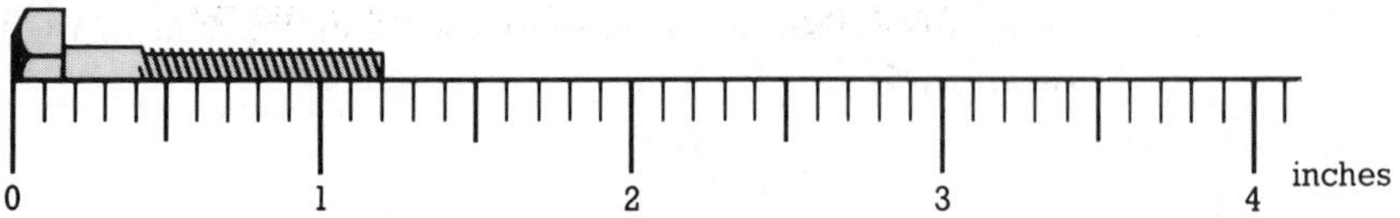

5.

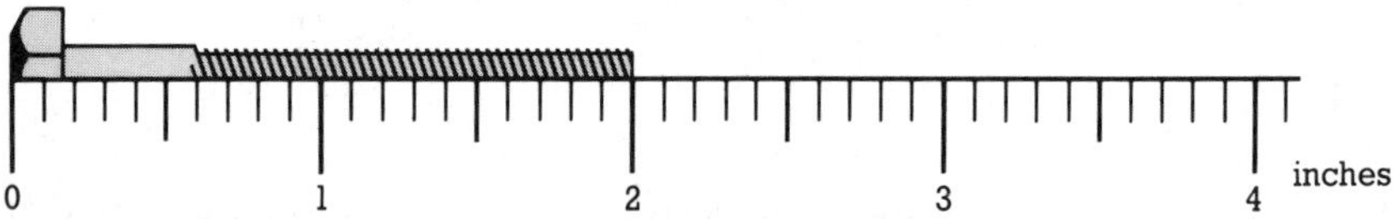

6.

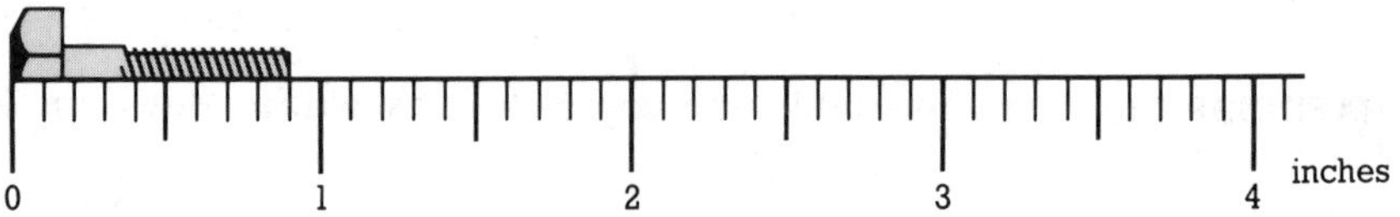

7.

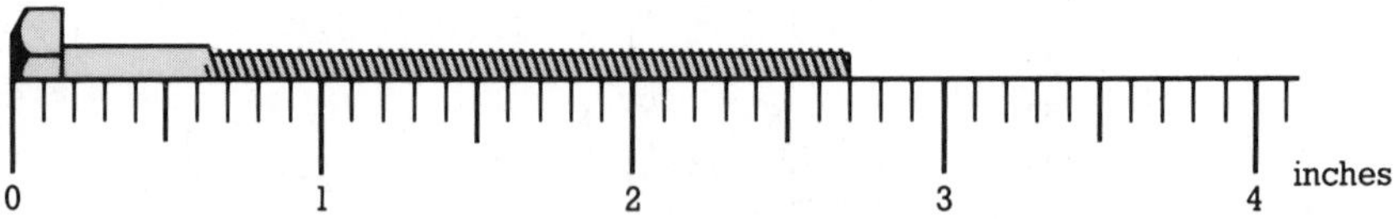

THE DECIMAL POINT

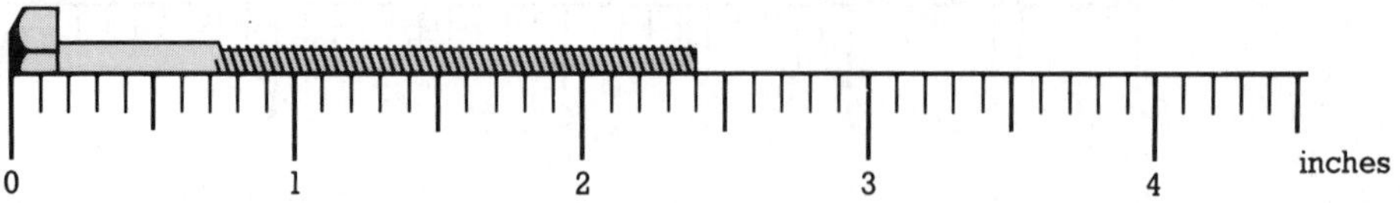

The length of this bolt is 2 inches and 4 tenths of an inch.

Using decimal notation, we write this length as 2·4 inches.

The dot is called the *decimal point* and we say *two point four* inches.

EXERCISE 11b **1.** Write the length of each bolt in Exercise 11a in decimal notation.

This bolt is being measured on a ruler marked in centimetres and tenths of a centimetre. Write its length in decimal notation.

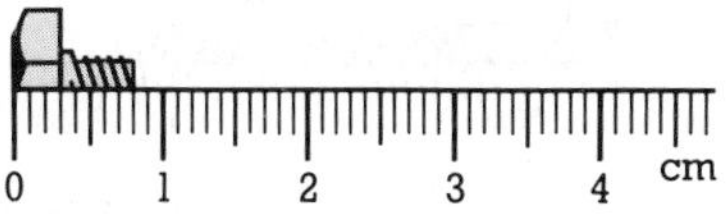

The length is 8 tenths of a centimetre.

In decimal notation we write 0·8 cm.

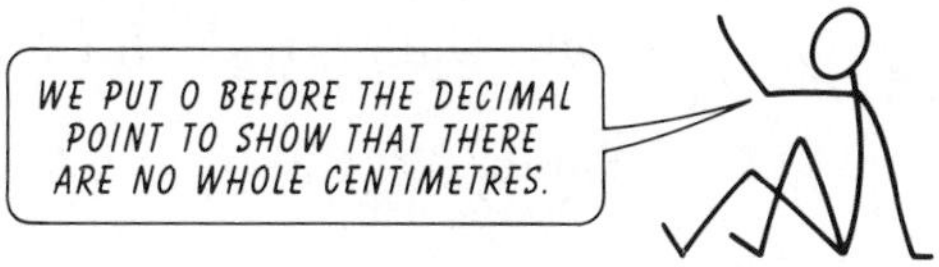

WE PUT 0 BEFORE THE DECIMAL POINT TO SHOW THAT THERE ARE NO WHOLE CENTIMETRES.

Write down the length of each bolt using decimal notation.

2.

3.

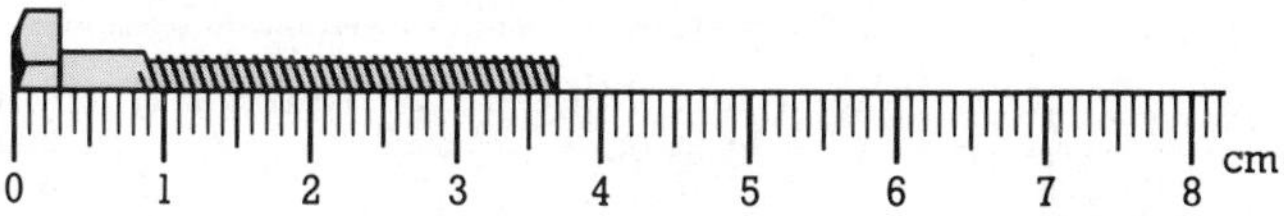

4.

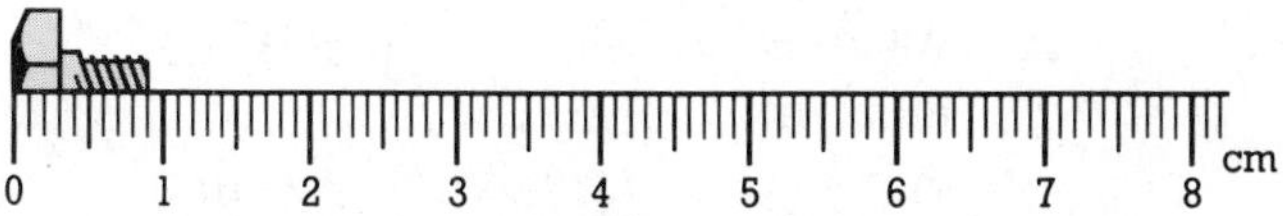

5.

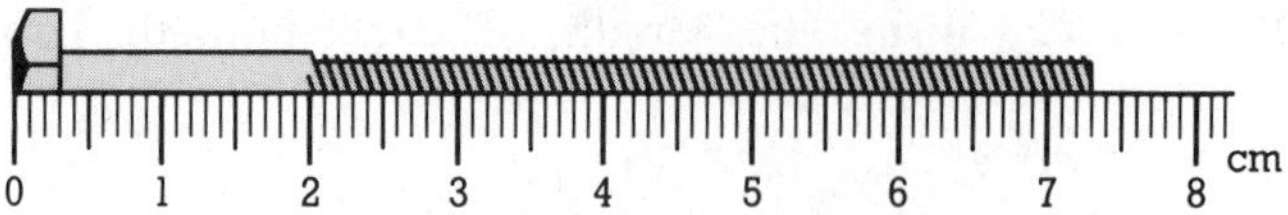

6.

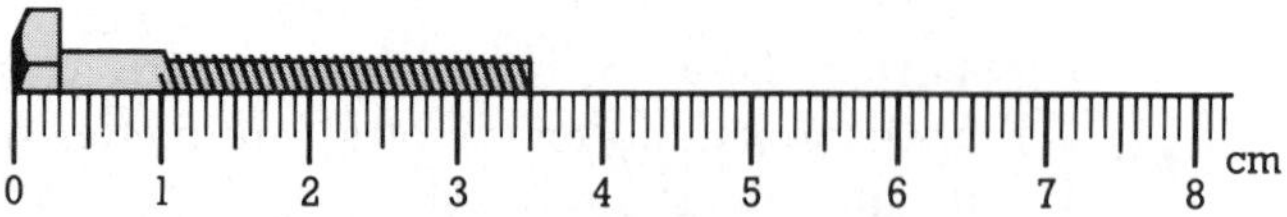

7.

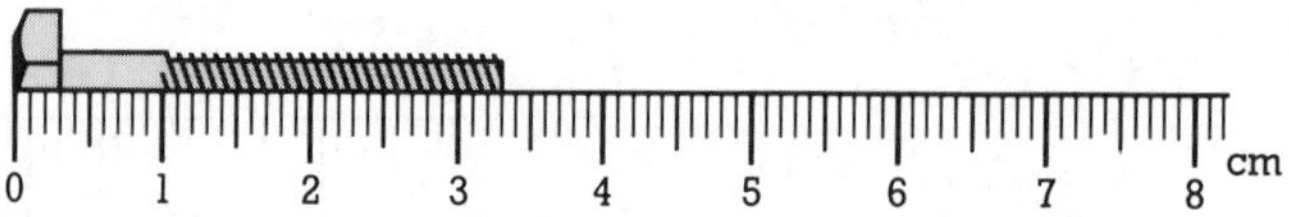

PLACE VALUE

One tenth $= \frac{1}{10} = 0{\cdot}1$

Three tenths $= \frac{3}{10} = 0{\cdot}3$

We know that 12·4 cm means 12 whole centimetres and 4 tenths of a centimetre.
Now 12 is 1 ten and 2 units, so 12·4 can be written in headed columns as

Tens	Units		Tenths
1	2	·	4

EXERCISE 11c **1.** Write each of the following numbers in headed columns.

a) 12·6 c) 6·3 e) 3·6 g) 7·2
b) 0·5 d) 0·2 f) 24·7 h) 17·9

What is the value of the figure 5 in the number 20·5 ?

The value of the figure 5 is 5 tenths.

2. What is the value of the figure 2 in each of the following numbers ?

a) 2·5 b) 21·5 c) 10·2 d) 72·6 e) 57·2

3. What is the value of the figure 7 in each of the following numbers?

a) 27·5 b) 13·7 c) 76·8 d) 52·7 e) 17·2

4. What is the value of each figure 5 in each of the following numbers?

a) 51·6 b) 5·3 c) 25·5 d) 54·5 e) 50·5

5. Write these numbers in order of size with the smallest number first.

21·5, 23·4, 20·6

6. Write each set of numbers in order of size with the smallest number first.

a) 15·1, 8·6, 12·9
b) 20·1, 15·5, 18
c) 20, 4·8, 7
d) 1·9, 1·2, 2

7. Two of these numbers are the same. Which are they?

3·0, 30, 3, 0·3

8. Which two of these numbers are the same?

5·0, 0·5, 50, 5

ROUNDING NUMBERS

Most things that we measure do not fall exactly on a division line. The length of this bolt is between 1·3 inches and 1·4 inches.

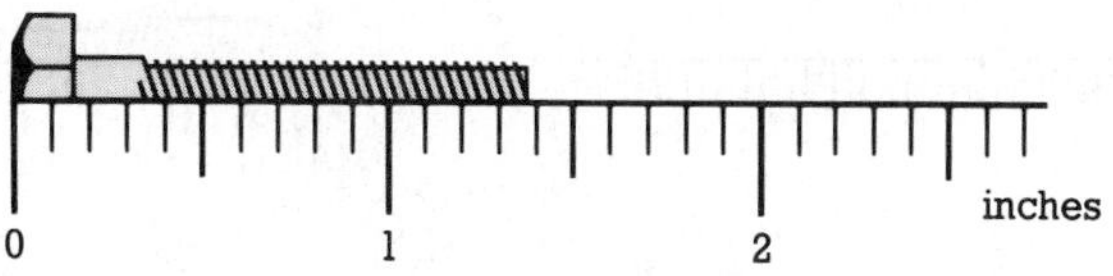

The end of the bolt is nearer 1·4 than 1·3, so its length is 1·4 inches to the nearest tenth of an inch.

If the end seems to be exactly halfway between divisions, we round the measurement up to the longer one.

EXERCISE 11d Give the length of each of the following objects to the nearest tenth of an inch.

1.

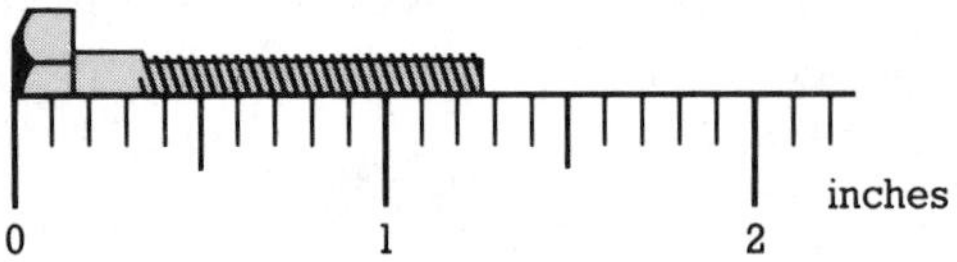

3.

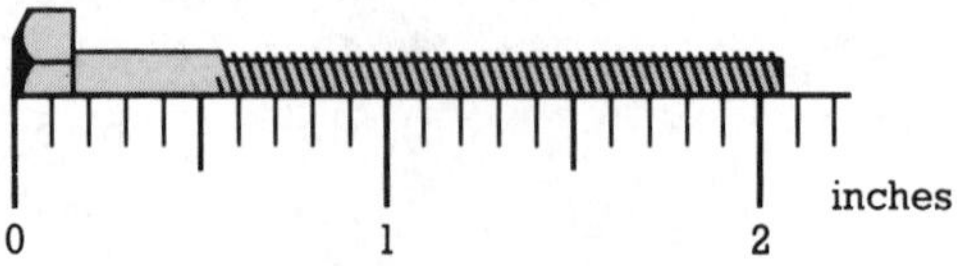

2.

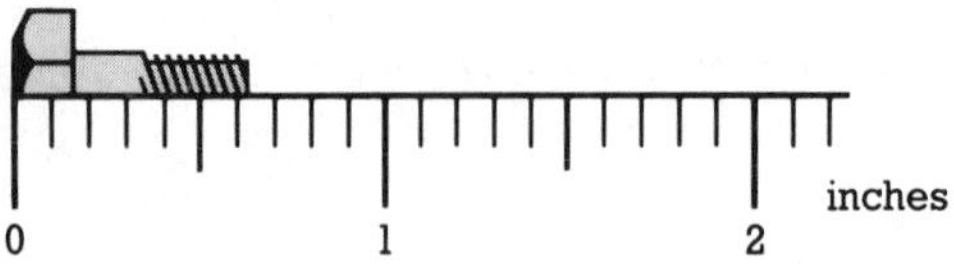

4.

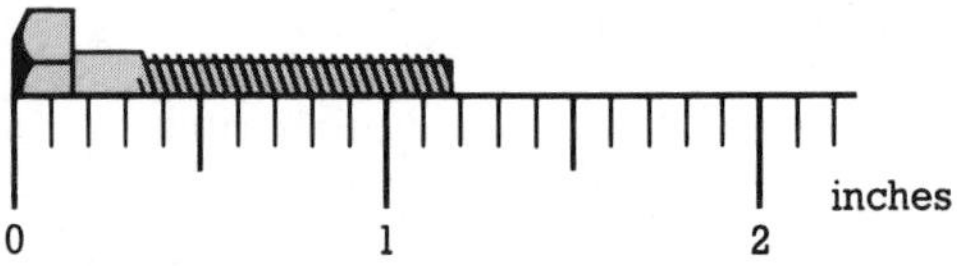

Give the length of each of the following objects to the nearest tenth of a centimetre.

5.

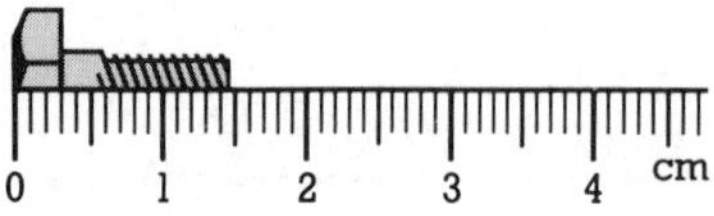

8.

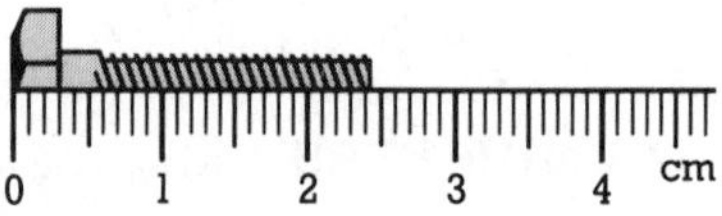

6.

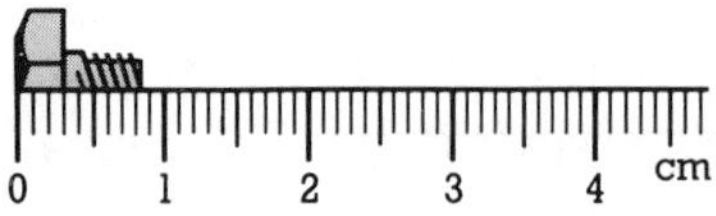

9.

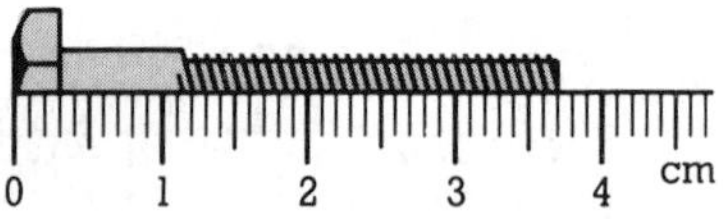

7.

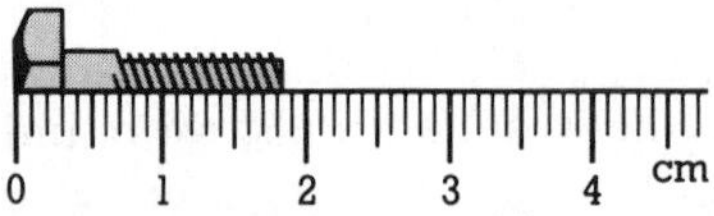

10.

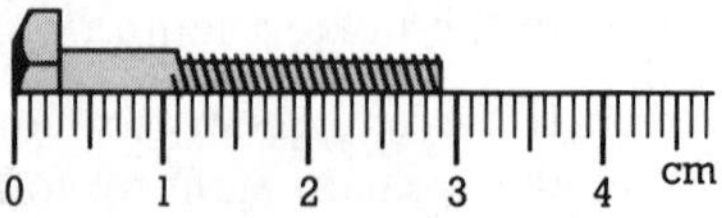

Each of the following diagrams shows the ruler through a magnifying glass.

Give the length of each of the bolts to the nearest tenth of a centimetre.

11.

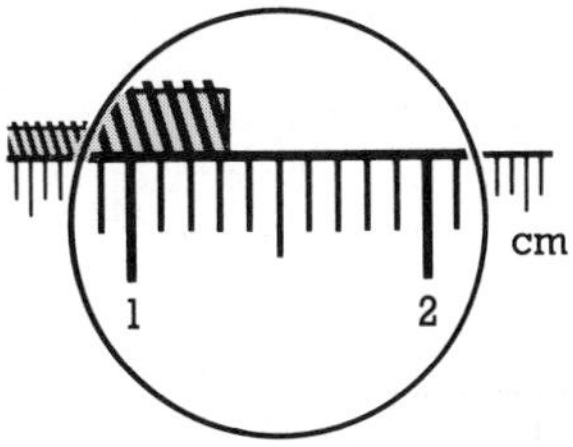

13.

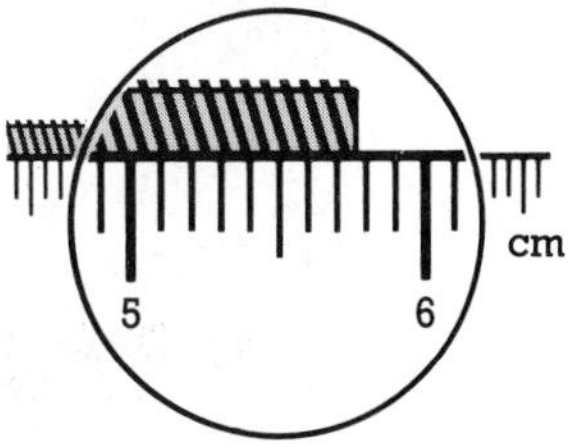

12.

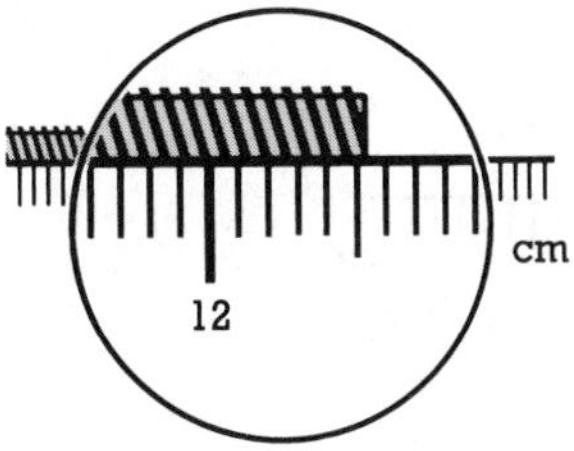

14.

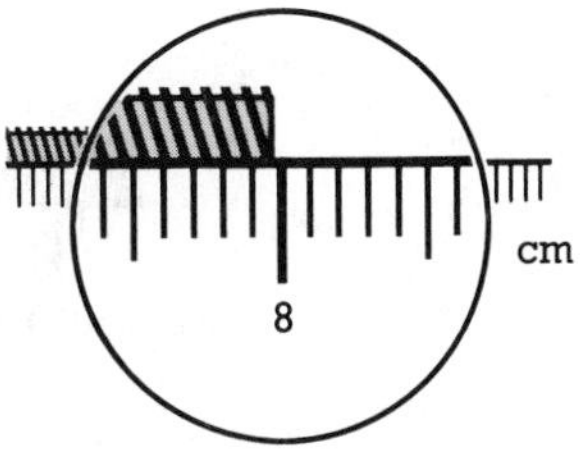

HUNDREDTHS

If we want to measure more accurately than to the nearest tenth of a centimetre, we have to magnify the scale.
This shows a magnification of the part of a ruler between 0·3 cm and 0·5 cm.

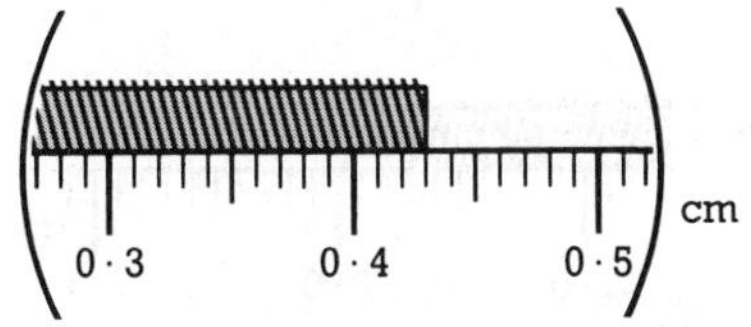

The space between each tenth mark is divided into ten parts, so each of these small parts represents one hundredth of a centimetre. The end of the bolt is 3 divisions along from the 4 tenths cm mark, so the reading is 4 tenths and 3 hundredths of a centimetre.

EXERCISE 11e Copy this table and write down the length of the bolt on each scale.

	cm	Tenths of a cm	Hundredths of a cm
1.			
2.			
3.			
4.			
5.			
6.			

1.

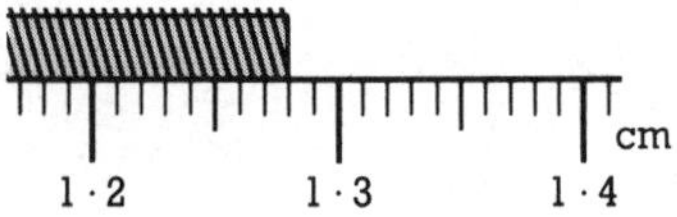

2.

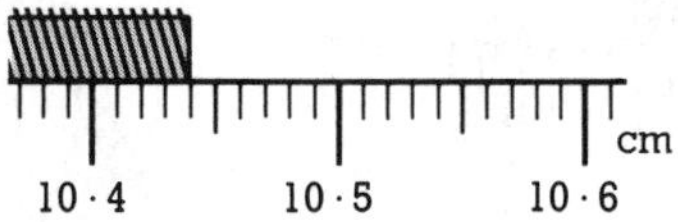

3.

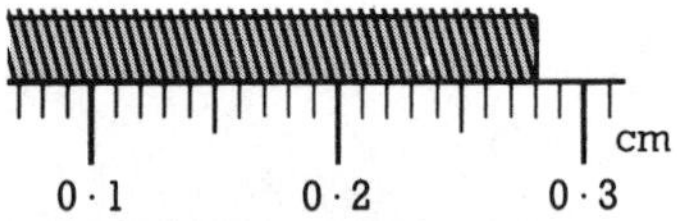

4.

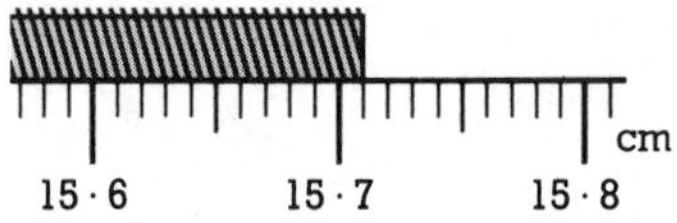

5.

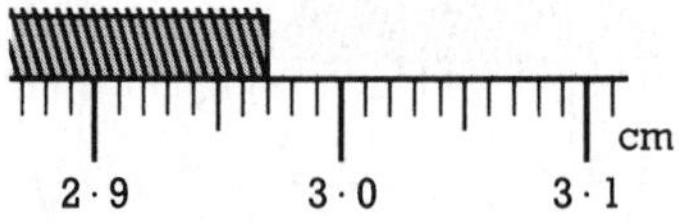

6.

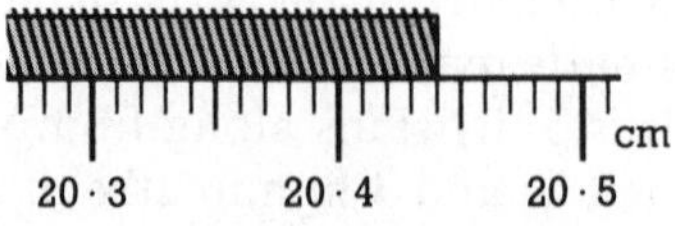

DECIMAL NOTATION

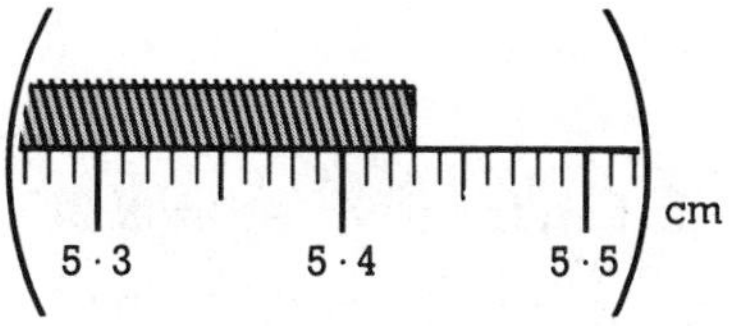

The length of this bolt is 5 cm, 4 tenths of a cm and 3 hundredths of a cm.
Using decimal notation we write this as 5·43 cm.
We say *five point four three* centimetres.

EXERCISE 11f **1.** Write down in decimal notation the length of each bolt in Exercise 11e.

Write down the length of each bolt using decimal notation.

2. 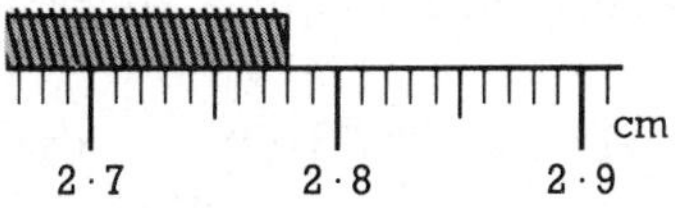

3. 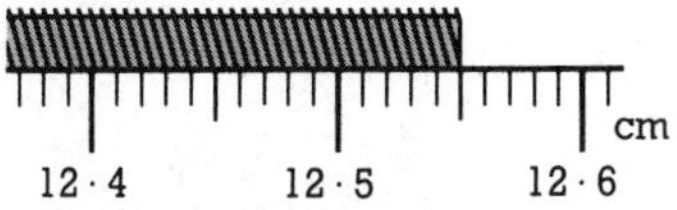

4. 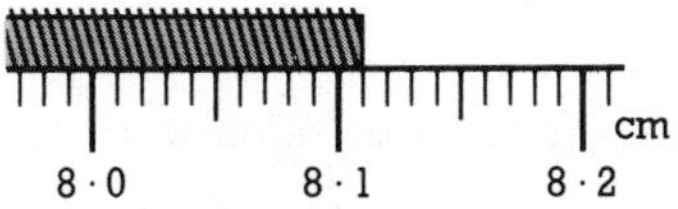

5. 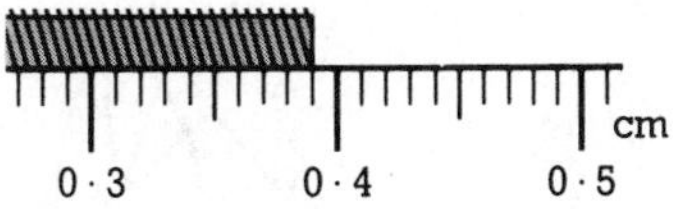

6. 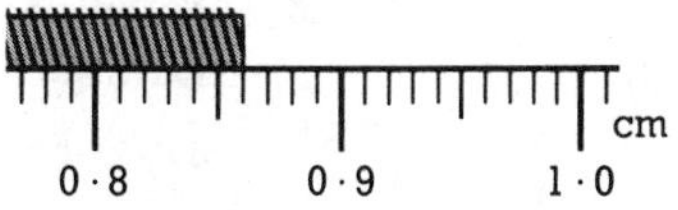

7. 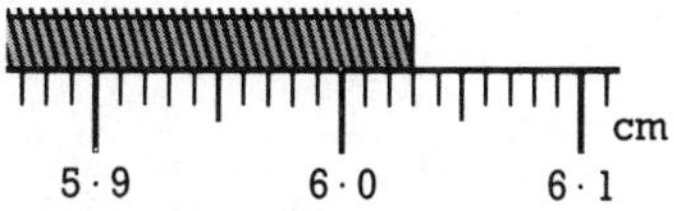

8. 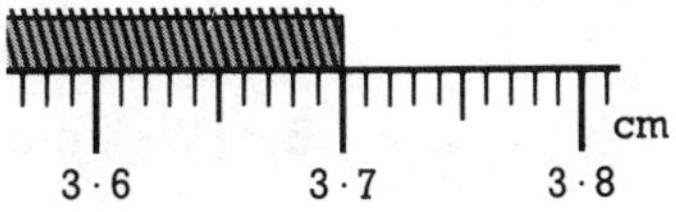

9. 

PLACE VALUE

THE 0 HERE MEANS THAT
THERE ARE NO TENTHS.

One hundredth $= \frac{1}{100} = 0{\cdot}01$

Two hundredths $= \frac{2}{100} = 0{\cdot}02$

We know that 23·47 cm means 23 cm, 4 tenths of a cm and 7 hundredths of a cm. Now 23 is 2 tens and 3 units, so 23·47 can be written in headed columns as

Tens	Units		Tenths	Hundredths
2	3	·	4	7

EXERCISE 11g

1. Write each of the following numbers in headed columns.

a) 14·56 c) 6·04 e) 4·08 g) 30·08
b) 5·87 d) 20·12 f) 41·99 h) 60·32

2. What is the value of the figure 7 in each of the following numbers?

a) 73·88 b) 62·75 c) 37·93 d) 21·97 e) 61·87

3. What is the value of the figure 4 in each of the following numbers?

a) 34·76 b) 2·45 c) 18·74 d) 41·33 e) 6·04

4. What is the value of each figure 3 in each of the following numbers?

a) 13·62 b) 25·03 c) 20·83 d) 30·11 e) 23·32

5. Which of these numbers is the smallest?

0·53, 17·2, 1·01

LOOK AT THE TENS,
THEN THE UNITS,
THEN THE TENTHS,
AND SO ON.

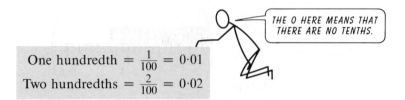

6. Which of these numbers is the largest?

1·71, 0·99, 1·17

7. Write these numbers in order of size with the smallest first:

2·5, 2·05, 2·55

8. Write these numbers in order of size with the largest first:

21·4, 12·04, 24·1

9. Write each set of numbers in order of size with the smallest first.

a) 4·3, 3·4, 4·03
b) 7·1, 1·07, 1·7
c) 15·7, 1·57, 7·15
d) 36·92, 63·29, 36·29

10. From each set, write down two numbers which are the same.

a) 2·10, 2·01, 2·1
b) 1·04, 1·40, 1·4
c) 5·7, 57, 5·70

ROUNDING TO THE NEAREST HUNDREDTH

This diagram shows a magnification of part of a ruler between 3·2 cm and 3·3 cm.

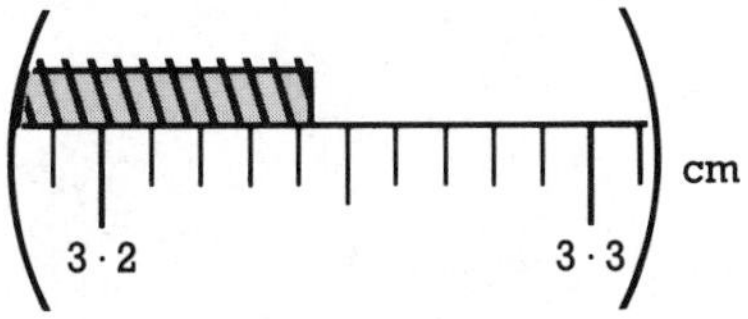

Each small division shows one hundredth of a centimetre.

The end of the bolt is nearer 3·24 than 3·25, so its length is 3·24 to the nearest hundredth of a centimetre.

If the end seems to be exactly halfway between divisions, round the measurement up to the larger one.

EXERCISE 11h Each bolt is measured with a ruler scaled in centimetres.

Give the length of each bolt to the nearest hundredth of a centimetre.

1. 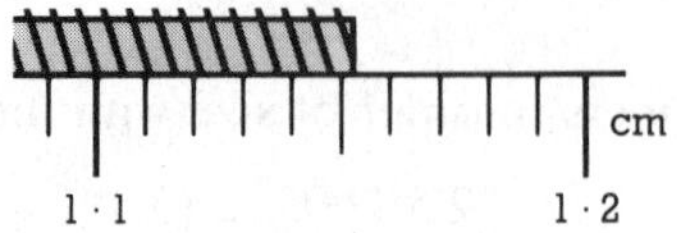

2. 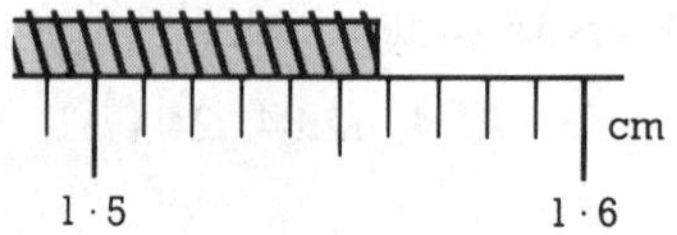

3. 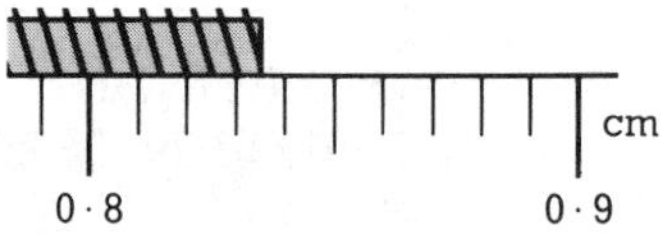

4. 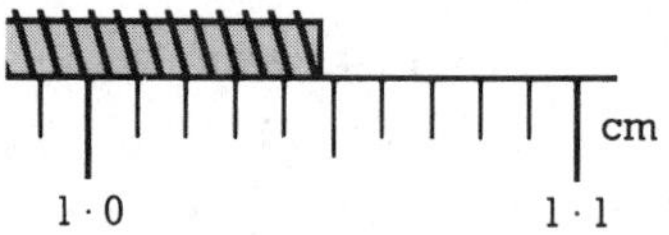

5. 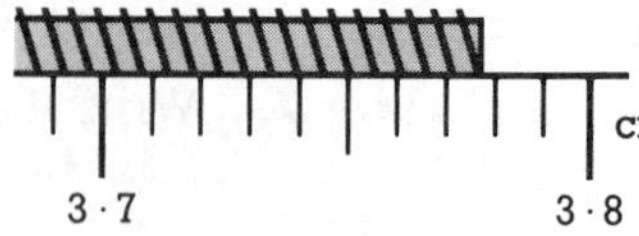

6. 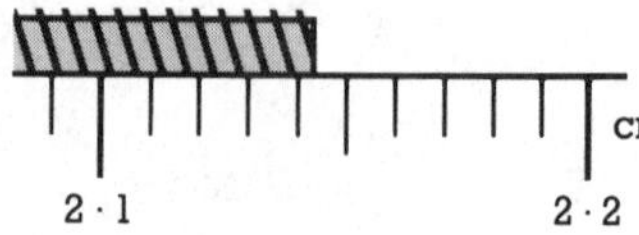

7. 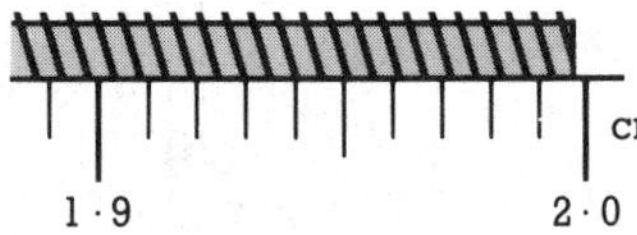

8. 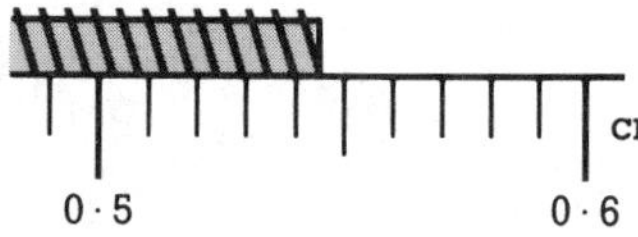

12 PERIMETERS

EXERCISE 12a Use a calculator.

1. John puts up fences. What length of fencing does he need for each of these fields?

a)
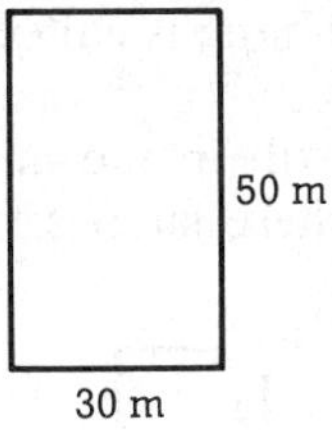

b)
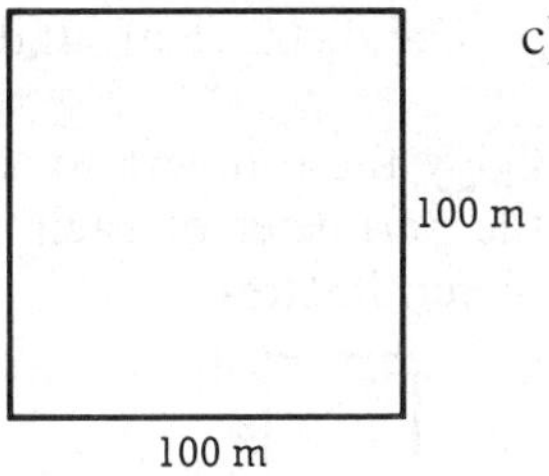

c)
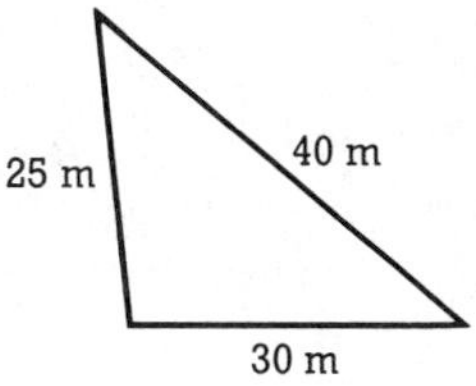

d)
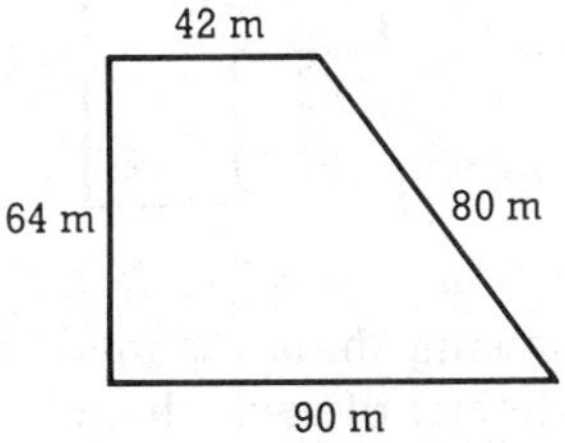

e)
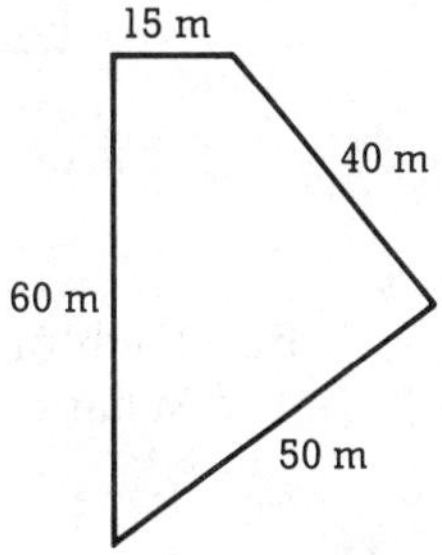

2. A roll of fencing is 25 metres long. How many rolls of fencing does John need for each of these fields?

a)
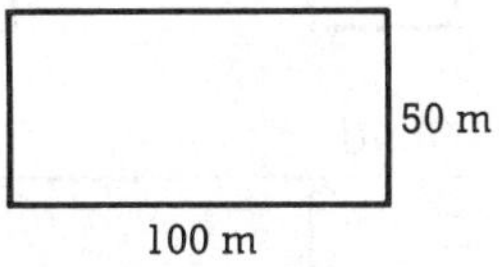

b)
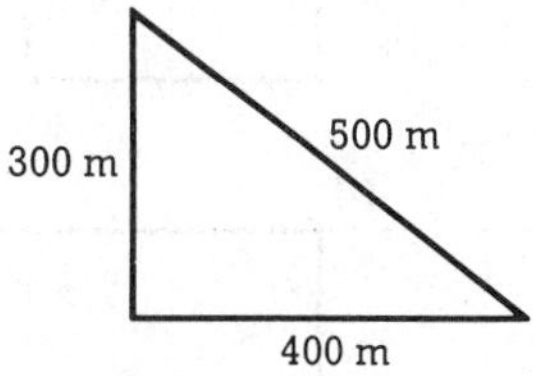

c)
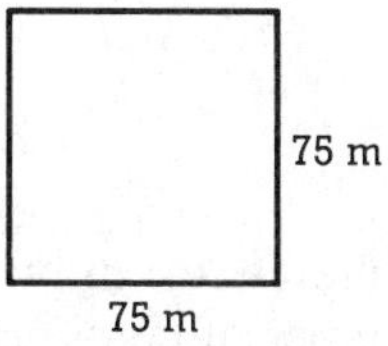

d)
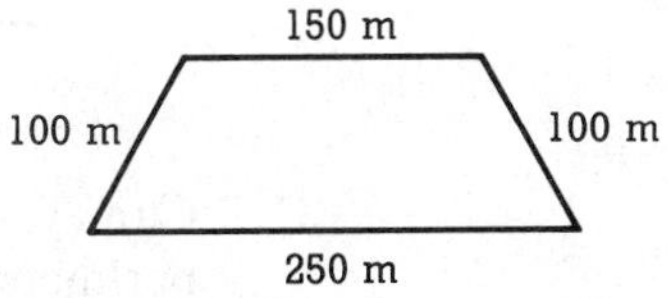

3. Would five 25 m rolls of fencing be enough to go all the way round this field?

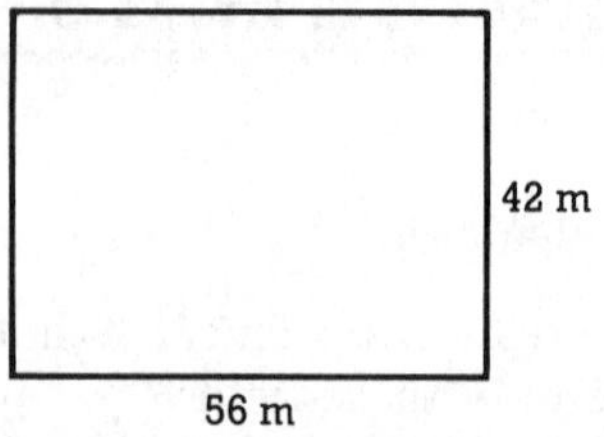

The distance around a shape is called its *perimeter*.

4. Copy these diagrams and fill in the missing lengths. What is the perimeter of each of these shapes? All measurements are in centimetres.

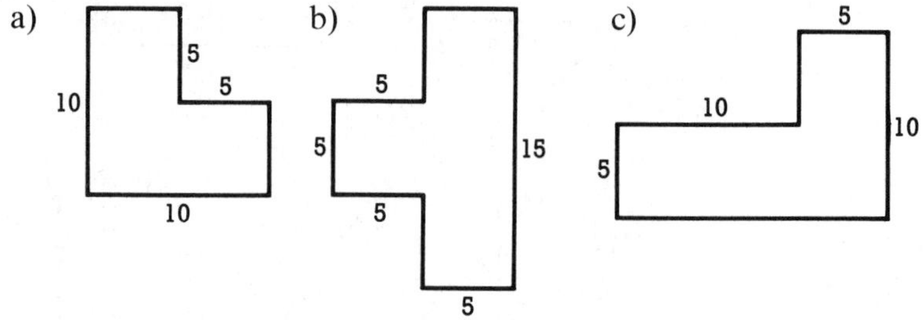

5. Each of the following shapes is made using four 1 cm squares. What is the perimeter of each shape?

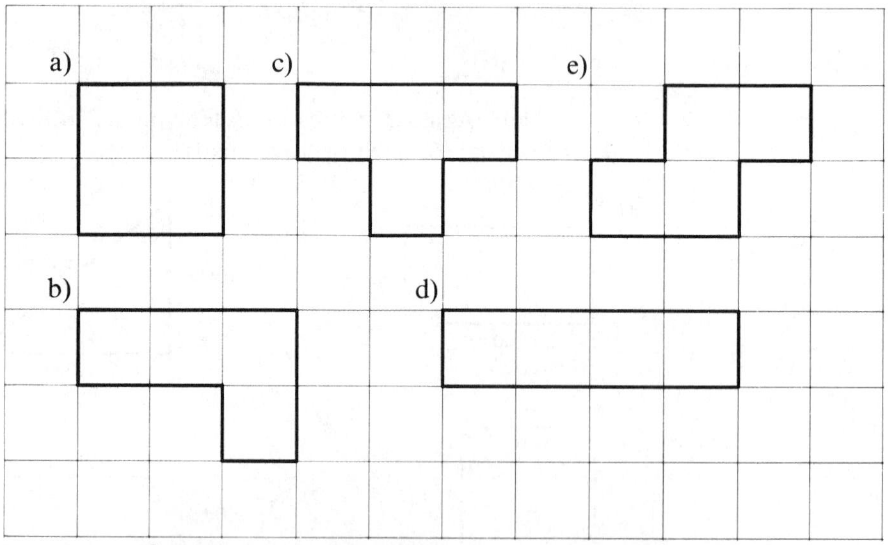

Can you use four squares to draw another shape whose perimeter is an odd number of centimetres?

6. Draw as many different shapes as you can each using 6 squares.

A different shape means one that cannot be obtained by turning another shape over or round. These two shapes, for example, are not different:

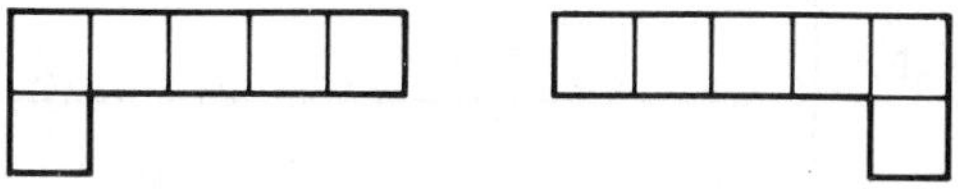

a) Write down the perimeter of each.
b) What is the largest perimeter you can get?
c) What is the smallest perimeter you can get?

7. On squared paper draw as many *different* shapes as you can that have a perimeter of 12 cm. Each side must be a whole number of centimetres.

8. Jawad wants to put a sheet of glass in this door.

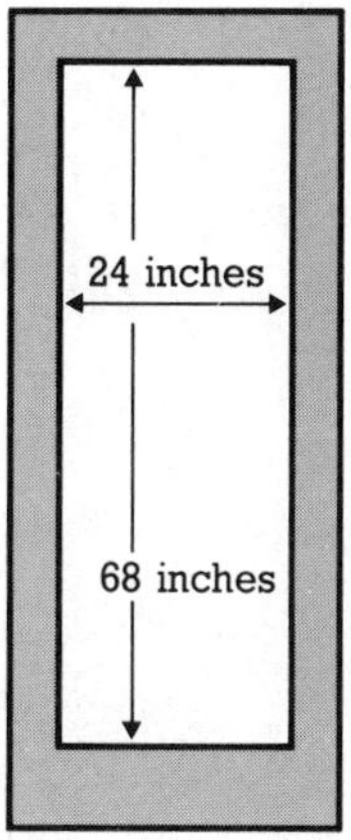

a) What length of wooden beading must he buy?
b) It is sold in 75 inch lengths. How many lengths must he buy?
c) How much is left over?
d) How much will it cost at 85 p for each length?

9. On squared paper, draw as many different rectangles as you can, each using 18 squares.
Write down the perimeter of each rectangle.

10. Draw one shape made of 4 squares and one made of 6 squares so that they have the same perimeter.

11.

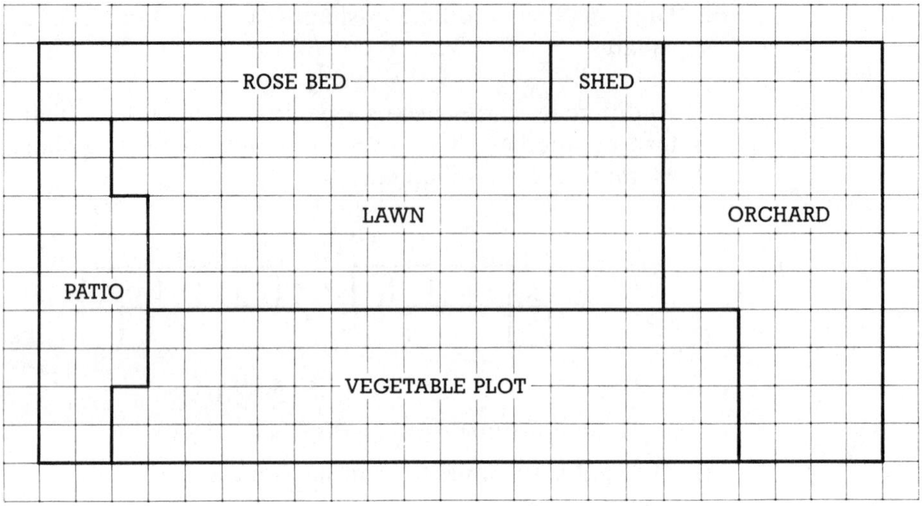

This is the plan of a garden. The side of each square represents 1 metre.

What is the perimeter of

a) the garden
b) the rose bed
c) the orchard
d) the patio
e) the base of the shed
f) the lawn ?

12.

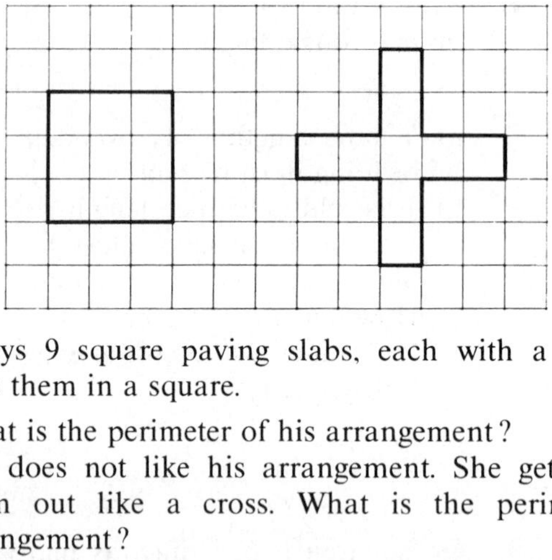

Bill buys 9 square paving slabs, each with a side of $\frac{1}{2}$ m. He lays them in a square.

a) What is the perimeter of his arrangement ?
b) Peg does not like his arrangement. She gets him to lay them out like a cross. What is the perimeter of her arrangement ?
c) Bill wonders if there is a way of getting an even greater perimeter. Can you find a way of doing this ?
(The paving slabs must meet along complete edges; they cannot be broken.)

13. Investigate the problem again starting with 16 paving slabs.

14. Investigate the problem again starting with 25 paving slabs.

15. You have found that different arrangements give different perimeters for the same number of slabs. Which shape gives the smallest perimeter?

16. If you had a 200 metre length of wire, which shape do you think would enclose the largest number of slabs?

17. a) Harry buys 36 paving slabs, each with a side of $\frac{1}{2}$ m, and lays them to form a square. He decides that he would like a larger perimeter, so he takes a slab from one corner and places it along the side as shown in the diagram.
By how much has he increased the total perimeter of his arrangement?

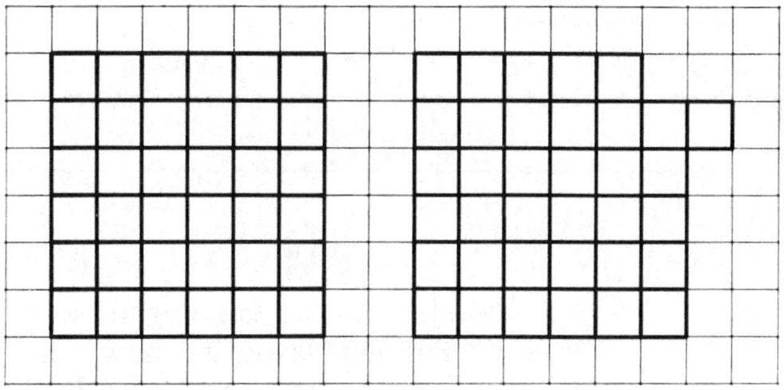

b) Harry decides to do the same with the other three corner slabs. On squared paper show the new arrangement so that the arrangement has rotational symmetry.

c) Can he take another slab away from the edge and place it in a new position so that the total perimeter is increased? If he can, show the new arrangement on a diagram.

18. Pete has 100 paving slabs, each with a side of $\frac{1}{2}$ m. He has 15 m of edging which he wants to place along the outside of the shape he makes.
Does he have enough edging to go all the way round?

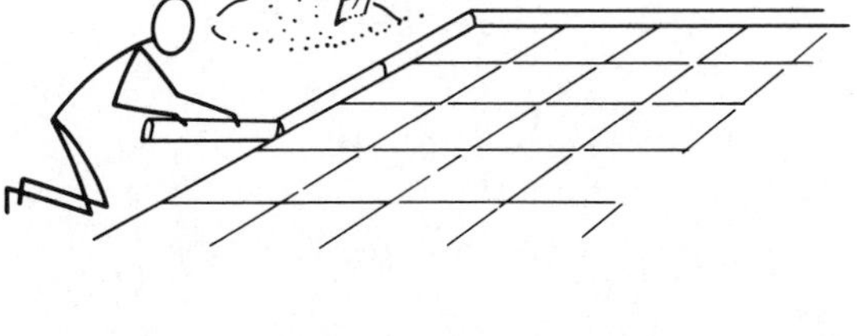

19. Ken has 64 square tiles, each with a side of 1 metre, which he lays in a large square (diagram A).

a) What is the perimeter of the square?

b) He decides to divide the square in half and puts one half alongside the other as shown in diagram B.
By how much has the perimeter of his layout increased?

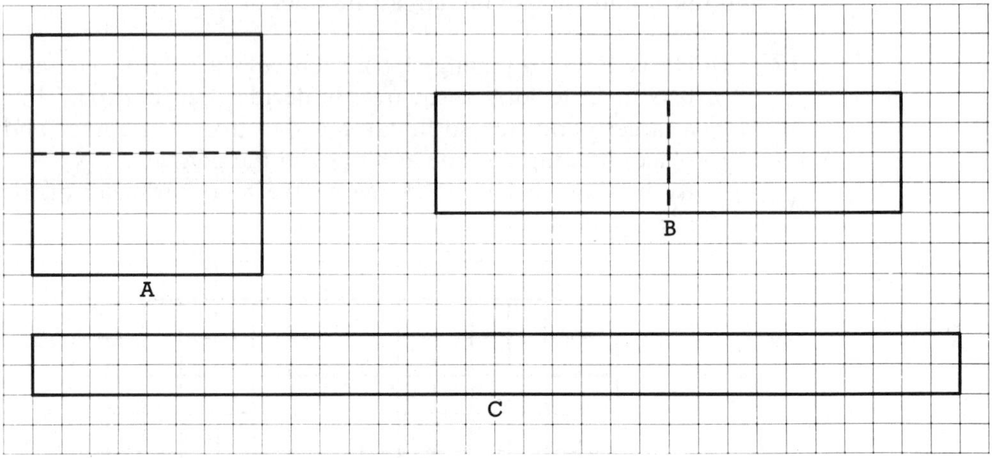

c) He does the same again so that his layout is half as wide. The new layout is shown in diagram C. He then does the same to get a new layout D. This layout is *not* shown.
Copy and complete the following table.

Shape	Length (m)	Breadth (m)	Number of tiles used	Perimeter (m)
Square A	8	8	64	
Rectangle B	16	4	64	
Rectangle C	32	2	64	
Rectangle D		1	64	

13 WORKING WITH UNITS

STANDARD UNITS

When we want to give the length of a room or the weight of a parcel, we give it in a unit that everyone can understand. These are called standard units.

We could give the length of a room as a number of metres. The metre is one of a set of units called metric units.

UNITS OF LENGTH

The units that are commonly used to measure length are

kilometres (km), metres (m), centimetres (cm), millimetres (mm).

You can see centimetres and millimetres on your ruler.

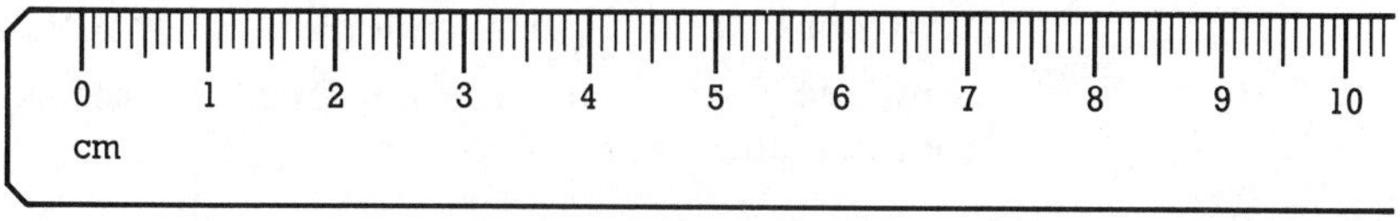

A standard bed is about 2 m long.

Ten football pitches, laid end to end, cover a distance of about one kilometre.

Which unit you choose to use depends on what you are measuring. It would be sensible to measure the length of a room in metres. We would not choose to measure the width of this page in metres however, because it is a lot less than one metre.

EXERCISE 13a **1.** Which unit would you use to measure

a) the length of your classroom
b) the length of your pencil
c) the length of a soccer pitch
d) the distance from Manchester to Liverpool
e) the length of a page in this book
f) the thickness of this book ?

2. Use your ruler to draw a line of length

a) 10 cm	d) 5 mm	g) 5 cm
b) 3 cm	e) 10 mm	h) 15 mm
c) 15 cm	f) 4 cm	i) 8 cm.

3. *Estimate* the length of each of the following lines

a) ______________________________

b) ________________

c) ____________________________________

d) _____________

e) ____

Now use your ruler to measure each line. How good were your estimates ?

4. Use plain paper and a straight edge (*not* a ruler with centimetres marked on it) to draw a line that is about

a) 10 cm long b) 5 cm long c) 2 cm long.

Now measure each of your lines to see how good your approximation was.

5. Estimate the width of your classroom in metres.

6. Estimate the height or width in centimetres of objects such as a milk bottle, lunch box, exercise book or text book.
Now use your ruler to find out how good your estimates were.

CHANGING FROM LARGE UNITS TO SMALLER UNITS

The relationships between the units are

$$1 \text{ km} = 1000 \text{ m}$$

$$1 \text{ m} = 100 \text{ cm}$$

$$1 \text{ cm} = 10 \text{ mm}$$

It is easier to compare lengths if both measurements are in the same unit.

Now 1 m is 100 cm, so 2 m is 200 cm.

If the bed is 200 cm long and the sheet is 250 cm long, we can see that the sheet is longer than the bed.

EXERCISE 13b

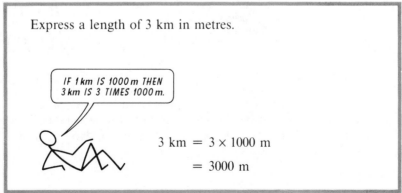

Express a length of 3 km in metres.

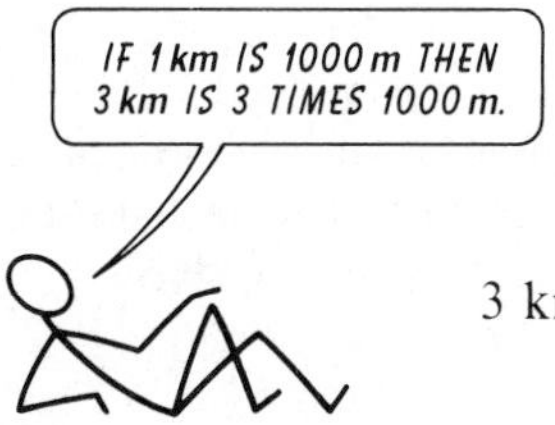

$$3 \text{ km} = 3 \times 1000 \text{ m}$$
$$= 3000 \text{ m}$$

1. a) Express a length of 2 cm in millimetres.
b) Express a length of 6 m in centimetres.

2. A strip of card is 16 cm long.

a) How long is the card in mm?
b) Will it fit into one of the envelopes?

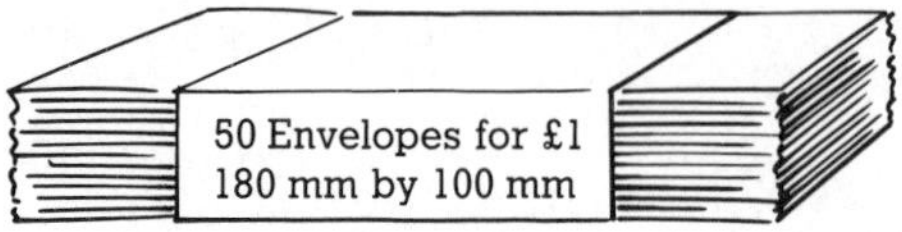

3. Express the length of each of these strips of card in millimetres.

a) 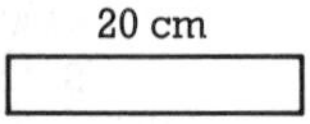

b) 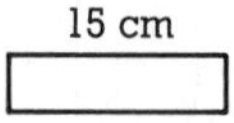

c) 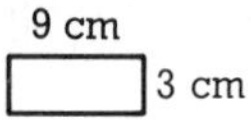

Which of these strips will fit into the envelopes?

4. Change each of these lengths into centimetres.

a) 3 m b) 25 m c) 12 m

Which is the shortest?

5.

a) Express $1\frac{1}{2}$ km in metres.
b) Write the distance from school of each child's home in order of size, with the shortest distance first.
c) Anita lives 5 km from school. How far is this in metres?

6. Convert each length to the unit in brackets.

a) 3 cm (mm)
b) 5 m (cm)
c) 2 km (m)
d) 24 m (cm)
e) 14 cm (mm)
f) 4 km (m)

UNITS OF WEIGHT

The most common units of weight are the kilogram (kg) and the gram (g).

1 kg = 1000 g

One eating apple weighs about 100 g, so one gram is a very small unit of weight. The most common bag of sugar on sale weighs 1 kg.

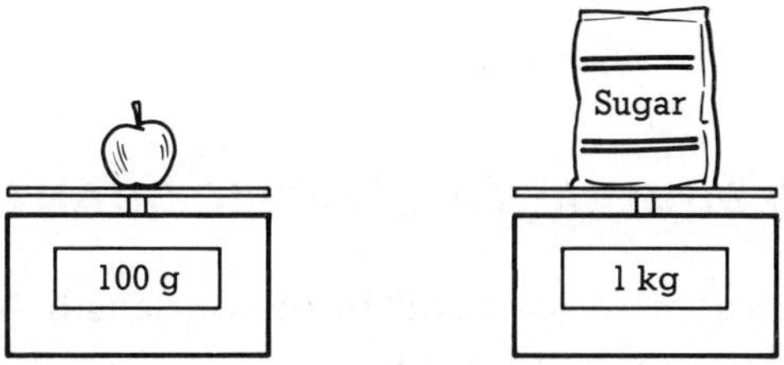
Sugar
100 g
1 kg

It is easy to remember the connection between kg and g (and between km and m) because the letter K is often used as an abbreviation for "thousand".

EXERCISE 13c

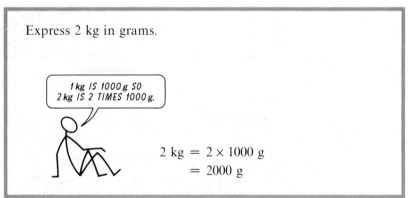

Express 2 kg in grams.

1 kg IS 1000 g SO
2 kg IS 2 TIMES 1000 g.

$$\begin{aligned} 2\text{ kg} &= 2 \times 1000\text{ g} \\ &= 2000\text{ g} \end{aligned}$$

1. Express in grams.

a) 4 kg b) 20 kg c) 5·2 kg

2.

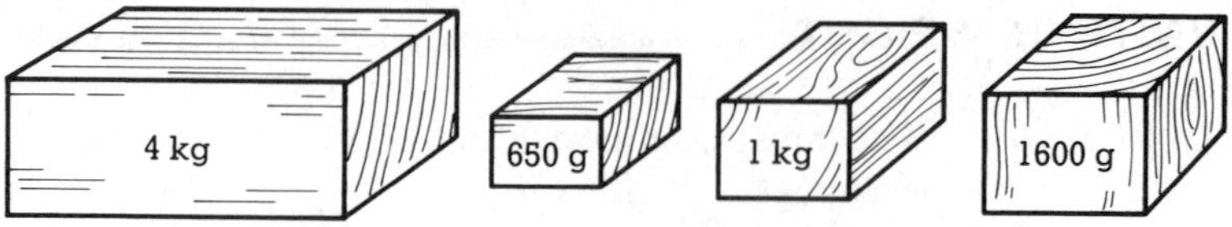

a) Give the weight of each piece of wood in grams.

b) What is the weight of the heaviest piece of wood?

c) What is the weight of the lightest piece of wood?

3. Express each of these weights in grams.

a) 3 kg b) 5 kg c) $\frac{1}{2}$ kg d) $1\frac{1}{2}$ kg

ADDING AND SUBTRACTING METRIC QUANTITIES

Before we can add these two lengths together, we must give them both in the same unit.

1 metre
58 cm

Before we can add or subtract *any* two quantities, they must both be given in the same unit.

EXERCISE 13d

If these two remnants of carpet are joined together end to end, how long will the total piece be?

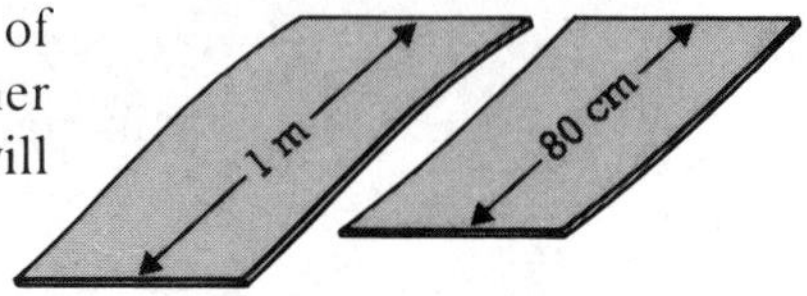
1 m
80 cm

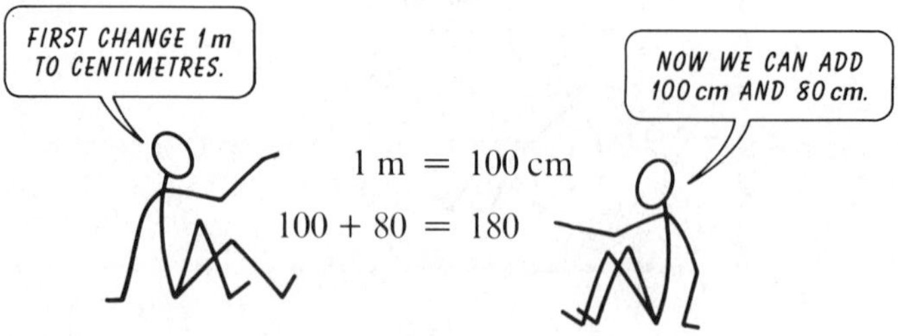
FIRST CHANGE 1 m TO CENTIMETRES.
NOW WE CAN ADD 100 cm AND 80 cm.

1 m = 100 cm

100 + 80 = 180

The total piece is 180 cm long.

1. Jason has to carry this shopping home.
How heavy is it?

2. Ming wants to put this table next to the cupboard.
What length of wall will they take up?

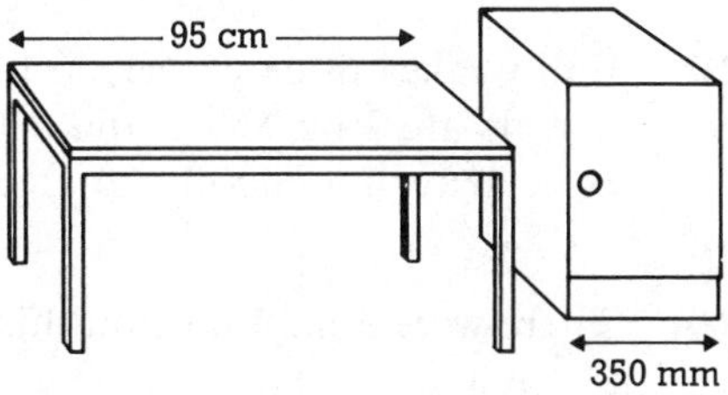

3. A roll of material is 5 metres long to start with. A length of 70 cm is cut off the roll.
What length of material is now left on the roll?

4. There is one kilogram of sugar in a bag. Peter takes 150 g of sugar out of the bag.
How much sugar is left?

5. Find a) 2 cm + 12 mm b) 2 km − 1500 m

6. Find a) 4 kg − 850 g b) 1 kg + 350 g + 540 g

7. Find a) 2 m − 54 cm b) 20 cm − 150 mm

8. Luke has to buy some wood to make two fence posts. One post is 1 m long and the other post is 85 cm long.

a) What length of wood should he buy to get the exact amount?
b) Luke decides that he needs an extra half metre of wood in case he has made a mistake when measuring the posts. How much wood does he buy?
c) Luke did make a mistake. The shorter post is 95 cm long. Did Luke buy enough wood?

9. Will these three kitchen units fit along a wall which is 300 cm long?

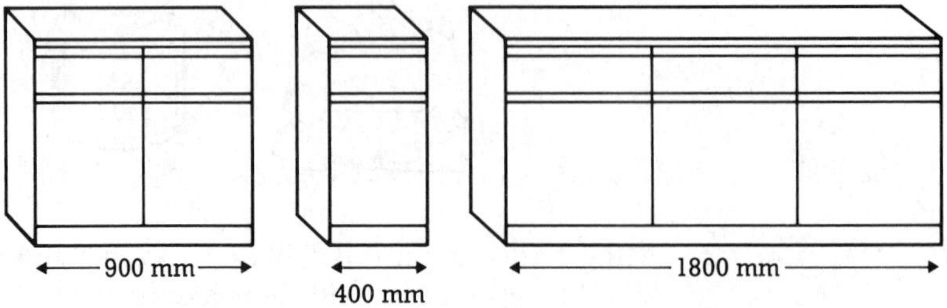

10. Emily takes three parcels to the post office. The weights of the parcels are 2 kg, 850 g, and 500 g.
How heavy are the three parcels together?

11. There were 5 m of tape on this roll at the beginning of a lesson.

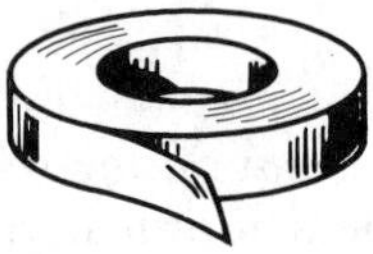

During the lesson, Peter cut off 50 cm, Jane helped herself to 30 cm and Mrs. Patel gave out two lengths of 70 cm each to other children in the class.
How much tape was left on the roll at the end of the lesson?

14 AREAS 1

EXERCISE 14a Use 1 cm line or dot grid for this exercise.

1. Sean has a lot of triangles like this.

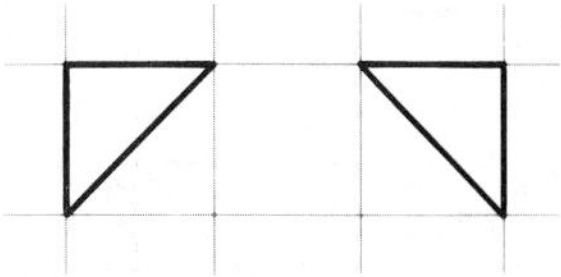

Copy the shapes A, B, C, D and E. How many of the triangles would he need to cover each of these shapes completely?

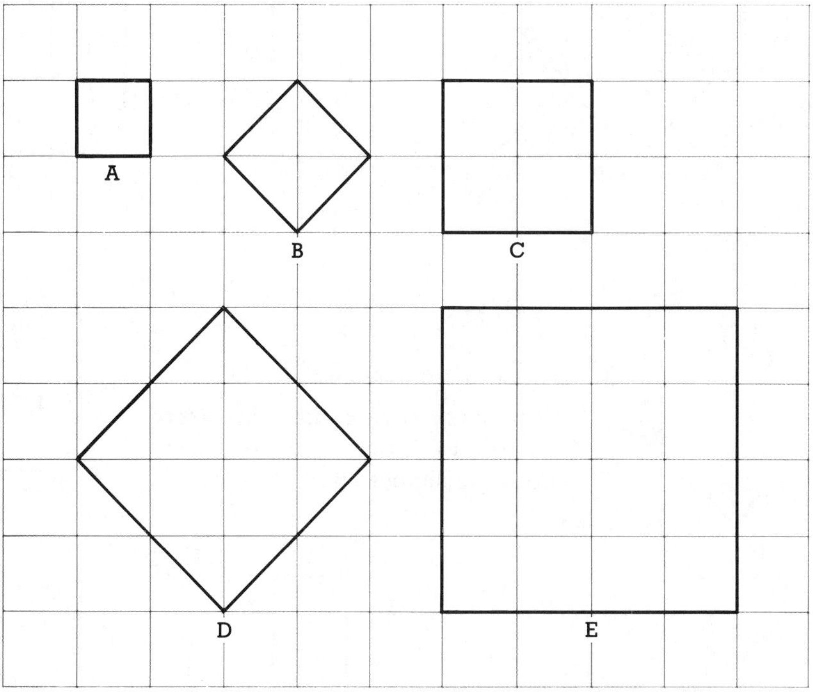

Copy and complete this table.

Square	A	B	C	D	E
No. of triangles to cover it	2				

2. Copy the shapes below.
How many triangles like this are needed to cover each shape completely?
The first one is done for you.

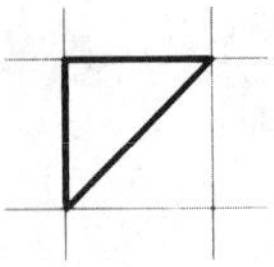

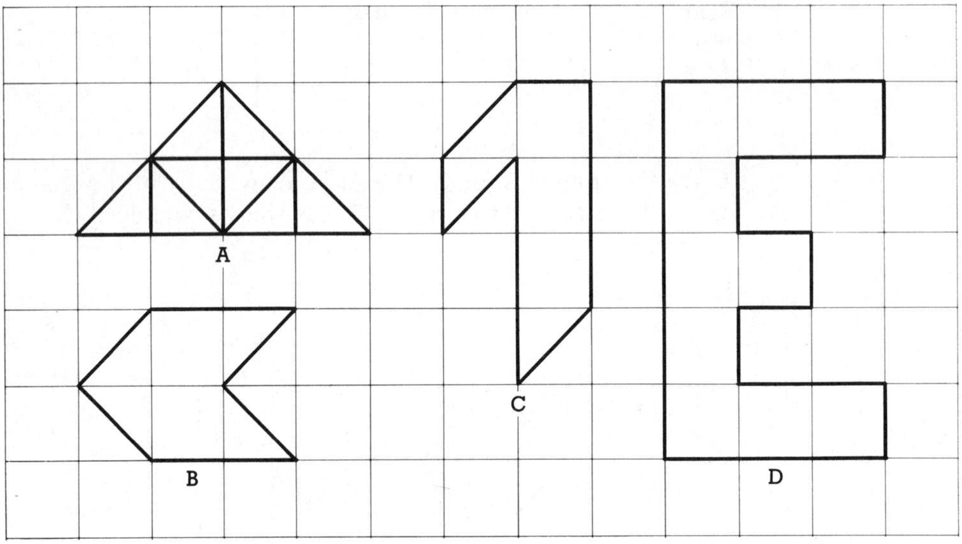

3. This is a 1 cm square.
How many squares like this are needed to cover each of the following shapes completely?

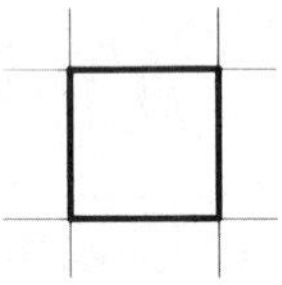

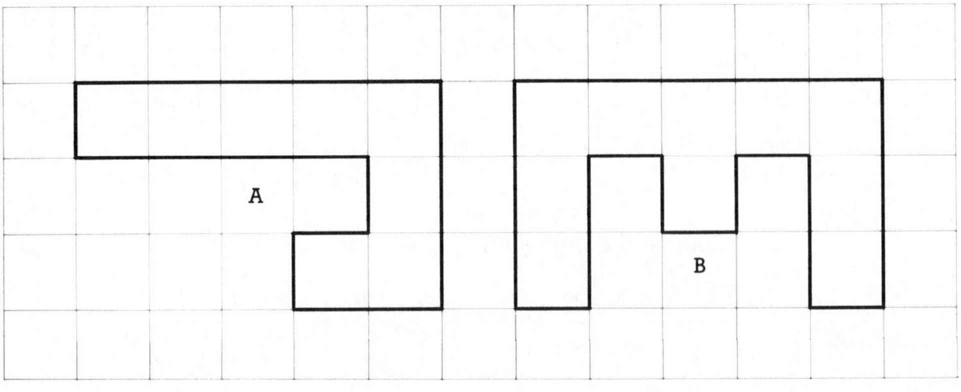

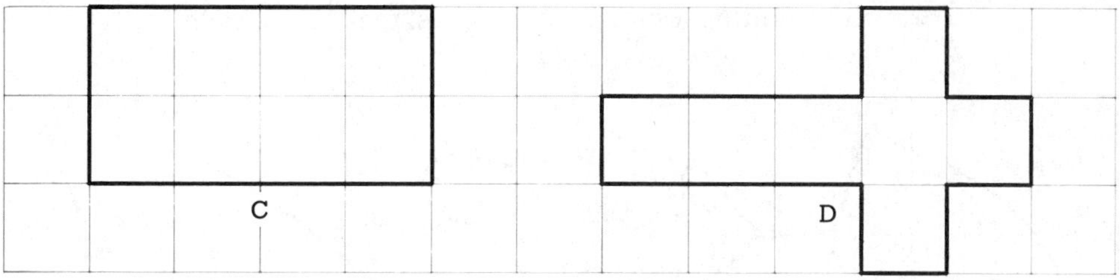

MEASURING AREA

The area of a shape is the amount of surface within the lines that enclose it.

The most convenient shape to use to describe the area of another shape is the square. We find the area of a shape by counting the number of squares of the same size needed to cover it.

One difficulty is that these squares do not always fit exactly into the area we are measuring. We get over this by using a simple rule:

If less than half of a square is inside the area we don't count it.
If more than half of a square is inside we count it as one square.

EXERCISE 14b **1.** By counting squares, estimate, in squares, the area of each island. St. John's is done for you.

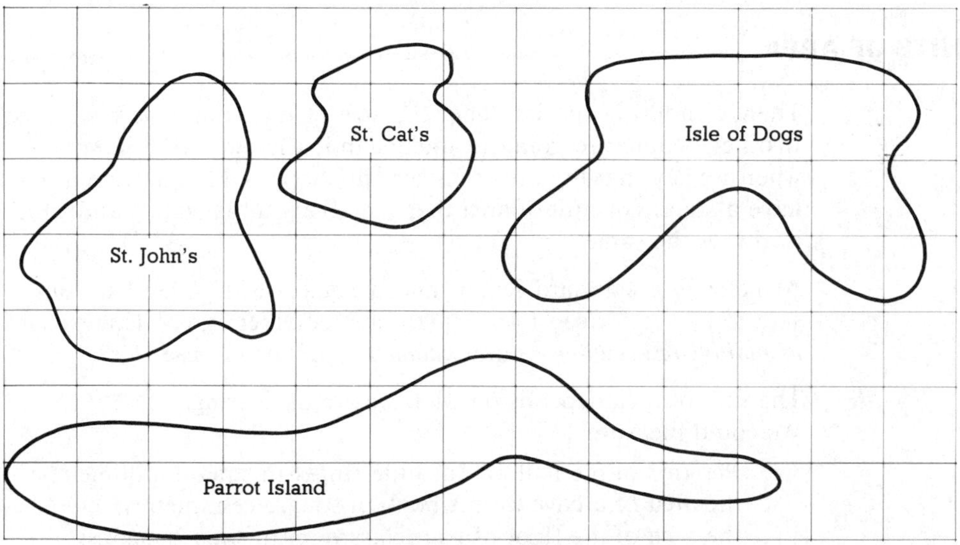

The area of St. John's is about 8 squares.

2. By counting, estimate, in squares, the area of each leaf.

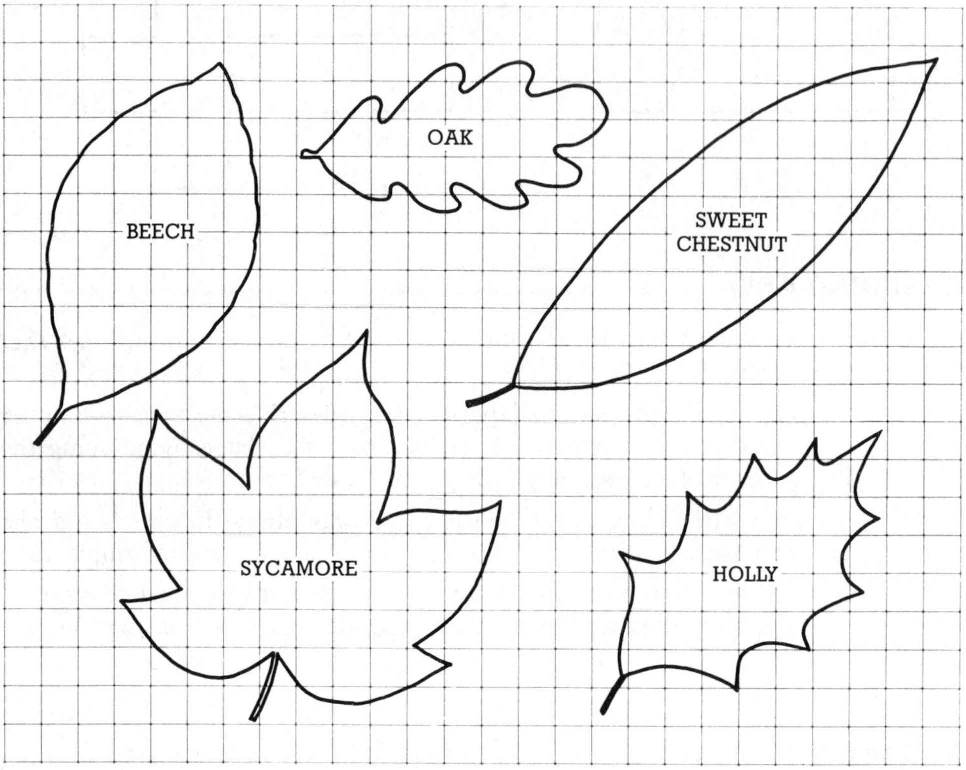

UNITS OF AREA

There is nothing special about the size of the square we have used. If other people are going to understand what we are talking about when we say that the area of a certain shape is 12 squares, we must have a square or unit of area that everybody understands and which is always the same.

A metre is a standard length and a square with sides 1 m long is said to have an area of one square metre. Other agreed lengths such as *millimetres*, *centimetres* and *kilometres*, are also in use.

The unit of area depends on what we are measuring.
We could measure:

the area of the nail on our little finger in square millimetres;
the area of a page in this book in square centimetres;
the area of the floor of your classroom in square metres;
and the area of a country in square kilometres.

EXERCISE 14c

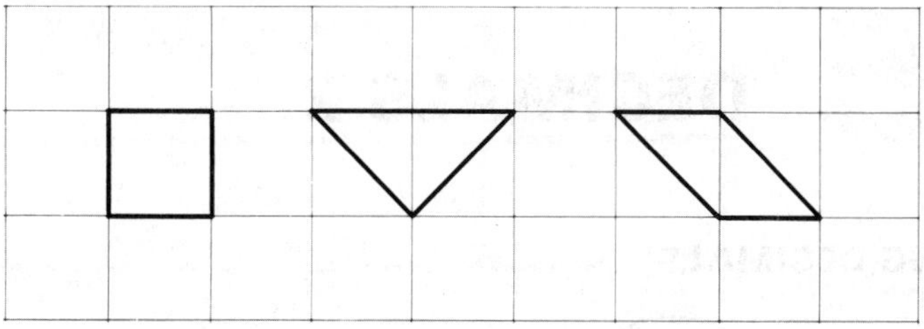

Each of these shapes has an area of 1 square centimetre. Use them to find the area of each of the shapes in Questions 1 to 10.

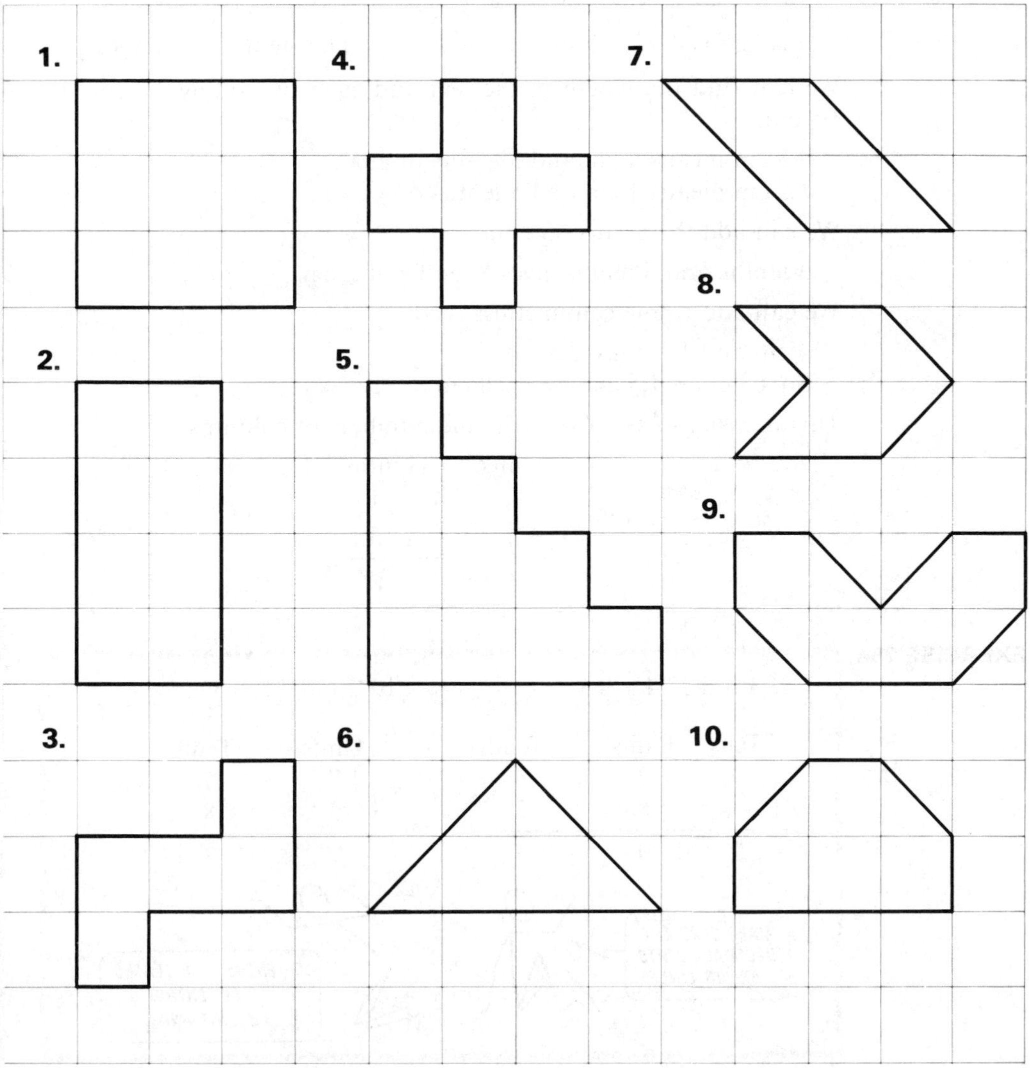

15 DECIMALS 2

ADDING DECIMALS

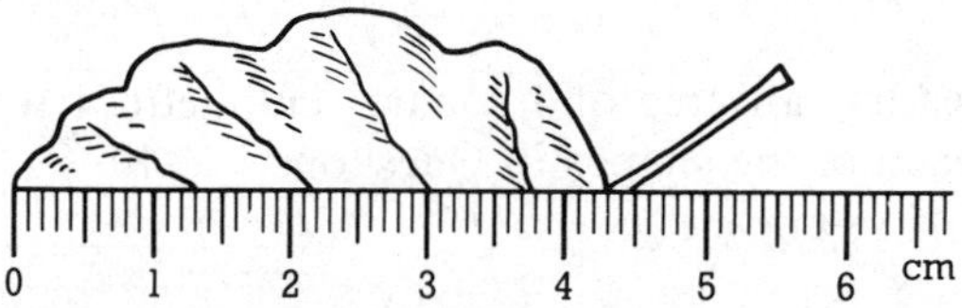

This leaf is 4·3 cm long.

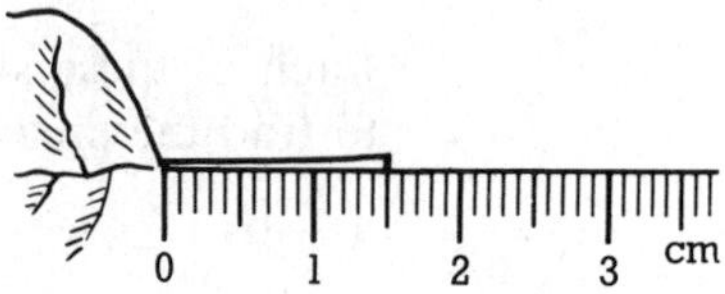

The stem is 1·5 cm long.

We can find the length of the leaf and stem by adding 4·3 cm and 1·5 cm.

4·3 cm means 4 cm and 3 tenths of a cm
1·5 cm means 1 cm and 5 tenths of a cm

We can add the tenths of a cm:

3 tenths and 5 tenths gives 8 tenths of a cm.

We can add whole centimetres:

4 cm and 1 cm gives 5 cm.
So 4·3 cm + 1·5 cm gives 5·8 cm.

This is easier to see if we write the numbers in columns:

Units		Tenths
4	·	3
+ 1	·	5
5	·	8

EXERCISE 15a

a) Find 12·4 + 8·3

	Tens	Units	·	Tenths
	1	2	·	4
+		8	·	3
	2	0	·	7

b) Find 7·5 + 3·8

Units	·	Tenths
7	·	5
+ 3	·	8
11	·	3

MAKE SURE THE DECIMAL POINTS ARE IN LINE.

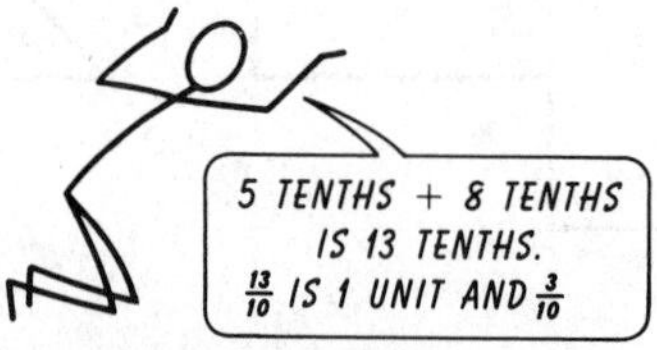

5 TENTHS + 8 TENTHS IS 13 TENTHS.
$\frac{13}{10}$ IS 1 UNIT AND $\frac{3}{10}$

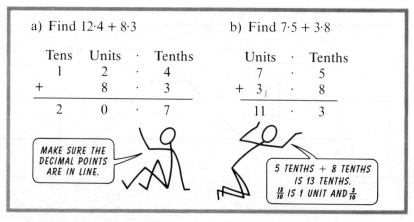

Find the total length of the leaf and stem.

1.

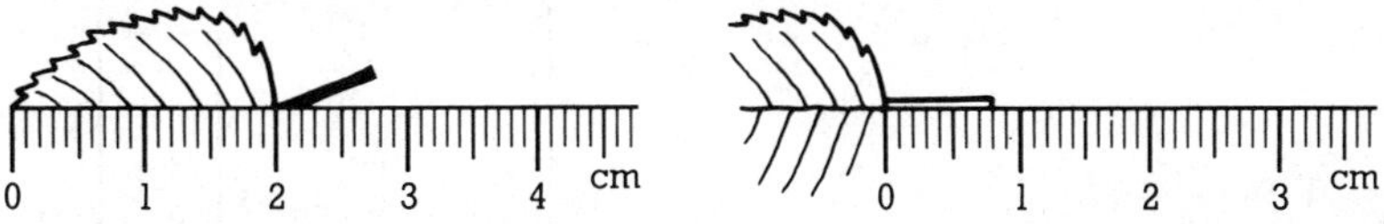

2.

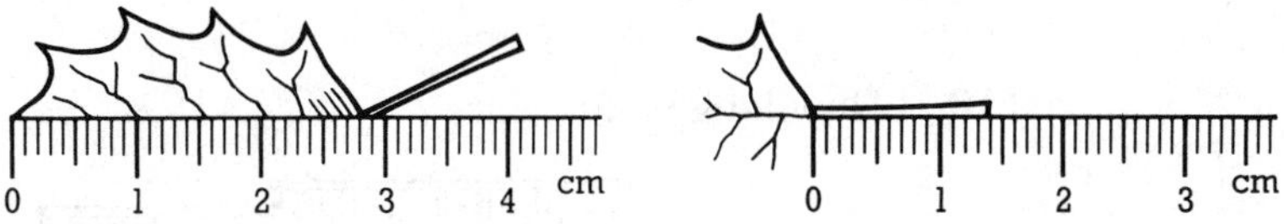

Find

3. 1·3 + 2·5

4. 8·5 + 2·3

5. 5·1 + 8·4

6. 18·6 + 21·3

7. 1·5 + 2·9

8. 3·8 + 5·5

9. 2·9 + 7·3

10. 12·7 + 22·6

11. 3·5 + 14·1

12. 23·4 + 9·8

13. 21·7 + 36·9

14. 101·5 + 72·8

15. This is the plan of a room.

a) How long is wall C?
b) How long is wall D?

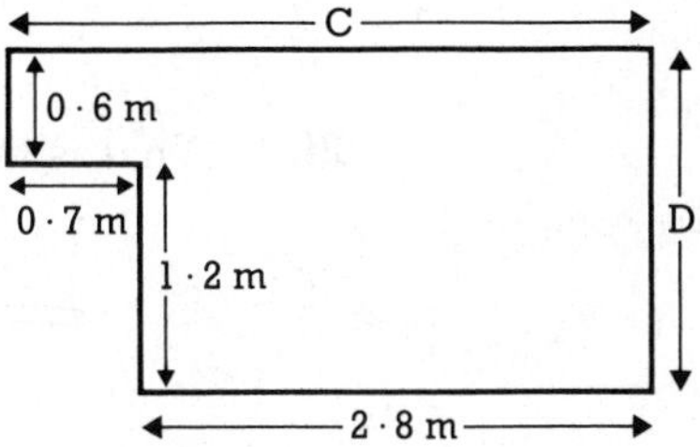

16. What is the total length of this lorry and trailer?

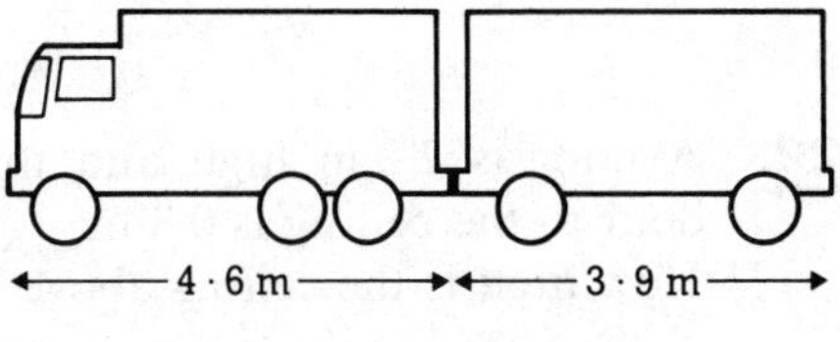

17. What is the overall length of this wall?

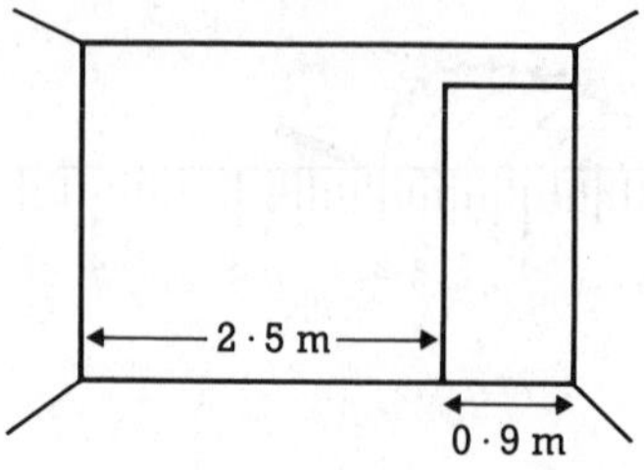

18. How long is this fence?

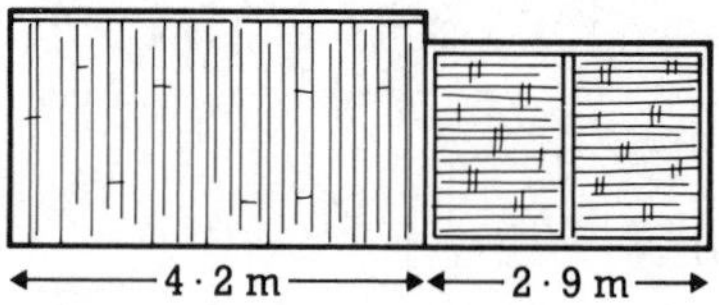

19. How tall is this tower?

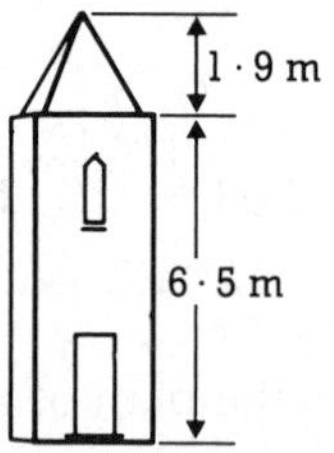

20. What is the total length of these two pipes?

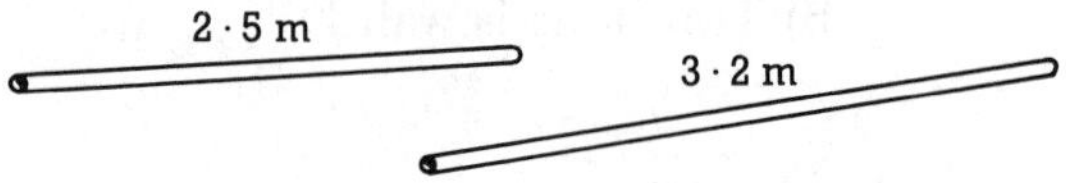

21. A corridor is carpeted for 2·6 m of its length and uncarpeted for 3·7 m.
How long is the corridor?

22. A door is 2·2 m high and the distance from the top of the door to the ceiling is 0·8 m.
How high is the ceiling above the floor?

We can add hundredths in the same way.

EXERCISE 15b

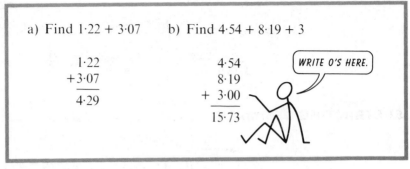

a) Find 1·22 + 3·07   b) Find 4·54 + 8·19 + 3

$$\begin{array}{r} 1{\cdot}22 \\ +3{\cdot}07 \\ \hline 4{\cdot}29 \end{array} \qquad \begin{array}{r} 4{\cdot}54 \\ 8{\cdot}19 \\ +\ 3{\cdot}00 \\ \hline 15{\cdot}73 \end{array}$$

Find

1. 3·22 + 4·04

2. 2·04 + 5·75

3. 7·21 + 3·04

4. 10·6 + 12·54

5. 12·1 + 6·64

6. 18 + 9·85

7. 4·07 + 18·49

8. 24·89 + 5·4

9. 26·81 + 25·55

10. 0·17 + 0·8

11. 10·09 + 8·11

12. 34·51 + 16·49

13. 2·15 + 5·23 + 1·49

14. 7·02 + 3·55 + 1·02

15. 17·8 + 15·22 + 51·09

16. 3·5 + 6 + 2·34

17. 7 + 0·59 + 3·5

18. 26·02 + 15 + 10·9

19. This is a rectangle with two rectangles cut off.

a) How long is the side AB?
b) How long is the side BC?

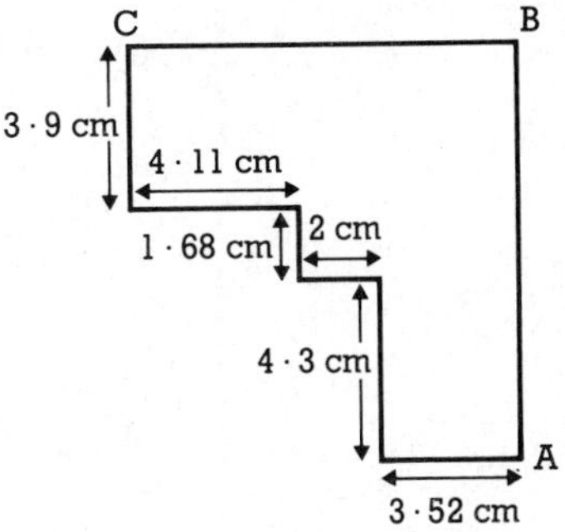

20. What is the overall width of the wall?

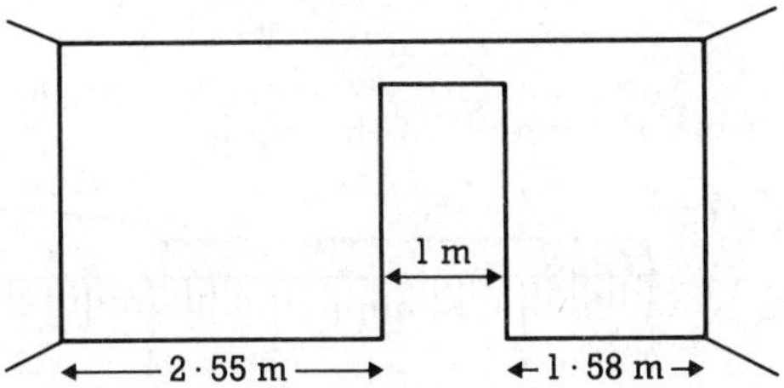

21. What length of floor can be covered with these three rugs if they are put end to end?

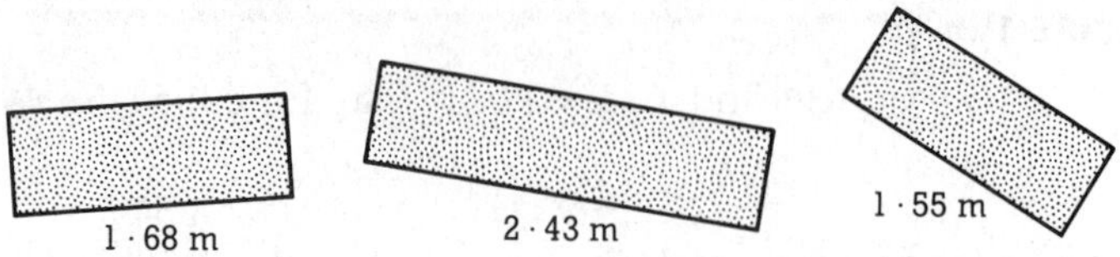

SUBTRACTING DECIMALS

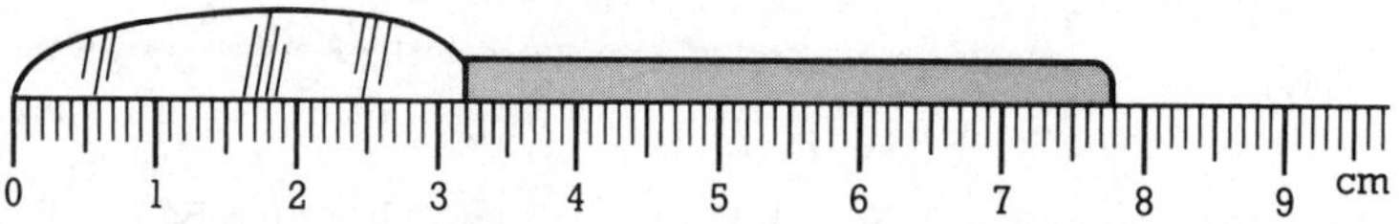

To find the length of the handle, we could count back on the scale, but it is easier to subtract the length of the blade from the overall length of the knife.

The length of the handle is 7·8 cm − 3·2 cm
= 4·6 cm

$$\begin{array}{r} 7{\cdot}8 \\ -3{\cdot}2 \\ \hline 4{\cdot}6 \end{array}$$

EXERCISE 15c

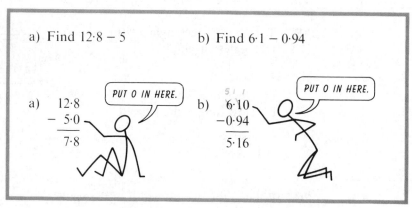

a) Find 12·8 − 5 b) Find 6·1 − 0·94

a) $\begin{array}{r} 12{\cdot}8 \\ -\ 5{\cdot}0 \\ \hline 7{\cdot}8 \end{array}$

b) $\begin{array}{r} 6{\cdot}10 \\ -0{\cdot}94 \\ \hline 5{\cdot}16 \end{array}$

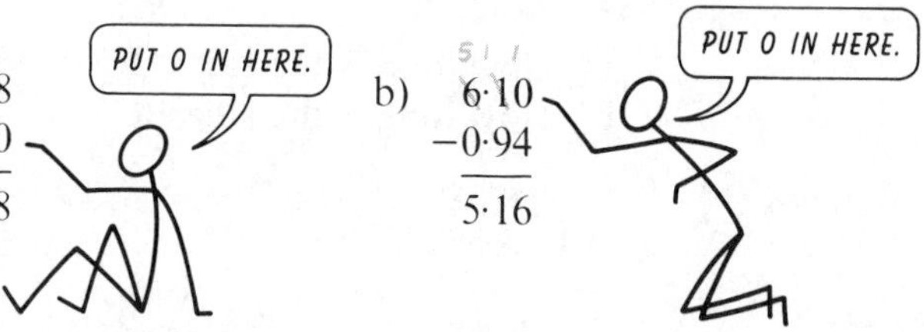

Find the length of the blade.

1.

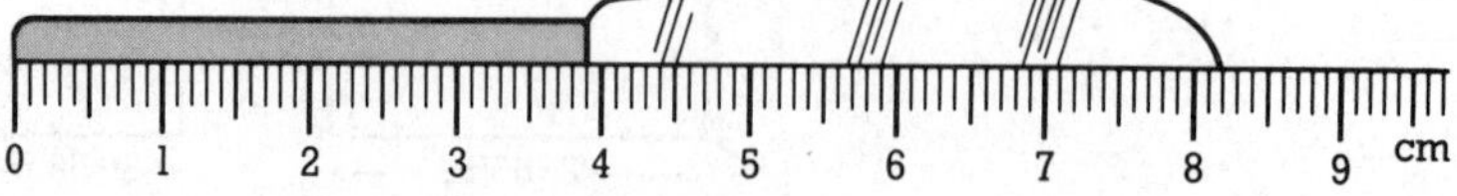

2.

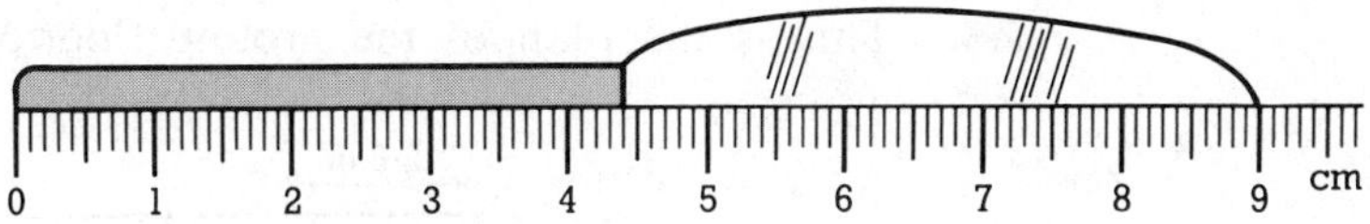

Find

3. 2·9 − 1·3 **5.** 8·3 − 4·5 **7.** 16·2 − 8·8

4. 5·8 − 4·5 **6.** 12·7 − 9·5 **8.** 21·4 − 17·5

9. 8·3 − 4 **13.** 25·6 − 8·14 **17.** 30 − 18·69

10. 7 − 2·5 **14.** 17·02 − 5·19 **18.** 6·9 − 0·05

11. 3·65 − 2·04 **15.** 51·8 − 36·04 **19.** 5 − 0·04

12. 7·09 − 5·84 **16.** 2 − 0·55 **20.** 10·02 − 9·89

21. A length of 2·5 m is cut off this roll of material.
How much is left?

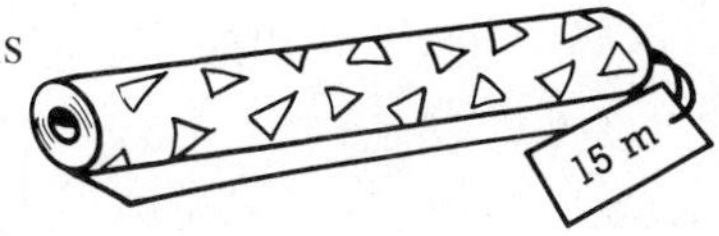

22. A room is 2·9 m long.
How much needs to be cut from this carpet if it is to fit the length of the room?

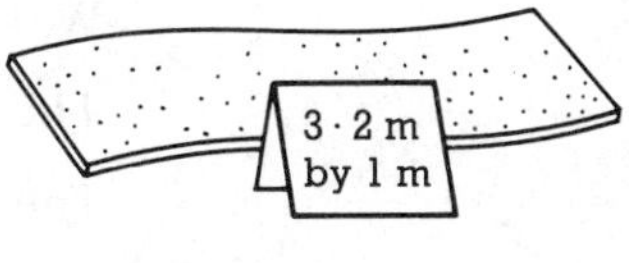

23. What is the length of the caravan?

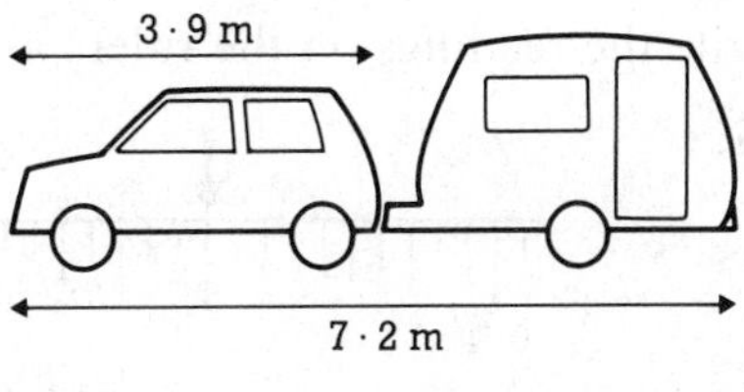

24. This is the plan of the ground floor of a house.

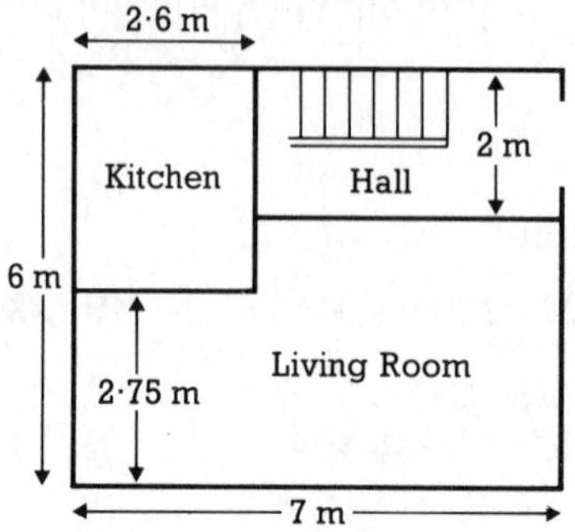

a) How long is the hall?
b) How wide is the kitchen?
c) What is the width of the wide end of the living room?

CHANGING DECIMALS TO FRACTIONS

This is a magnified section of a ruler showing tenths and hundredths.

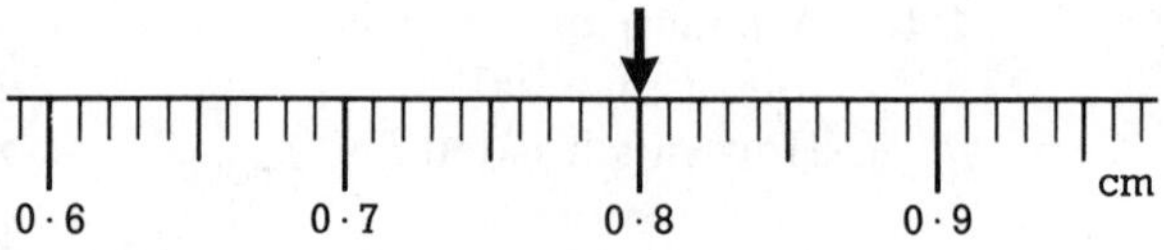

We know that one tenth $= \frac{1}{10} = 0{\cdot}1$.

The reading on the ruler is 0·8 cm, or $\frac{8}{10}$ cm.

The fraction $\frac{8}{10}$ can be simplified to $\frac{4}{5}$.

Therefore $0{\cdot}8 = \frac{4}{5}$

EXERCISE 15d Write the readings on the rulers as fractions.

1.

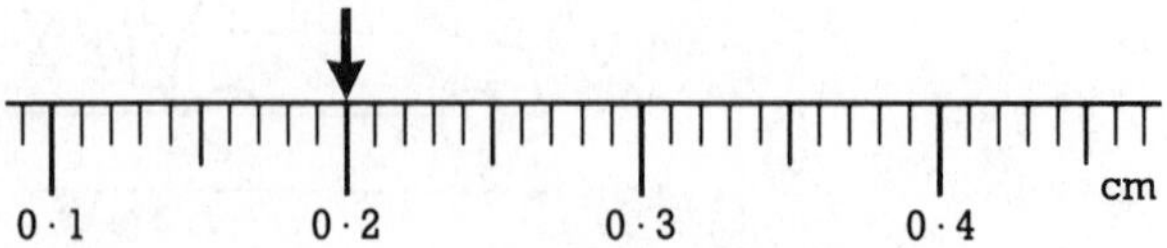

2.

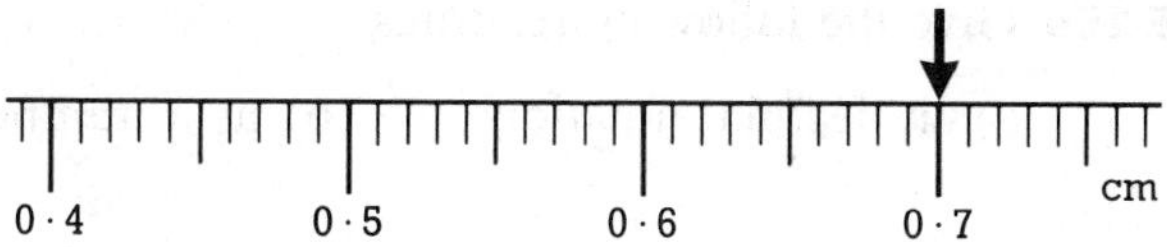

3.

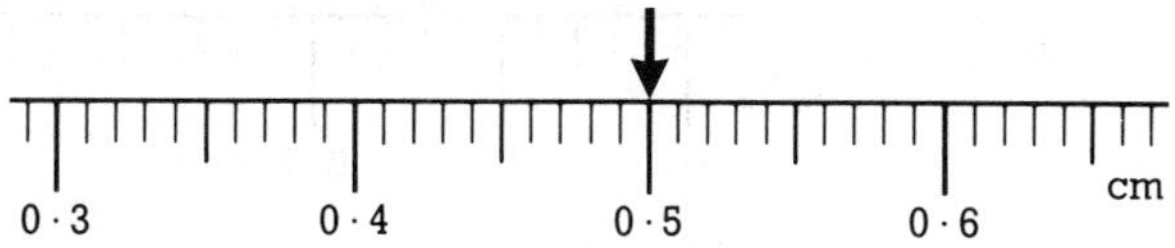

Write 0·4 as a fraction in its simplest form.

$$0{\cdot}4 = \frac{\overset{2}{\cancel{4}}}{\underset{5}{\cancel{10}}} = \frac{2}{5}$$

Write each of the following decimals as a fraction in its simplest form.

4. 0·1 **6.** 0·3 **8.** 0·7 **10.** 0·2

5. 0·5 **7.** 0·9 **9.** 0·6 **11.** 0·8

TENTHS AND HUNDREDTHS

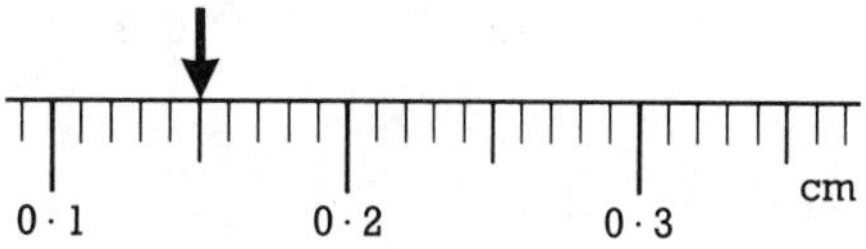

In decimal notation, the reading on this ruler is 0·15 cm.
Now 0·15 means 1 tenth and 5 hundredths.

i.e. $0{\cdot}15 = \frac{1}{10} + \frac{5}{100}$, but $\frac{1}{10} = \frac{10}{100}$

So $0{\cdot}15 = \frac{10}{100} + \frac{5}{100} = \frac{15}{100}$

i.e. the reading on this rule can also be given as the fraction $\frac{15}{100}$

This fraction can be simplified: $\frac{15}{100} = \frac{3}{20}$

EXERCISE 15e Give the following readings

a) in decimal notation b) as a number of hundredths.

1.

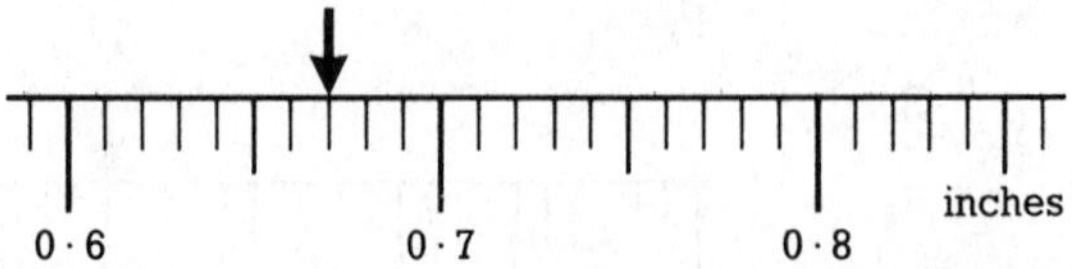

2.

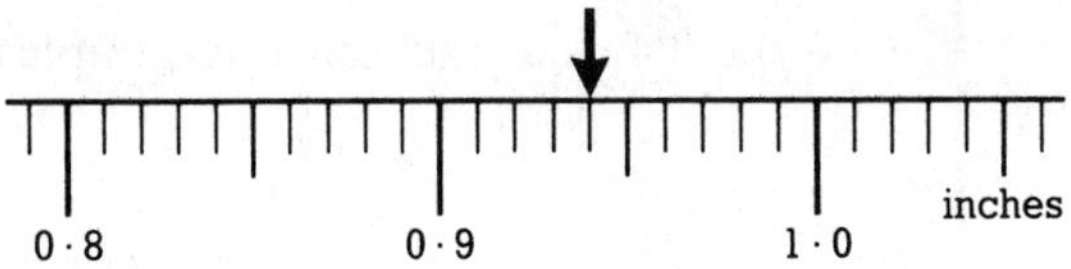

3.

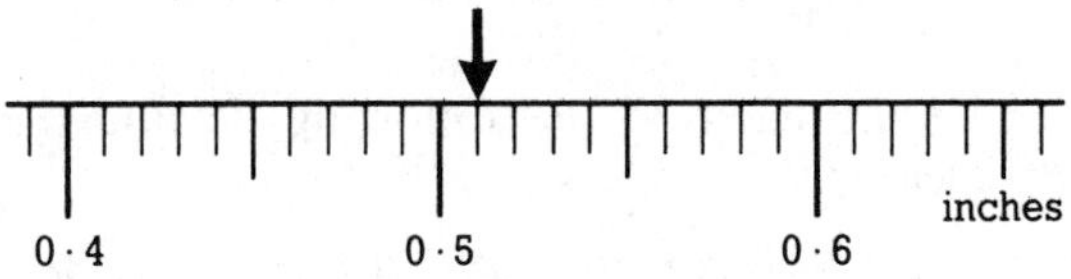

4.

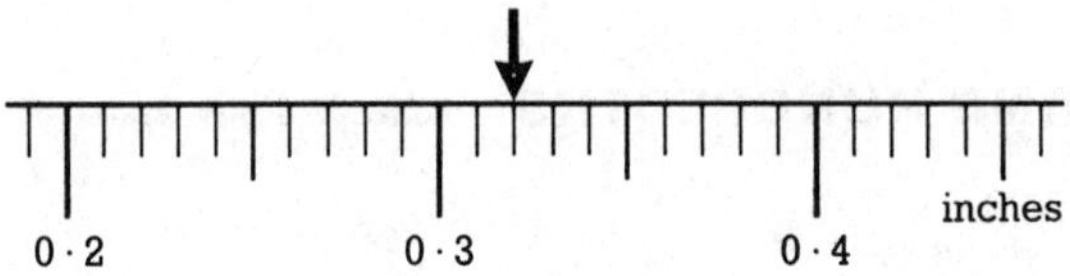

5.

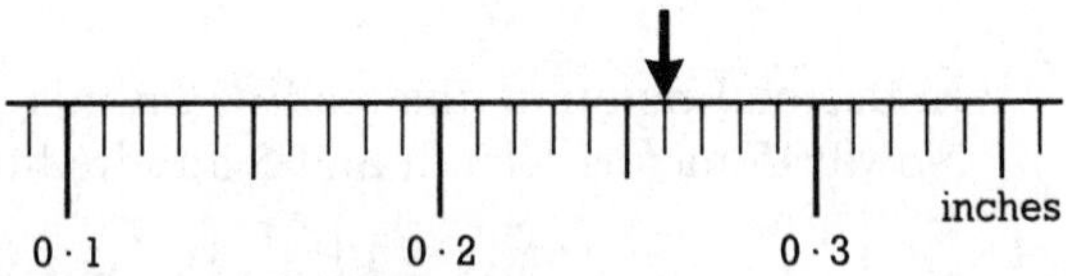

6.

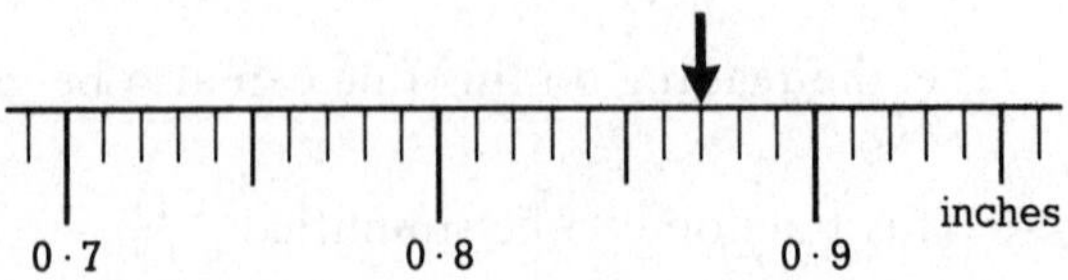

Express 0·25 as a fraction in its lowest terms.

$$0\cdot25 = \frac{25}{100} = \frac{1}{4}$$

Express each of the following decimals as a fraction in its lowest terms.

7.	0·16	**11.**	0·44	**15.**	0·08	**19.**	0·6
8.	0·36	**12.**	0·55	**16.**	0·05	**20.**	0·03
9.	0·75	**13.**	0·15	**17.**	0·80	**21.**	0·3
10.	0·24	**14.**	0·92	**18.**	0·35	**22.**	0·81

These equivalent decimals and fractions are worth remembering.

$0\cdot5 = \frac{1}{2}$ $\quad$ $0\cdot25 = \frac{1}{4}$ $\quad$ $0\cdot75 = \frac{3}{4}$

MIXED EXERCISES

EXERCISE 15f

1. What is the value of the figure 6 in each of these decimals?
a) 6·49 b) 43·62 c) 7·06 d) 68·5

2. Find a) 1·6 + 5·9 b) 2·8 − 1·9 c) 2·59 + 1·5

3. Give the measurements on these rulers to the nearest tenth of an inch.

a)

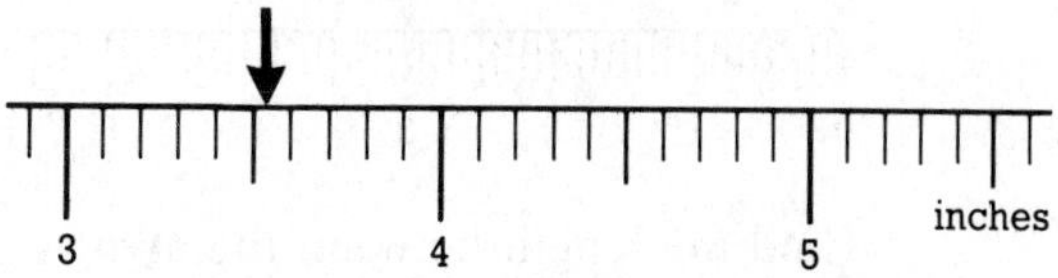

b)

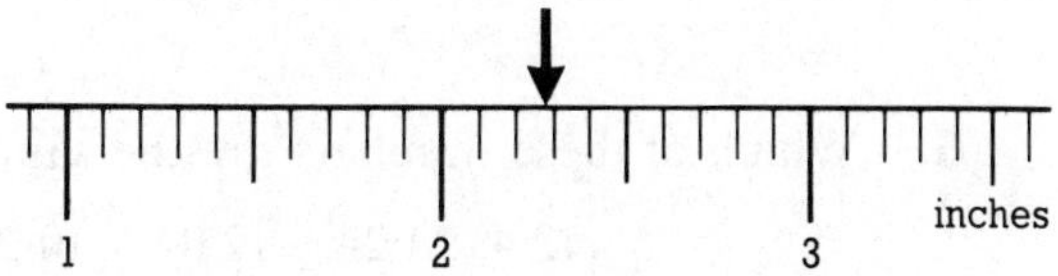

4. Write the following decimals in order of size with the smallest first.

1·5, 0·5, 5·1

5. Which two of these numbers are the same?

1·5, 15, 1·05, 1·50, 0·15

EXERCISE 15g

1. What is the value of the figure 9 in each of these decimals?

a) 89·5 b) 15·39 c) 0·91 d) 95·2

2. Write each set of numbers in order of size with the largest first.

a) 1·04, 0·41, 4·1 b) 59·6, 9·56, 90·5

3. Give the measurements on these magnified sections of a ruler to the nearest hundredth of a centimetre.

a)

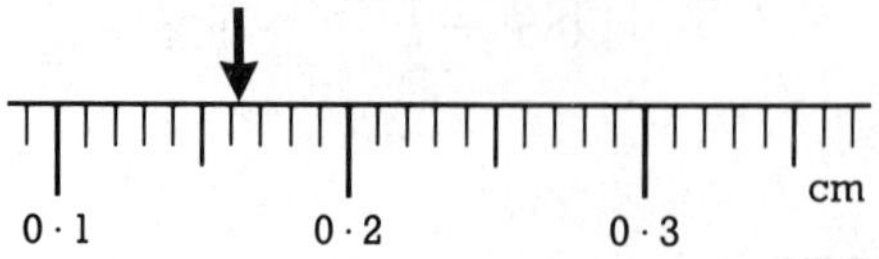

b)

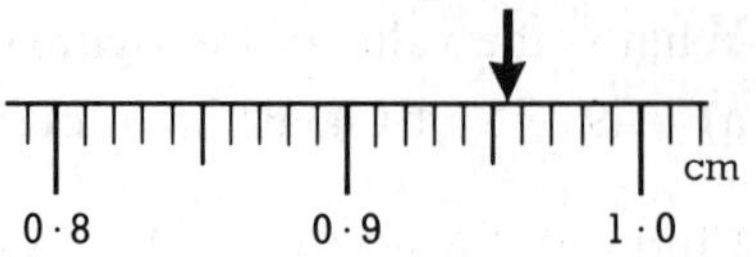

4.

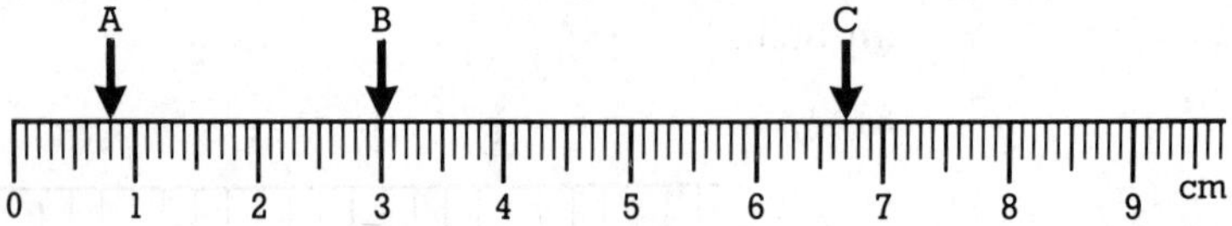

Find the length between the arrows

a) A and B b) A and C

5. Which of these numbers are the same?

12·4, 1·24, 12·04, 10·24, 124, 12·40

EXERCISE 15h **1.** Write each set of numbers in order of size with the smallest first.

a) 2·5, 0·25, 25, 5·02 b) 5·5, 0·5, 0·05, 5

2. Give each of these measurements to the nearest hundredth of a centimetre.

a)

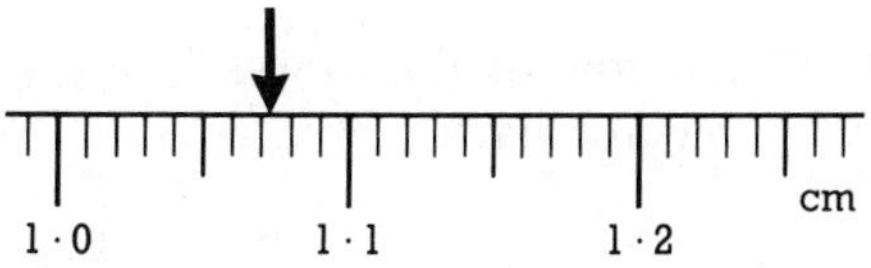

b)

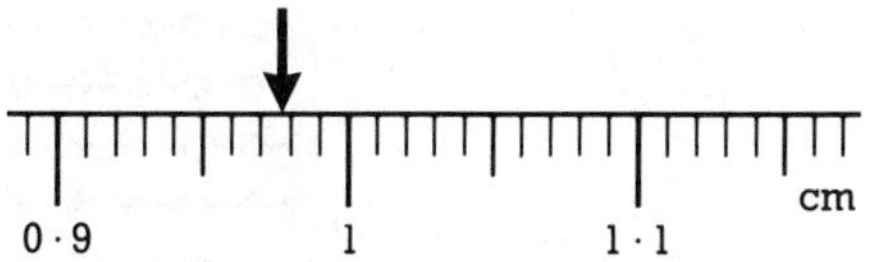

3. This is the floor plan of an office block.

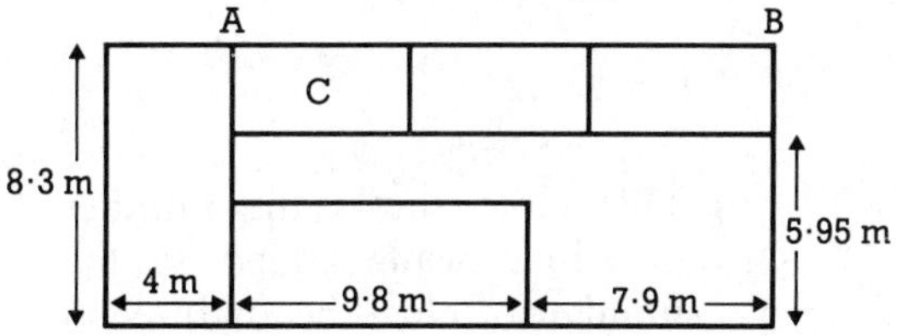

Find

a) the length of the wall AB
b) the width of the room C
c) the overall length of the block.

4. Find a) 17·02 − 9·8 b) 2·61 + 1·5 + 0·07

5. Which of these numbers are the same?

81·07, 81·70, 87·1, 80·17, 87·01, 81·7, 801·7

16 NUMBER PATTERNS

NUMBER PAIRS

EXERCISE 16a 1. Each row of this frame holds six beads: some are white and some are black.

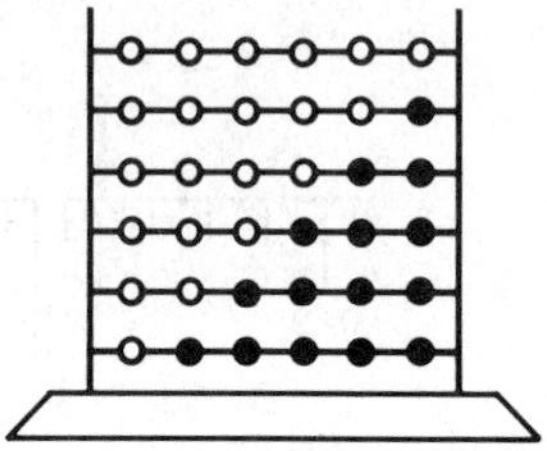

a) This table shows the number of white beads added to the number of black beads in each row.
Copy and complete the table.

6 + 0	6
5 + 1	6
4 + 2	
3 +	
2	
1	

b) Are there any more pairs of whole numbers that add up to 6?

c) The pattern of beads has a line of symmetry.
Copy the pattern onto squared paper and mark the line of symmetry on it.

2. The board on the opposite page has ten squares across and down. There are black and white counters on the squares as shown.

a) Copy and complete the table at the side of the board.

b) Is there a line of symmetry on the board?

c) Are there any other pairs of whole numbers that add up to 10?

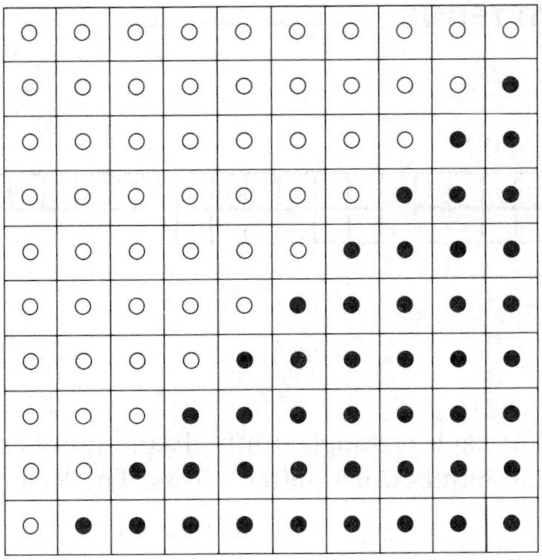

10 + 0	10
9 + 1	
8 +	
7	
2 +	
1 + 9	

We saw in Chapter 2 that it helps when adding numbers mentally if you know the pairs of numbers that add up to 10.

Make use of the number pairs in Question 3 to do these mental additions.

a) 3 + 7 + 8 + 2 + 3 c) 2 + 6 + 8 + 4

b) 1 + 9 + 6 + 14 + 1

a) 3 + 7 + 8 + 2 + 3 = 10 + 10 + 3 = 23

b) 1 + 9 + 6 + 14 + 1 = 10 + 20 + 1 = 31

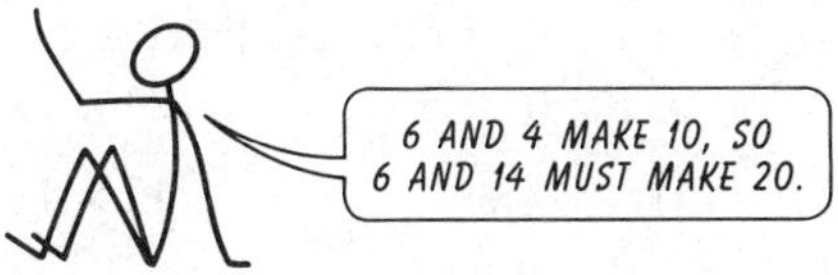
6 AND 4 MAKE 10, SO
6 AND 14 MUST MAKE 20.

c) 2 + 6 + 8 + 4 = 10 + 10 = 20

Add the following numbers in your head.

3. 5 + 5 + 4 + 6 + 7

4. 9 + 1 + 3 + 7 + 7 + 3

5. 5 + 3 + 5 + 7

6. 9 + 1 + 3 + 7 + 2 + 8

7. 6 + 2 + 4 + 8 + 6

8. 1 + 6 + 9 + 4 + 8

MULTIPLICATION PATTERNS

EXERCISE 16b 1.

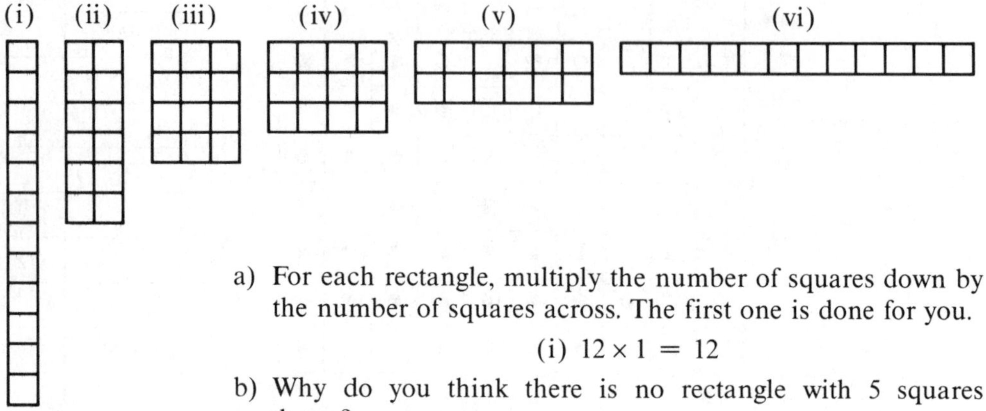

a) For each rectangle, multiply the number of squares down by the number of squares across. The first one is done for you.

(i) $12 \times 1 = 12$

b) Why do you think there is no rectangle with 5 squares down?

Start with the product $24 \times 2 = 48$.

a) Halve the first number (24), double the second number (2) and write down the result.
b) Carry on halving the first number and doubling the second one until you cannot go any further with whole numbers.
c) Do you get 48 as the answer every time?
d) How many steps are you able to write down, *not* counting the given product?

$24 \times 2 = 48$

a) $12 \times 4 = 48$

b) $6 \times 8 = 48$

$3 \times 16 = 48$

We cannot go any further because half of 3 is not a whole number.

c) We get 48 each time.

d) There are 3 steps.

2. Start with $32 \times 2 = 64$.

a) Halve the first number and double the second one as many times as you can using whole numbers, as in the worked example.
b) Do you get 64 every time?
c) Not counting the given product, how many steps are there?

3. Do the same again starting with $28 \times 2 = 56$.

4. If you start with $18 \times 2 = 36$, how many steps are possible?

5. If you start with $11 \times 2 = 22$, how many steps are possible?

6. Think of a reason why some numbers that we start with allow more steps than others.

SHAPES WITH PATTERNS

This square is made from four matchsticks.

Another square can be added on to either side.

We can carry on adding extra squares on either side.

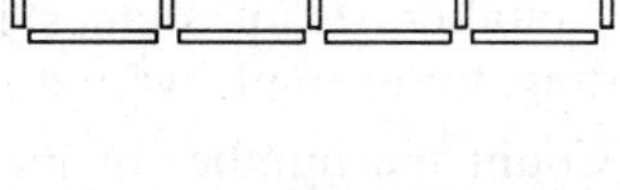

By making a list of the numbers of matchsticks needed to form a row of one, two, three squares, and so on, we can see whether these numbers have a pattern.

EXERCISE 16c **1.**

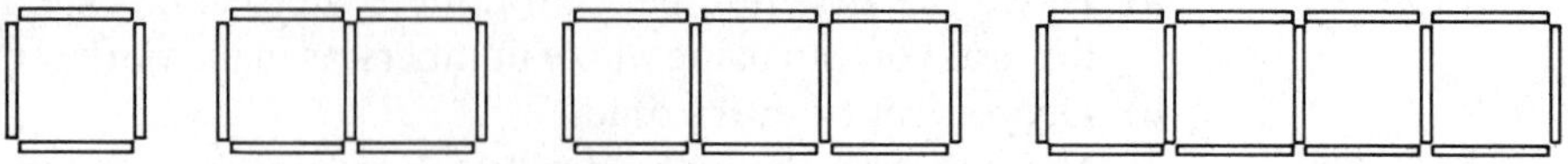

a) Count the number of matchsticks needed to make each of these shapes.

b) Copy this table and enter your results in it.

Number of squares	1	2	3	4
Number of matchsticks				

c) Without drawing the diagram, can you say how many matchsticks would be needed to make 5 squares in a row?

d) Write down the number missing from the following sentence. The number of *extra* matchsticks needed for each extra square is . . .

2. In this question matchsticks are used to form triangles.

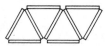

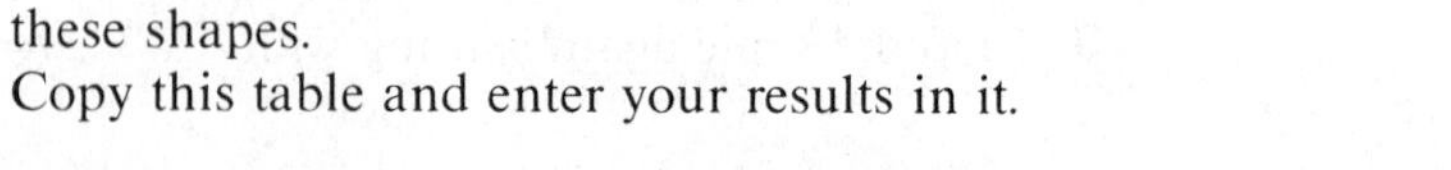

a) Copy the table and complete part of it by counting the number needed to make each shape.

Number of triangles	1	2	3	4	5	6
Number of matchsticks						

b) Without drawing the diagrams write down the number of matchsticks needed for the next two shapes.

c) How many extra matchsticks are needed for each extra triangle in the row?

3. Try another set of shapes like those in Questions 1 and 2, starting, for example, with a five-sided or a six-sided object.

a) Count the number of matchsticks in each shape and enter them in a table.

b) Decide how many extra matchsticks you need to go on to the next diagram.

4. a) Copy this table and complete it by using the answers you found in the first three questions.

Basic shape	Square	Triangle	Five-sided (Pentagon)	Six-sided (Hexagon)
Number of matchsticks for each extra shape				

b) Can you say how many extra matchsticks would be needed for each extra shape if you started with
i) an eight-sided shape ii) a ten-sided shape?

5. Now let us see what happens if the shapes we draw are not kept in a row.

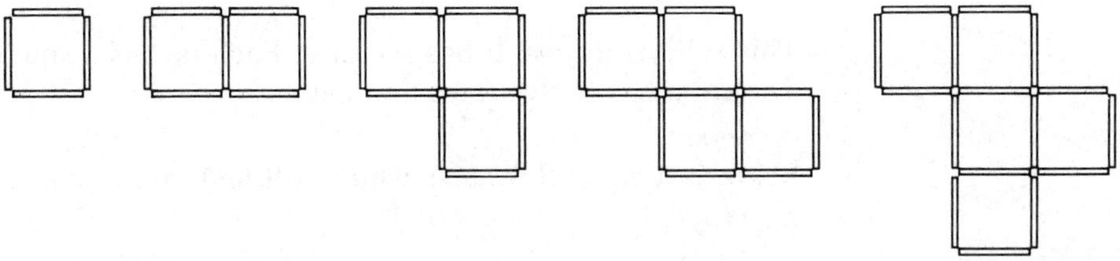

This time extra squares can be added on either side or above or below.

a) Using squared paper, copy the shapes above.
b) Draw four more shapes by adding an extra square each time. The last shape should have 9 squares.
c) Copy and complete this table

No. of squares	1	2	3	4	5	6	7
No. of matchsticks							

d) Compare the numbers in your table with those in your neighbour's table. If some of the numbers are different can you give a reason for this?

17 SOLIDS

EXERCISE 17a 1.

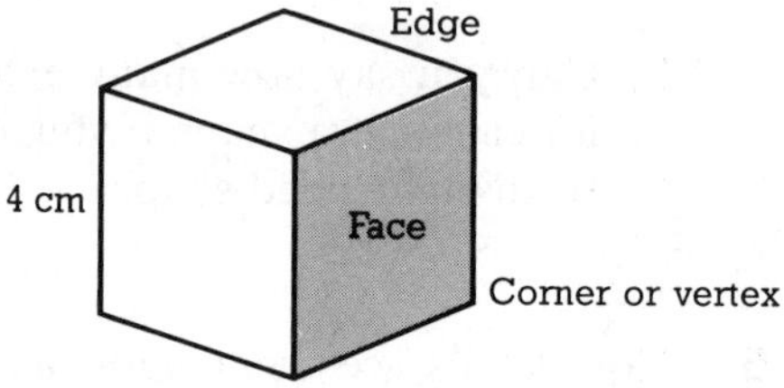

This solid is a *cube*. It has six *faces*. Each face is a square. The cube has twelve *edges* and eight *corners*.

Below is a *net* of this cube, which will fold up to make the solid.

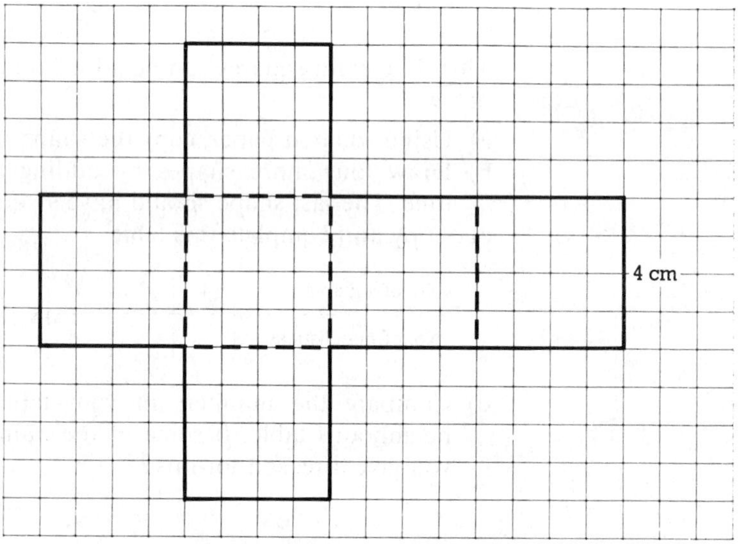

a) Draw the net on 1 cm squared paper or dotted paper and cut it out. Fold it along the broken lines.
   It will fold up into a cube. Fix it together with sticky tape.
b) Are all the edges the same length?
c) Are all the faces the same shape?

2.

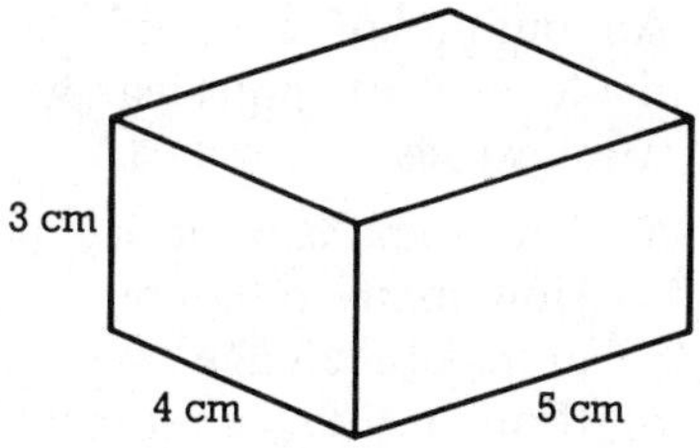

This is a picture of a *cuboid.* It is sometimes called a *rectangular block*.
Each face is a rectangle.

Below is a net for this cuboid. Make it up in the same way as for the cube in Question 1.

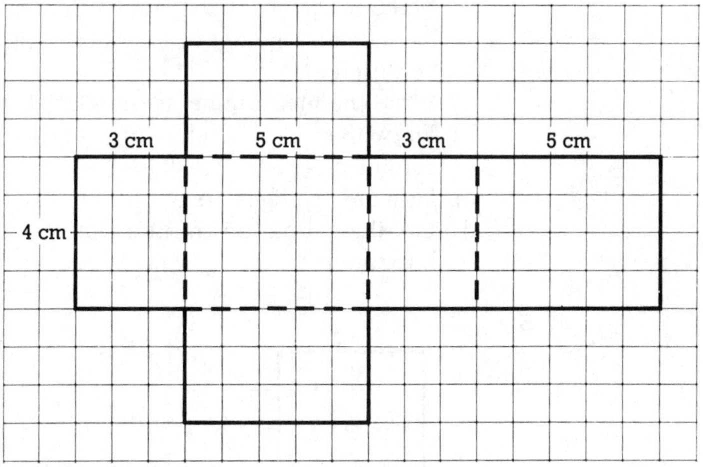

a) How many faces has the cuboid?

b) How many edges does it have?

c) How many edges are 3 cm long?

d) How many faces measure 4 cm by 3 cm?

e) Put the cuboid down on a flat surface. How many edges are vertical (upright)?

f) If an outline of the cube were made of rods, how many rods of each length would be needed?

3. An outline of a cube can be made out of pipecleaners or wire or rods.

a) The rods cannot be bent. How many rods are needed to make the cube?

b) If one rod is 6 cm long, how long must the other rods be?

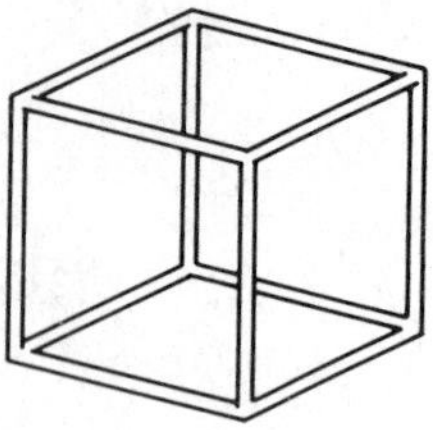

4.

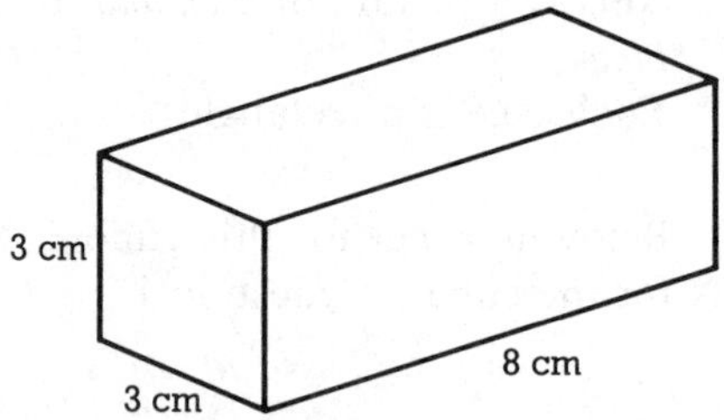

a) Make a sketch of the net of this cuboid. It will be roughly the same as the net in Question 3 but the measurements will be different.
Write the measurements on your sketch.

b) Draw the net accurately on squared paper and make up the cuboid.

c) How many edges are 3 cm long?

d) Lay the cuboid down on a flat surface. How many edges are horizontal?

5.

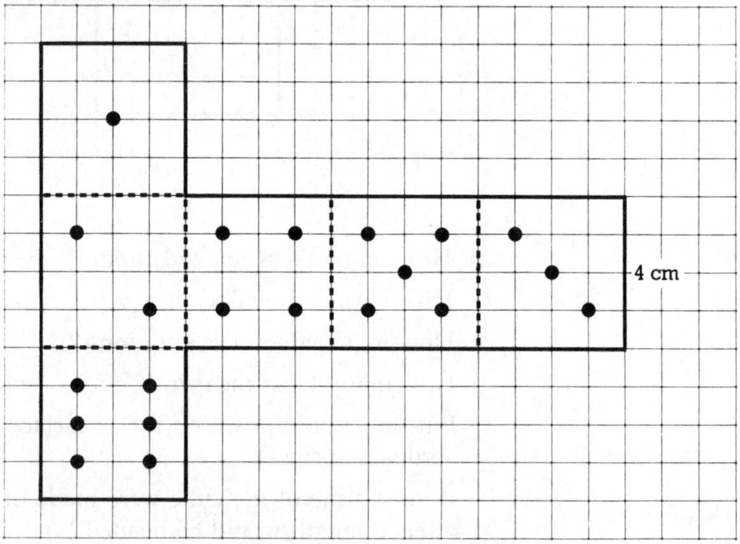

a) Draw the net full size on 1 cm squared paper and make it up into a dice.

b) What is the name for the shape of the solid?

c) How many spots are there on the face opposite the one with 3 spots? Add together the number of spots on these 2 faces.

d) How many spots are there opposite the 2-spot face? Add the two numbers together. What do you notice?
Test your idea on the remaining two faces.

e) Look at some real dice. Are the spots arranged in the same way?

6.

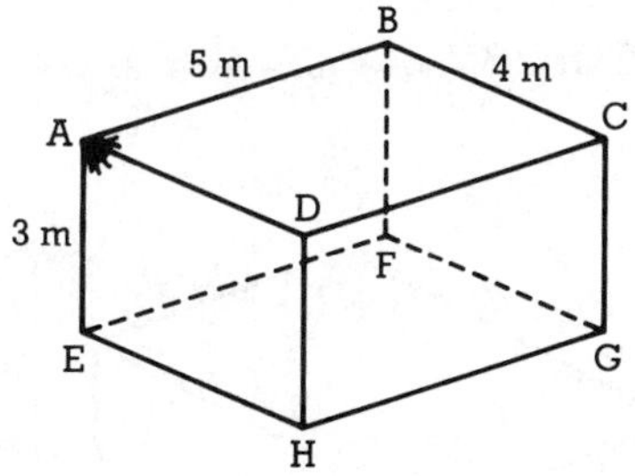

This is a diagram of a room. A spider is at corner A and wants to get to G.
The spider will walk only along the edges of the room but there are several routes it can follow.

a) One route is from A to E to H to G.
We can write this AEHG.
How far will the spider walk if it takes this route?

b) Write another possible route (give the letters). What is its length?

c) Find as many other routes as you can and give the length of each.

d) Is there a shortest route?

e) If the spider did not mind crossing a ceiling or a wall, could it find a shorter route?

7.

John wants to make a wire outline of a cube with sides of 7 cm. He has 84 cm of wire. He does not need any overlap at any of the corners as he is cutting the wire into pieces and welding it together.

a) Is there enough wire to make the cube? Will there be any left over?

b) If he does not cut the wire, can he bend it to form the outline of a 7 cm cube?

CUBES AND CUBOIDS

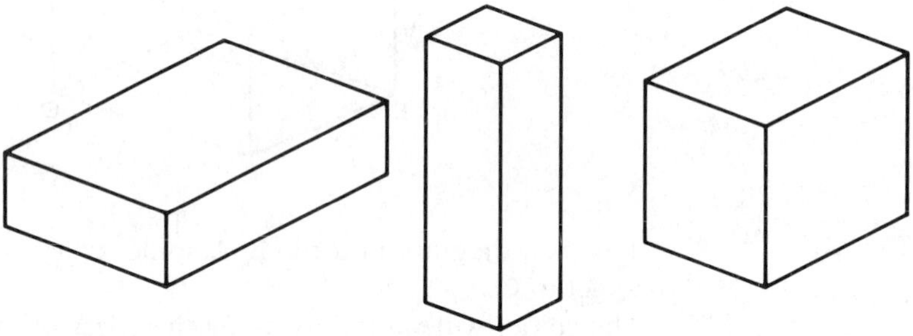

As we have seen, cuboids can have many different sizes and shapes.

A cube is a cuboid but it is a special one, with all its edges the same length and all its faces the same size.

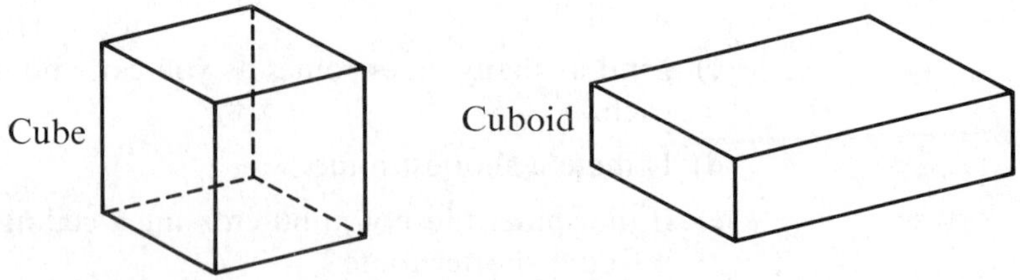

Each face of a cube is a square.

A face of a cuboid is a rectangle.

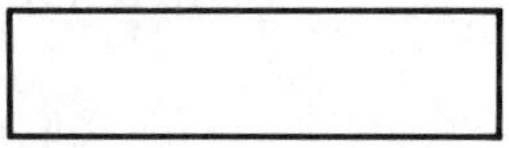

VOLUME

Three-dimensional objects occupy space. We use the word *volume* for this space.

The space occupied by a 1 cm cube is called 1 cubic centimetre, i.e. its volume is 1 cubic centimetre.

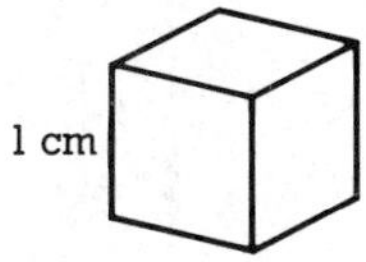

The volume of an object can be measured by finding the number of 1 cm cubes that fill the same space as the object.

EXERCISE 17b **1.** a) How many 1 cm cubes like this are needed to cover the bottom of the box below?

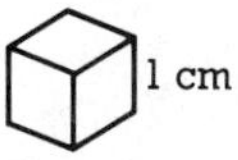

b) How many layers of 1 cm cubes would be needed to fill this box?

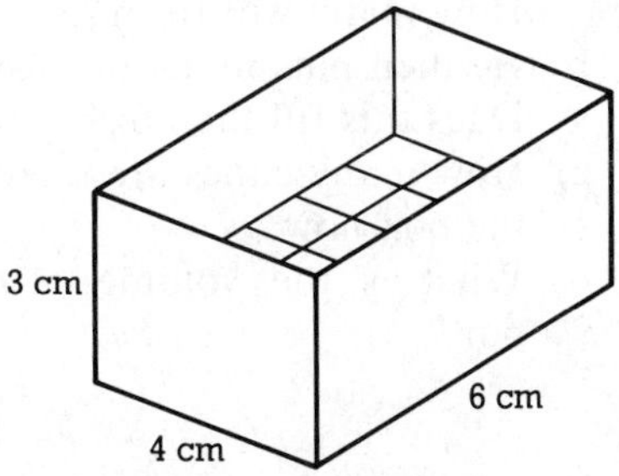

a) How many 1 cm cubes are needed to fill a box 3 cm by 6 cm by 5 cm?

b) What is the volume of the box?

a)

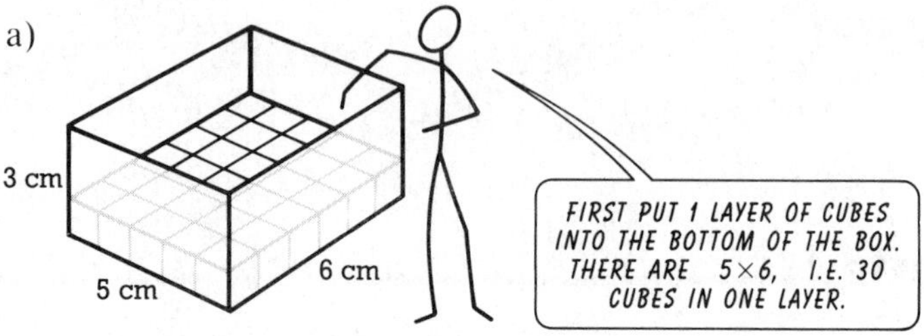
3 cm
5 cm
6 cm
FIRST PUT 1 LAYER OF CUBES INTO THE BOTTOM OF THE BOX. THERE ARE 5×6, I.E. 30 CUBES IN ONE LAYER.

THEN FILL UP WITH MORE LAYERS. THERE ARE 3 LAYERS NOW. 3×30=90.

There are 90 cubes in the box.

b) The volume is 90 cubic centimetres.

2. Azim has a box like this. He wants to know how many 1 cm cubes will fit into the box.

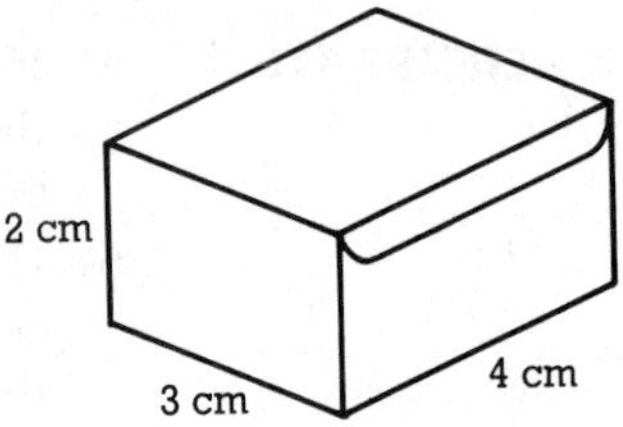

a) He fills the base of the box with one layer of cubes. How many will fit in?
b) He then puts in another layer. Does this fill the box?
c) How many cubes are there in the box now?
d) What is the volume of the box?

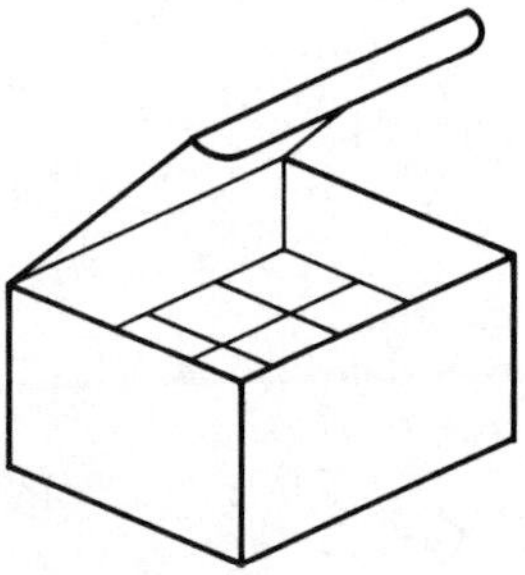

3. Dawn's box is a different size.

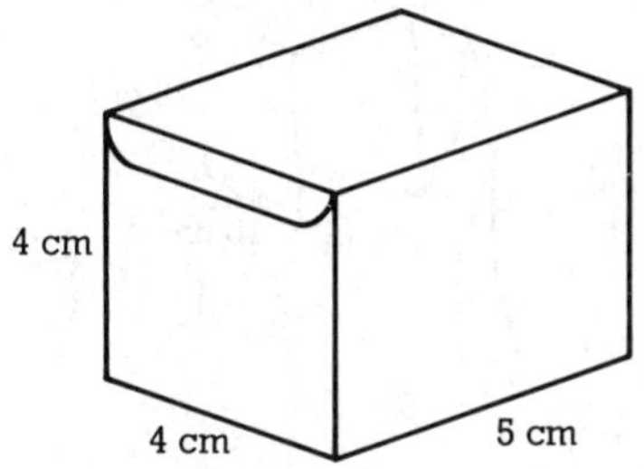

a) How many 1 cm cubes can Dawn fit into the base of her box?
b) How many layers are needed to fill the box?
c) How many cubes will fit into the box altogether?
d) What is the volume of the box?

4. Find the volume of each of the following boxes.

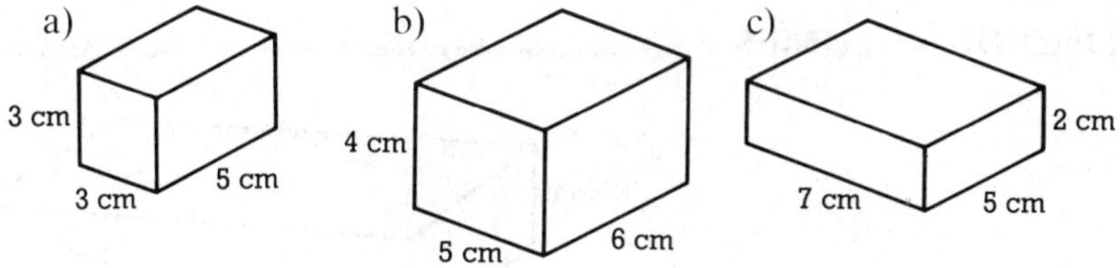

5.

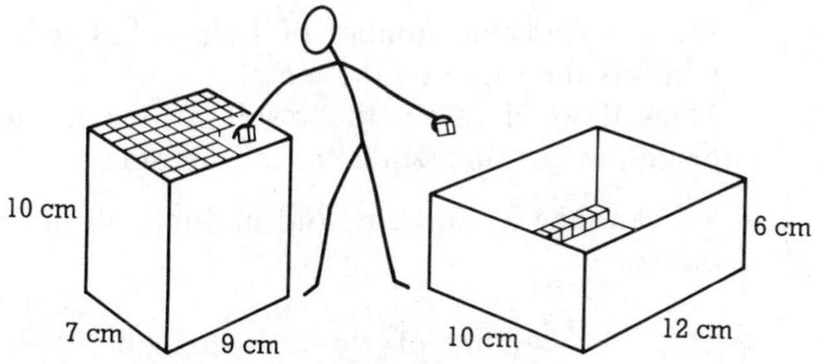

Julie takes all the 1 cm cubes out of the first box and fits them into the second box.

a) Do the cubes fill the second box?
b) If not, how many more are needed?

6.

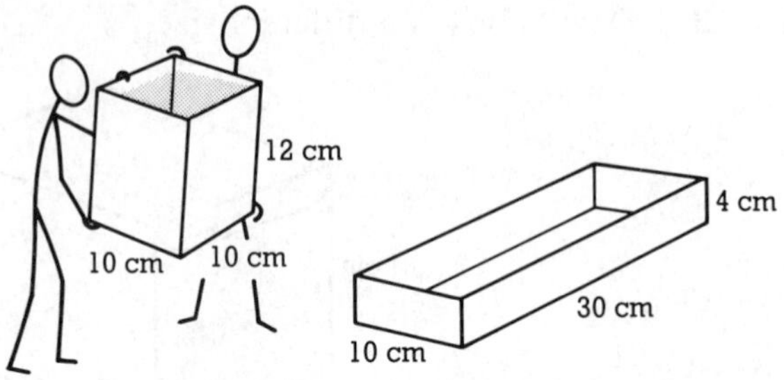

The first tin box is full of water. The water is poured from the first box into the second.
Does the water just fill the second box exactly or does it overflow?

7. A round tin is full of sand.
Suggest a way of finding the volume of the sand.

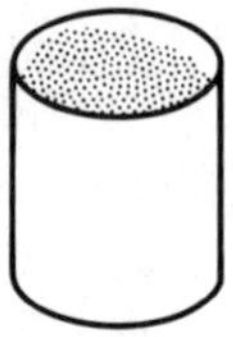

FINDING VOLUMES

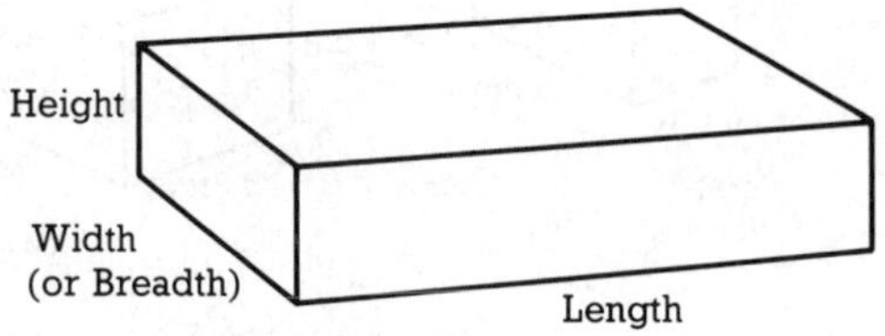

We can find the number of 1 cm cubes in the bottom layer if we multiply the width by the length.
Then if we multiply the result by the number of layers, i.e. the height, we get the volume of the cuboid.

We can take a short cut, and multiply all three numbers together in one go.

Volume of cuboid $=$ Length $\times$ Width $\times$ Height

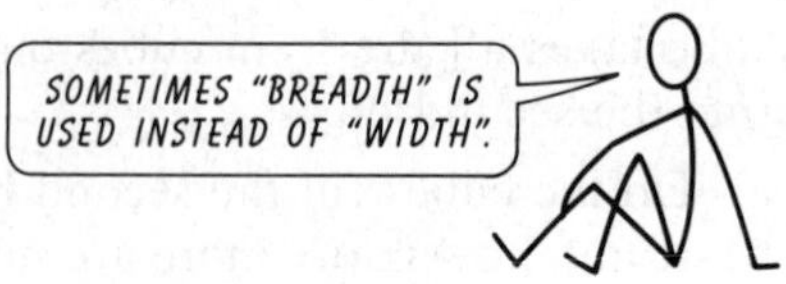

EXERCISE 17c

Find the volume of the box.

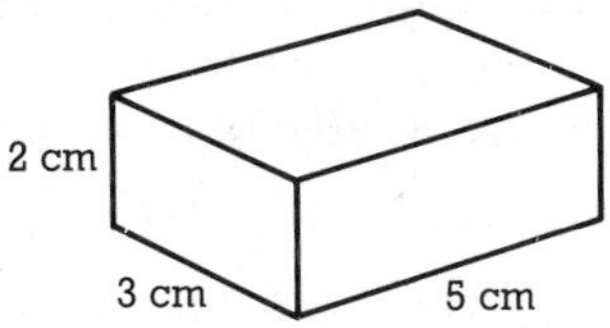

Volume = Length × Width × Height

= 2 × 3 × 5 cubic centimetres

= 30 cubic centimetres

1. Find the volume of each of the following cuboids.

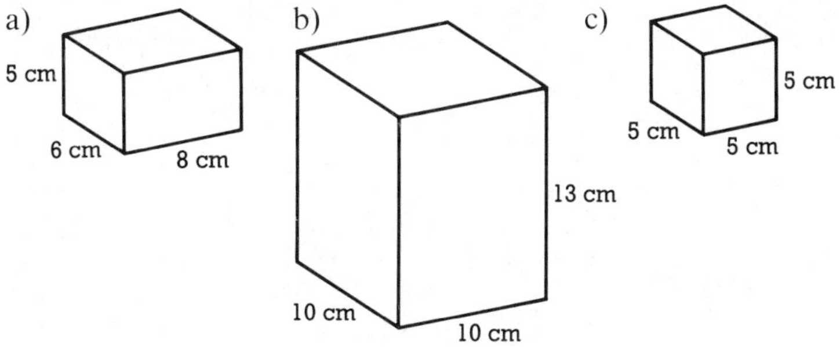

2. Find the volume of a rectangular block measuring 10 cm by 6 cm by 8 cm.

3. A room measures 5 m by 5 m by 4 m.

a) How many 1 m cubes would fill the room?
b) The volume of a 1 m cube is 1 cubic metre. What is the volume of the room?

4. A cuboid measures 30 mm by 40 mm by 9 mm.

a) How many 1 mm cubes would fill the cuboid?
b) The volume of a 1 mm cube is 1 cubic millimetre. What is the volume of the cuboid?

5. A rectangular box measures 12 cm by 8 cm by 4 cm.

a) How many 1 cm cubes are needed to fill it?

b) The volume of a 1 cm cube is 1 cubic centimetre. What is the volume of the rectangular box?

6. Find the volume of each of the following cuboids.

	Length	Breadth	Height
a)	12 cm	5 cm	6 cm
b)	30 mm	8 mm	7 mm
c)	8 mm	4 mm	3 mm

18 PROBABILITY

CHANCE

The people in these cartoons are talking about the chances of something happening.

Other words that we use to describe whether or not something might happen are: impossible, unlikely, fifty-fifty chance, probable, certain.

The measure of the chance of something happening is called *probability*.

EXERCISE 18a Use your own words to describe the probability of each of the following events happening.

1. You will have maths homework tonight.

2. It will snow on December 25th.

3. You will have a meal after school.

4. If you toss a coin it will land heads up.

5. You will play football for England.

6. You will win the women's final at Wimbledon.

7. You will watch a film next Saturday.

8. The next car to pass the school gate will have been made in Europe.

9. England will beat the West Indies in the next Test Match Series.

10. If you throw a dice, it will score a six.

11. If you draw a card from an ordinary pack of playing cards, it will be black.

OUTCOMES

When James tosses the dice, there are six possible scores that he can get. These are 1, 2, 3, 4, 5, 6.

The act of tossing the dice is called an *experiment.*
The score that you get is called an *outcome* or an *event.*
The set of numbers {1, 2, 3, 4, 5, 6} is called the set of *all possible outcomes.*

When you toss a dice there are six possible outcomes.

EXERCISE 18b List all the possible outcomes of each experiment and write down the number of outcomes in each case.

1. Tossing a 10 p coin. (Assume that it lands flat.)

2. Taking one disc from a bag containing 1 red, 1 blue and 1 yellow disc.

3. Choosing one letter from the letters in the word MASTER.

4. Choosing one number from the first five even numbers.

5. Choosing one letter from the vowels of the alphabet.

6. Taking one disc from a bag containing 1 red, 1 blue, 1 brown, 1 yellow and 1 orange disc.

7. Choosing one card from a hand of ordinary playing cards containing just the four aces.

8. Tossing a 10 p coin and a 5 p coin. (Assume that they both land flat.)

QUANTIFYING CHANCE

Some events are impossible; throwing a seven with an ordinary dice, for example.

Some events are certain; that a disc taken out of a bag that has only red discs in it will be red, for example.

For most events, the chances are somewhere between impossibility and certainty. We can measure chance on a scale going from 'impossible' at one end to 'certain' at the other end.

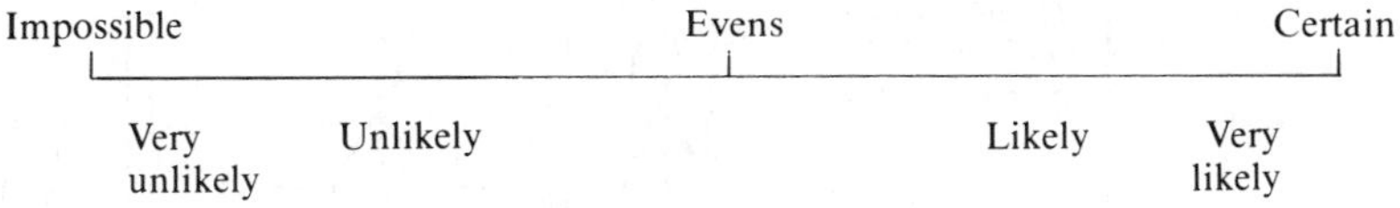

EXERCISE 18c Copy the scale above. For each question use an arrow to mark the place on the scale that measures the chance of the event happening. The first one is done for you.

1. Throwing a six with an ordinary dice.

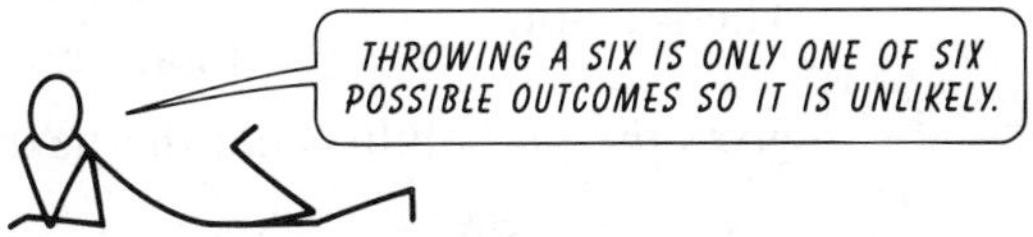

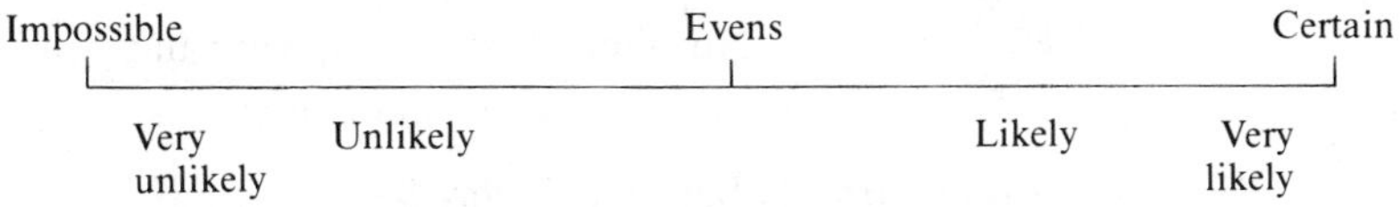

2. Tossing a 10 p coin and getting a head.

3. Taking a red disc from a bag containing 1 red, 1 blue and 1 yellow disc.

4. Choosing the letter M from the letters in the word MASTER.

5. Throwing a nine with an ordinary dice.

6. Getting a score of less than five with an ordinary dice.

7. Drawing the ace of spades from a full pack of ordinary playing cards.

8. Taking a blue disc from a bag containing 5 blue discs and 3 red discs.

9. Taking a pencil out of a box that contains only pencils.

10. Choosing a vowel from the letters in the word OUR.

PROBABILITY

Hannah kept a tally of the number of buses that passed her bus stop, and ringed those that were 168s.
About half the tally marks were ringed, so Hannah was right to say that there was an even chance that the next bus would be a 168.

The fraction $\dfrac{\text{Number of 168s}}{\text{Total number of buses}}$

gives the probability that the next bus is a 168.

> The probability that an event happens is the fraction
>
> $$\frac{\text{Number of times an event happens}}{\text{Total number of events}}$$
>
> This fraction is between 0 and 1.

When this fraction is $\frac{1}{2}$, we say that the chance is even, or fifty-fifty.

If an event is impossible, the probability of it happening is 0.

If an event is certain, the probability of it happening is 1.

EXERCISE 18d 1. Peter wanted to know which way up his badge was more likely to land when he tossed it.
He tossed the badge twenty times. This is a record of what happened.
F stands for face-side up and P stands for pin-side up.

F, F, F, P, F, P, F, F, F, P, F, F, P, P, F, P, F, F, F, F

a) How many times did the badge land pin-side up?

b) What is the probability that Peter's badge will land pin-side up?

c) Which of these words best describes the probability of the badge landing pin-side up?

Even chance, unlikely, probable.

d) What is the probability that the badge will land on its edge?

2. Find a pin-badge of your own. Toss it fifty times, recording the result of each toss as F or P.

a) How many times did the badge land pin-side up?

b) What is the probability that your badge will land pin-side up?

c) Copy this scale and use an arrow to mark where your answer to (b) best fits.

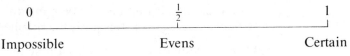

0	$\frac{1}{2}$	1
Impossible	Evens	Certain

3.

WHAT ARE THE CHANCES THAT THIS DRAWING PIN WILL LAND WITH ITS PIN STICKING UP?
I'VE NO IDEA! LET'S FIND OUT.

a) Find a drawing pin and then drop it 50 times.
Record your results as P for point-up, O for any other position.

b) How many times did the drawing pin land point-up?

c) What is the probability that your drawing pin will land point-up?

d) Is your answer to (c) greater than evens, or less than evens?

e) Copy the scale given in Question 2, part (c). Use an arrow to show where the answer to part (c) of this question fits on the scale.

f) Would you get a similar result for (c) if you used a different make of drawing pin?

19 FUNCTION MACHINES

FUNCTION MACHINES

To find out how many pegs he needs, John has to follow these instructions:

Count the towels that need to be hung up.
Double that number: this gives the number of pegs needed.

This instruction can be written as a function machine.
(Function is the mathematical word for the rule that changes one number to another number.)

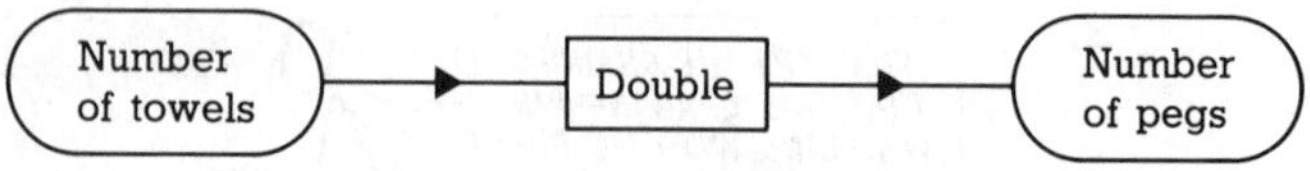

The arrows show which way to work.

EXERCISE 19a

John has 4 towels to hang up. Use the function machine to find the number of pegs that he needs.

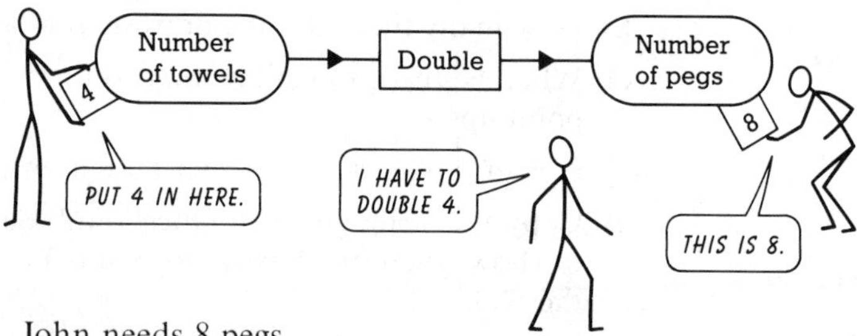

John needs 8 pegs.

1. Copy this table.

Use the function machine on the opposite page to fill in the second column.

Number of towels		Number of pegs
4	⟶	8
6	⟶	
10	⟶	
12	⟶	
20	⟶	

2. This function machine works out how long it takes to defrost bread in a microwave.

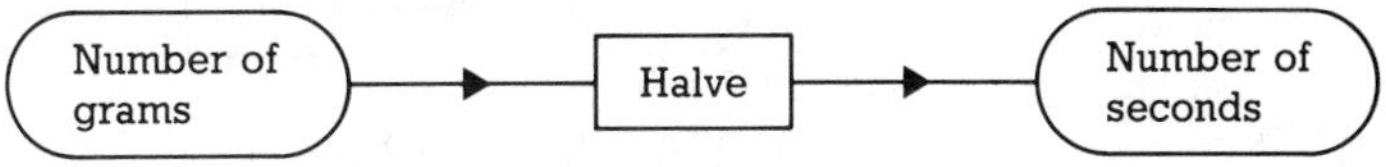

Copy this table and then fill in the right-hand column.

Weight (number of grams)	Time (number of seconds)
60	30
100	
200	
500	
800	

USING SYMBOLS

Here is the function machine for the pegs again.

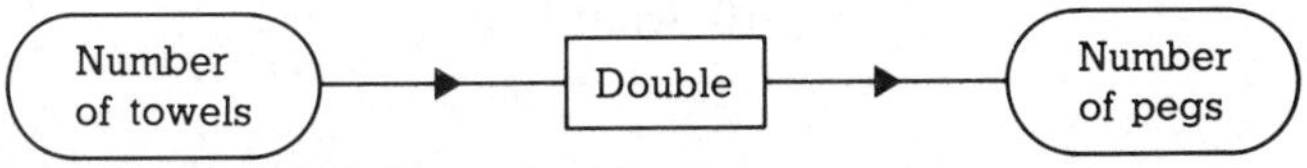

It takes time to write out the words in the boxes, so we use symbols to make the job quicker.

We use x to stand for the *number* of towels and y to stand for the *number* of pegs. The instruction "double" means "multiply by 2", so we use $\times 2$ for "double". The function machine then looks like this.

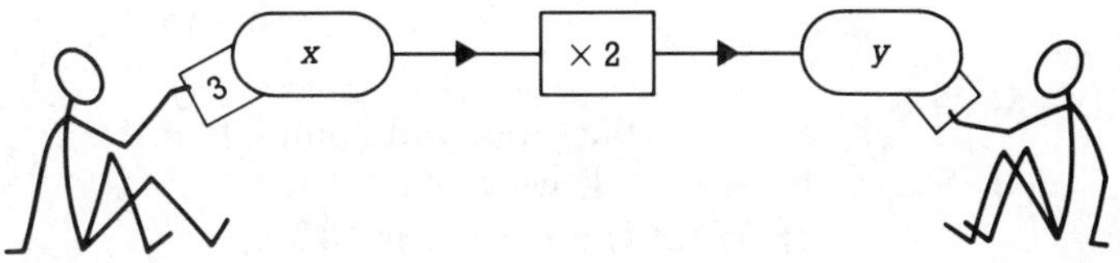

EXERCISE 19b **1.** Use the function machine to answer this question.

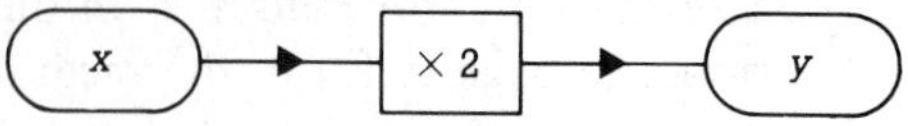

a) If x is 3, what is y? b) If x is 9, what is y?

2. Here is the function machine for working out the time needed to defrost bread. The letter p stands for the *number* of grams of bread and q stands for the *number* of seconds needed.

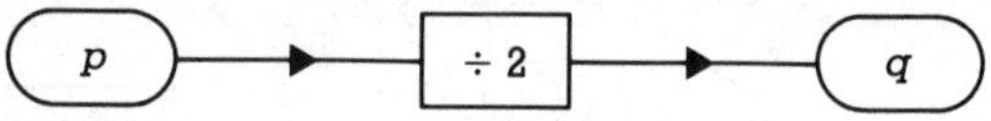

a) If p is 120, what is q?
b) If p is 80, what is q?
c) If a loaf weighs 140 grams, how long does it take to defrost?

3. This function machine changes the numbers in the top row to the numbers in the bottom row.

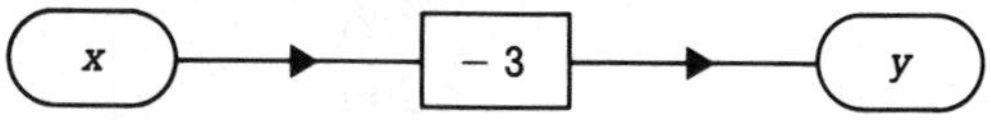

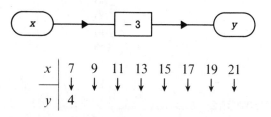

x	7	9	11	13	15	17	19	21
	↓	↓	↓	↓	↓	↓	↓	↓
y	4							

a) Copy and complete the table.
b) If x is 6, what is y?
c) If x is 10, what is y?

4. The function machine changes the numbers in the top row to the numbers in the bottom row.

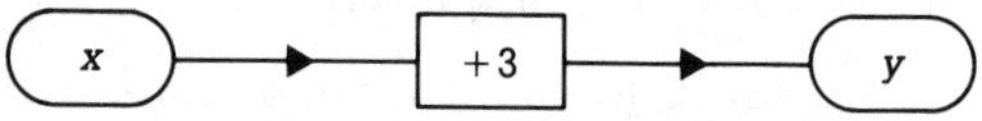

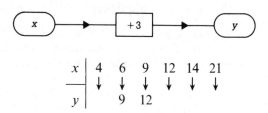

x	4	6	9	12	14	21
	↓	↓	↓	↓	↓	↓
y		9	12			

a) Copy the table and complete it.
b) If x is 11, what is y?
c) What is y when x is 18?

5. Copy the table and use the function machine to complete it.

a)

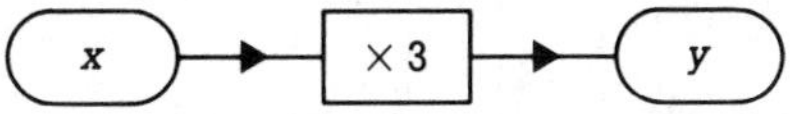

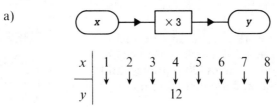

x	1	2	3	4	5	6	7	8
	↓	↓	↓	↓	↓	↓	↓	↓
y				12				

If x is 10, what is y?

b)

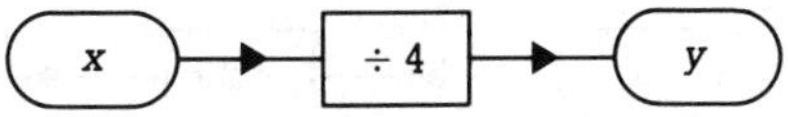

x	8	20	36	40	80	100
	↓	↓	↓	↓	↓	↓
y						

What is y when x is 12?

c)

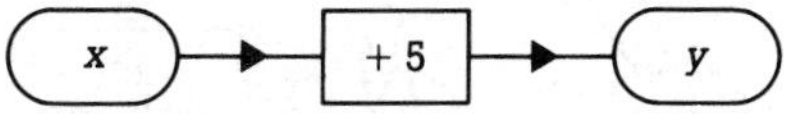

x	1	2	3	4	10	15	20
	↓	↓	↓	↓	↓	↓	↓
y							

What is y when x is 5?

d)

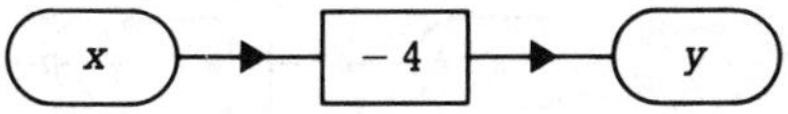

x	7	9	11	13	15	17	19
	↓	↓	↓	↓	↓	↓	↓
y							

What is y when x is 10?

TWO OPERATIONS

To work out the time needed to cook a 3 lb chicken, we need to find 3 times 20 minutes and then add another 20 minutes.

FRESH CHICKEN
COOKING TIME
20 minutes per lb
plus 20 minutes

We can write these instructions in a function machine.
We will use x for the *number* of pounds that the chicken weighs and we will use y for the *number* of minutes needed to cook the chicken.

EXERCISE 19c

Use the function machine given above to find the time taken to cook a chicken that weighs 6 lb.

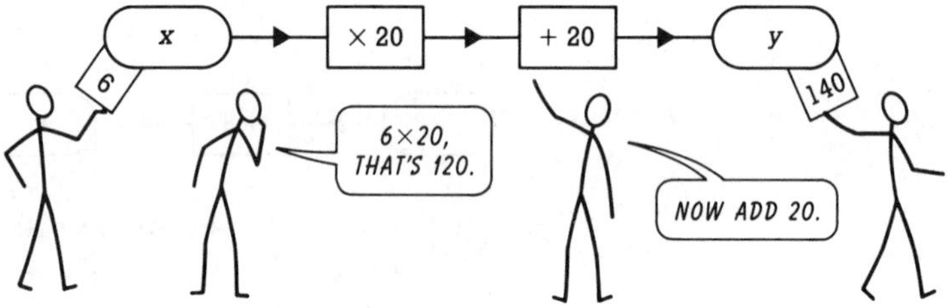

The chicken needs to be cooked for 140 minutes.

Use the function machine to complete the table.

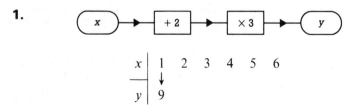

1.

x	1	2	3	4	5	6
	↓					
y	9					

If x is 8, what is y?

2.

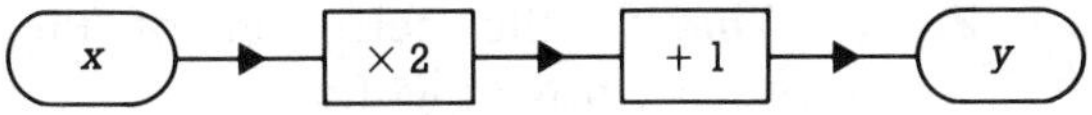

x	1	2	3	4	5	6
	↓					
y	3					

If x is 10, what is y?

3.

x	1	2	3	4	5	6
	↓					
y	10					

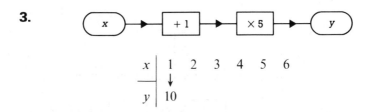

What is y when x is 9?

MAKING A FUNCTION MACHINE

If we can work out the instructions we can make our own function machine.

EXERCISE 19d **1.** Each pot has two seedlings in it.

a) If there are 5 pots, how many seedlings are there altogether?

b) In this table,

t is the number of pots and

s is the number of seedlings.

t	1	2	3	4	5	8	10	15
	↓	↓						
s								

Copy the table and then complete it.

c) Copy and complete this function machine.

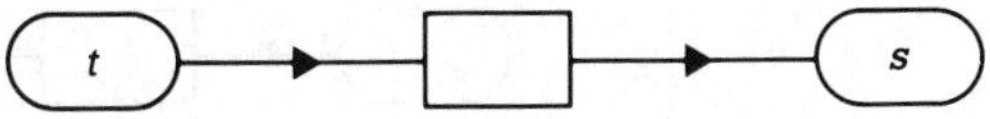

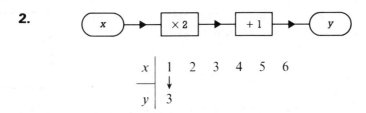

2. a) What is the perimeter of the square in the picture?

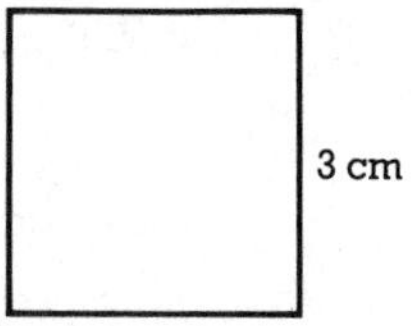

b) What is the perimeter of a square whose side is 2 cm long?

c) l is the number of centimetres in the length of a side of the square and p is the number of centimetres in the perimeter. Copy this table and complete it.

l	2	4	6	7	10	12	20
	↓	↓					
p							

d) Copy and complete the function machine:

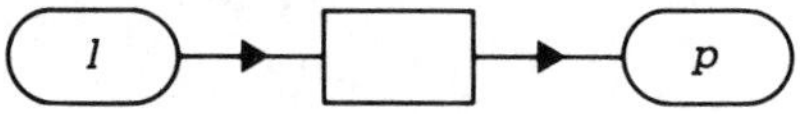

e) If l is 3, what is p?

3.

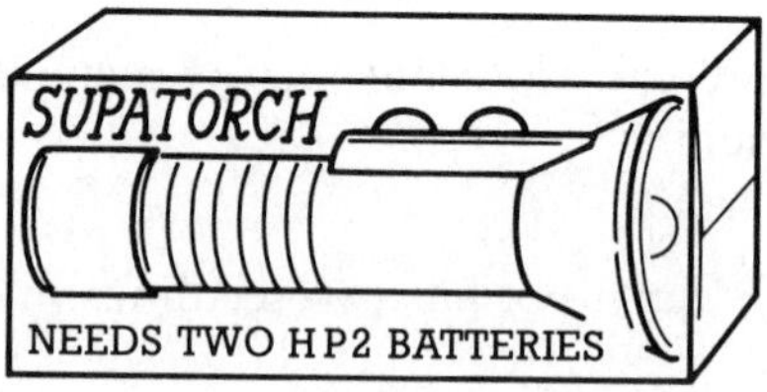

a) Ann buys 2 of these torches.
How many batteries should she buy?

b) Sunil buys 6 of these torches.
How many batteries does he need?

c) t stands for the number of torches and b stands for the number of batteries. Copy and complete this table.

t	1	2	3	5	10	50
	↓	↓				
b						

d) Make a function machine like this one for the table.

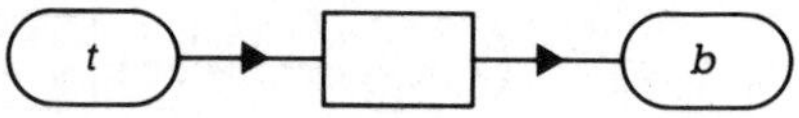

4. Look at this table.

x	1	2	3	4	6	12	18
	↓	↓	↓	↓	↓	↓	↓
y	3	4	5	6	8	14	20

a) The next number in the top row is 24. What is the number below it in the bottom row?
b) If x is 8, what is y?
c) If x is 5, what is y?
d) Make a function machine like this one for the table.

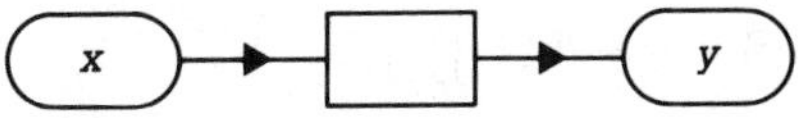

5. The rule for finding the numbers in the bottom row of this table is

"add 2 and then multiply by 2".

h	1	2	4	7	11	16
	↓	↓				
t	6	8				

a) Copy and complete the table.
b) Make a function machine like this one for this rule.

c) If h is 3, what is t?

6. Look at this table.

a	1	2	3	4	5	6
	↓	↓	↓	↓	↓	↓
b	9	19	29	39	49	59

a) If a is 7, what is b?
b) If a is 9, what is b?
c) Can you see the rule for getting the lower set of numbers?
d) Make a function machine for the rule like this one.

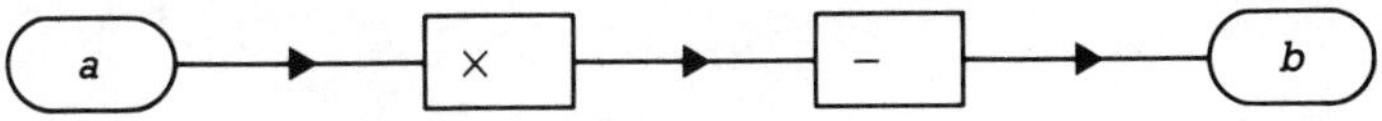

20 MISSING NUMBERS

MISSING NUMBERS

EXERCISE 20a Copy each of the following statements and write the missing number in the box.

1. $4+6=\square$

2. $2+\square=7$

3. $4\times\square=8$

4. $\square+4=18$

5. $6-\square=2$

6. $\square\times 3=6$

Sometimes the missing number is indicated by a question mark.

In Questions 7 to 12, what are the missing numbers?

7. $3+9=?$

8. $?+5=7$

9. $9+?=12$

10. $5\times ?=15$

11. $8-?=4$

12. $?-3=4$

MISSING NUMBERS IN SENTENCES

EXERCISE 20b Write down the missing number as a word.

1.

Gita had six apples and James had _____ apples. Together they had nine apples.

2. Gary set off for the newsagent with 78 p and spent _____ p on a magazine. He came out of the shop with 36 p.

3.

The fence at the front of the Browns' house is ____ feet wide and the gate is 3 feet wide. The total width is 24 feet.

4. Sabrina bought ____ pens at 11 p each and paid 88 p.

5. Joanna spent 54 p at the coconut shy where each throw cost ____ p. She had six throws.

6. I think of a number, ____, and add six. The result is nine.

USING LETTERS

Instead of using ____ or ? we can write a letter in place of a missing number.

EXERCISE 20c

Copy, replacing the letter by the missing number.

$8 + x = 12$

$8 + 4 = 12$

Replace each letter by the missing number.

1. $a + 3 = 7$

2. $4 + x = 8$

3. $b - 1 = 4$

4. $c - 3 = 2$

5. $6 + 9 = d$

6. $7 \times x = 14$

$3 + y = 13$ What number does y stand for?

$$3 + y = 13$$
$$y = 10$$

In each question, what number does the letter stand for?

7. $5 + x = 7$

8. $e + 4 = 9$

9. $7 = f - 1$

10. $3 \times z = 6$

11. $5 = w + 2$

12. $x - 5 = 2$

Alan has two hamsters and David has _____ hamsters.
Together they have seven.
Write this in numbers with a letter in place of the missing number.

$$2 + x = 7$$

YOU CAN USE ANY LETTER YOU WISH EXCEPT O.

Write the following sentences in numbers and letters as in the worked example.

13. A bookshelf holds _____ English books and nine mathematics books. There are seventeen books on the shelf.

14.

I spent 62 p at a snack bar where I had coffee at 35 p and a pastry at _____ p.

15. Three sections of fencing, each _____ metres long, are joined together to make a fence of length 18 metres.

16. On a shelf are seven large plates and _____ small plates. There are fifteen plates altogether.

EXERCISE 20d

I think of a number, add 4 and the result is 9. What is the first number I thought of?

Try 6: result is $6 + 4$ i.e. 10 Wrong

Try 5: result is $5 + 4$ i.e. 9 Right

The number first thought of is 5.

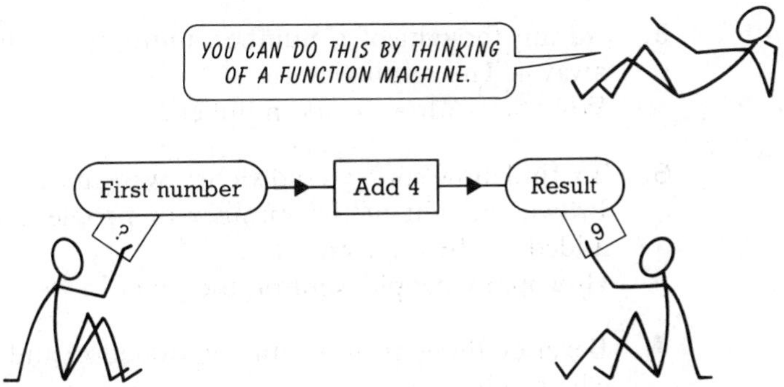
YOU CAN DO THIS BY THINKING OF A FUNCTION MACHINE.
First number
Add 4
Result
?
9

1. Jenny thought of a number and added 7. The result was 10. What was the number Jenny first thought of?

2. Mark thought of a number and multiplied it by 3. The result was 21.
What number did Mark think of?

3. Maya thought of a number. When she subtracted 9, she got 8. What was Maya's first number?

4. Sian thought of a number and divided it by 2. The result was 16. What number did Sian first think of?

I thought of a number, doubled it and then added 3. The result was 9. What was the first number I thought of?

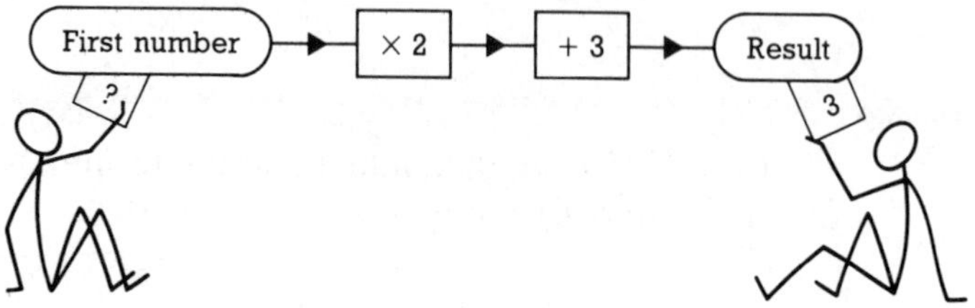

Try 4:	$4 \times 2 = 8$	$8 + 3 = 11$	Wrong
Try 3:	$3 \times 2 = 6$	$6 + 3 = 9$	Right

The first number I thought of was 3.

5. Adrian thought of a number, multiplied it by 5 and then took away 4. The result was 16.
What was Adrian's first number?

6. To find how many sandwiches were needed for a picnic, Mrs Brown thought of the number of people, multiplied by 3 and added 6. The total was 18.
How many people went on the picnic?

7. Beverley thought of a number, added 6, and then divided by 2. The result was 5.
What was Beverley's first number?

8.

21 ANGLE FACTS

MEASURING ANGLES

We use a *protractor* to measure angles. This is what a protractor looks like.

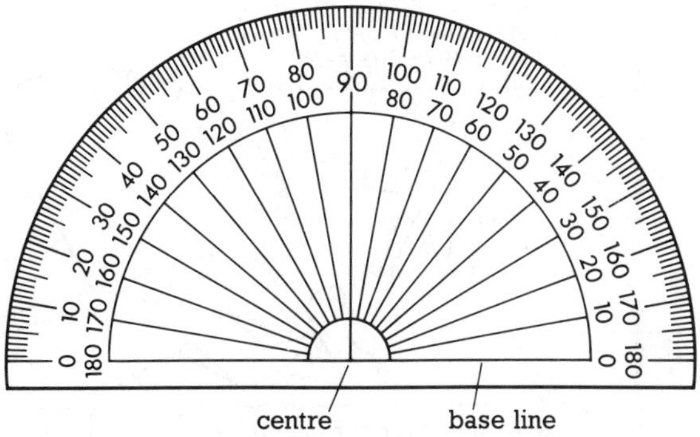

The line near the straight edge is called the *base line*; there is a mark at its *centre*.

You can see that there are two scales marked in degrees. Each scale goes from 0 to 180 but they start at opposite ends of the base line.

SO WE HAVE TO BE CAREFUL TO USE THE RIGHT SCALE.

For example, this angle is small, so we know that it is 30° and not 150°.

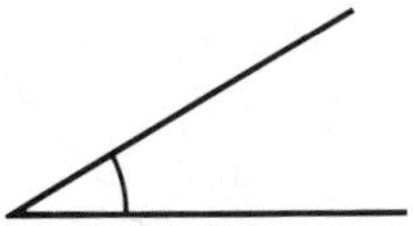

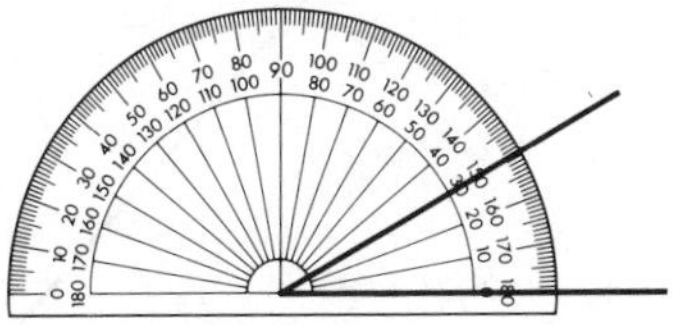

It is always a good idea to *estimate* the size of an angle before measuring it, so that we can check the measurement.

EXERCISE 21a

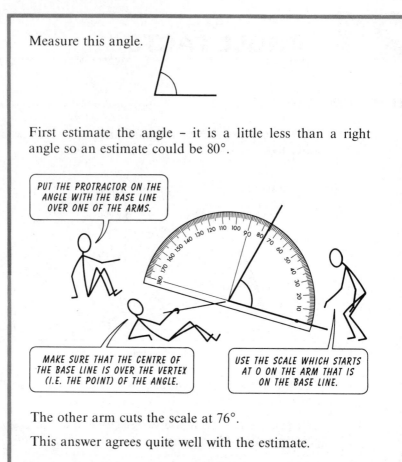

Measure this angle.

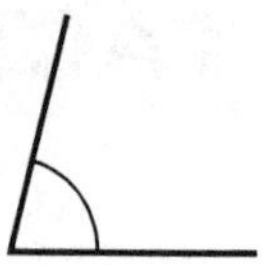

First estimate the angle – it is a little less than a right angle so an estimate could be 80°.

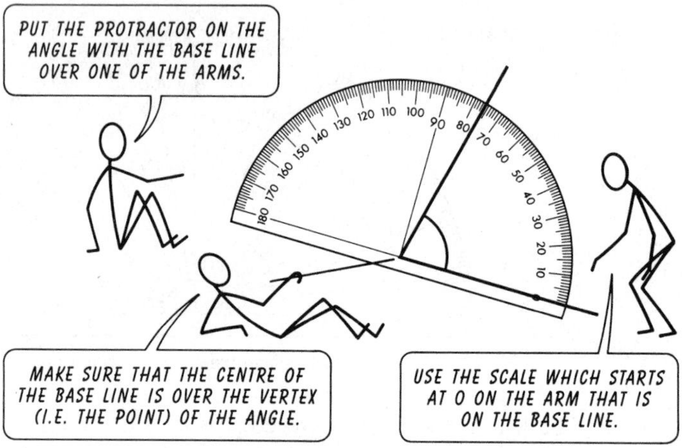

PUT THE PROTRACTOR ON THE ANGLE WITH THE BASE LINE OVER ONE OF THE ARMS.
MAKE SURE THAT THE CENTRE OF THE BASE LINE IS OVER THE VERTEX (I.E. THE POINT) OF THE ANGLE.
USE THE SCALE WHICH STARTS AT 0 ON THE ARM THAT IS ON THE BASE LINE.

The other arm cuts the scale at 76°.

This answer agrees quite well with the estimate.

First estimate, and then measure, each of the following angles.

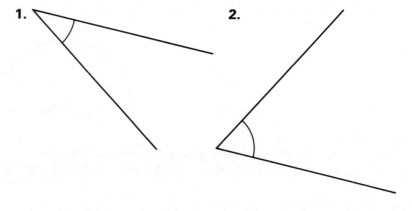

1.

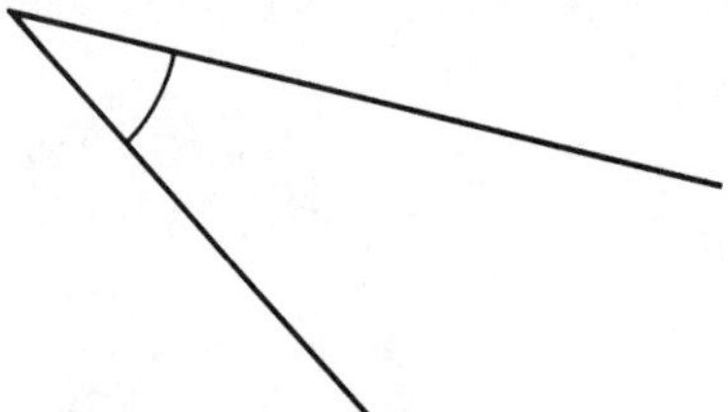

2.

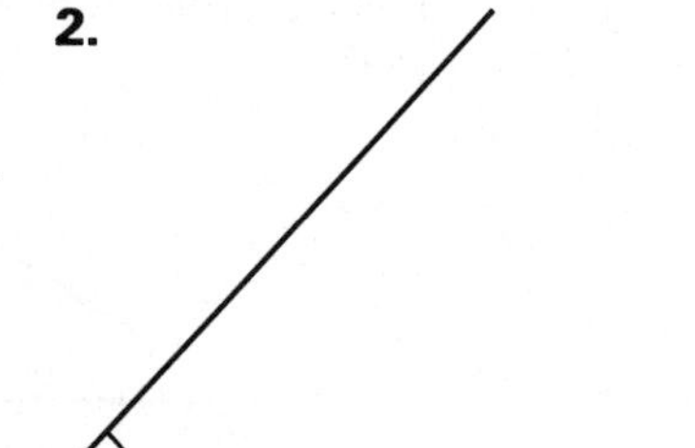

3.

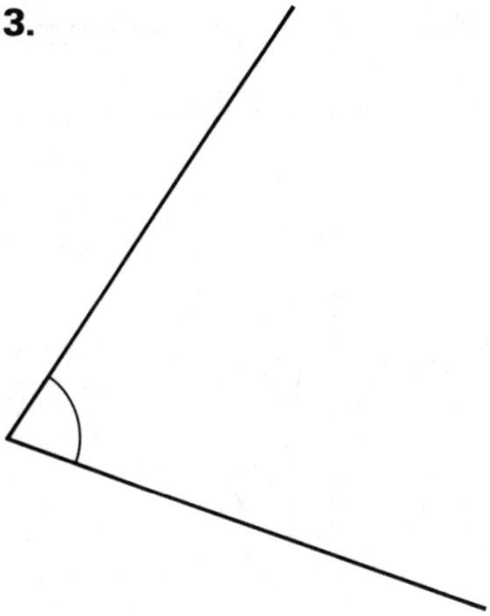

4.

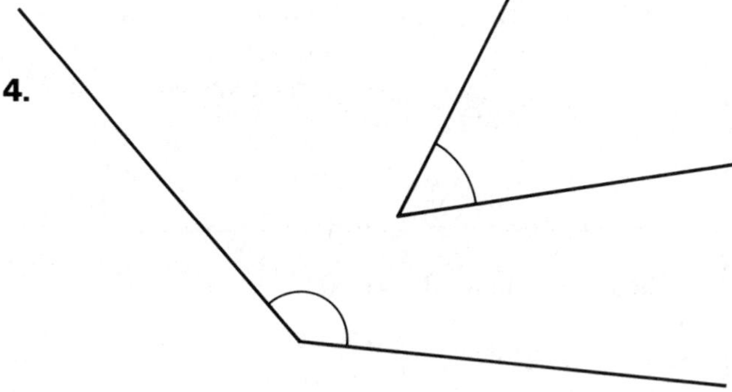

5.

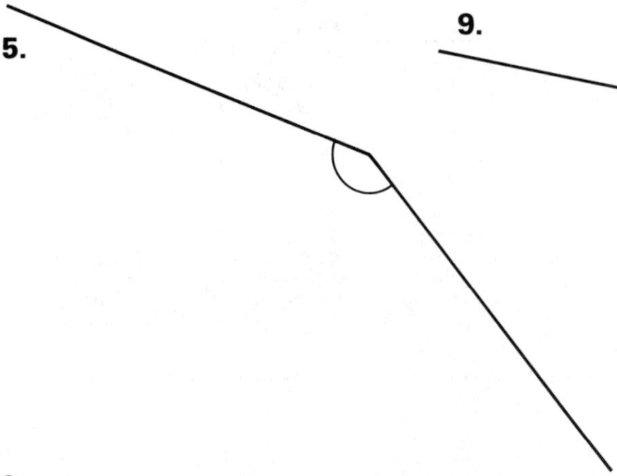

6.

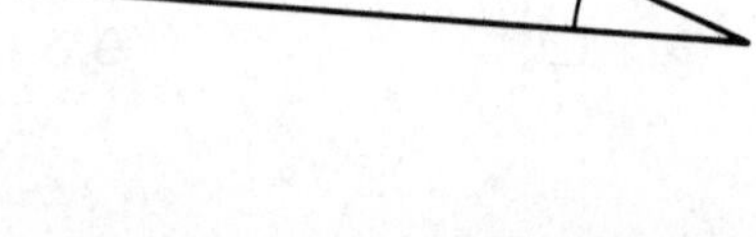

7.

8.

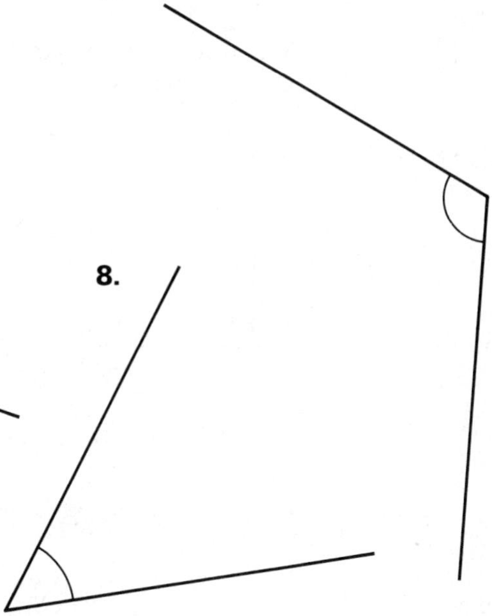

9.

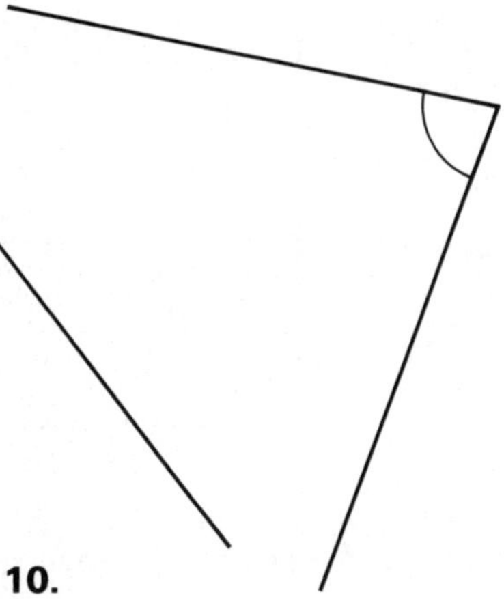

10.

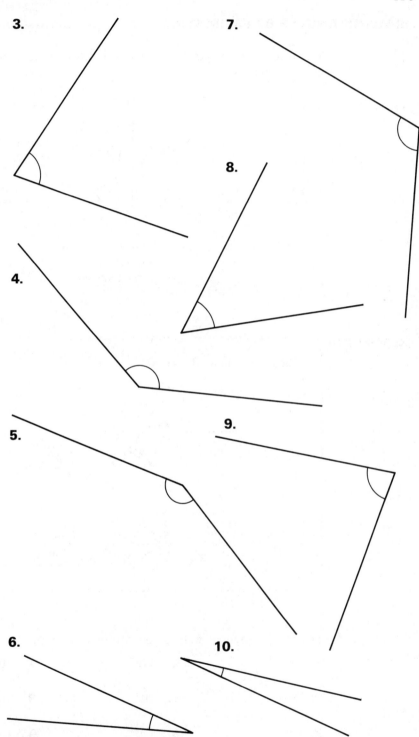

DRAWING ANGLES BY ESTIMATING

When we want to sketch an angle it helps to remember the shape of certain angles such as

90°

90° is a right angle.

60°

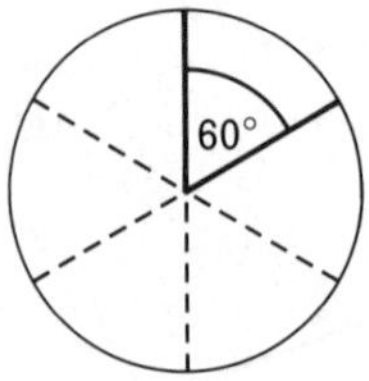

Dividing a circle into six equal parts gives 60°.

45°

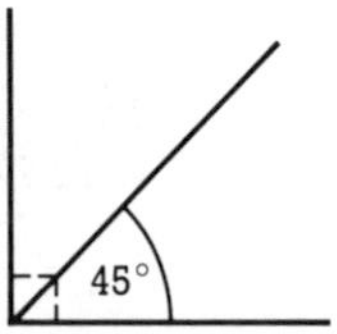

45° is half a right angle.

EXERCISE 21b

Sketch an angle of a) 50° b) 105°

a)

b)

Draw each angle as well as you can by estimation.

1. 40°

2. 80°

3. 70°

4. 170°

5. 20°

6. 120°

7. 30°

8. 100°

9. 10°

DRAWING ANGLES BY USING A PROTRACTOR

Suppose that we want to draw an angle of 140°.

First draw a line for one of the arms and mark the vertex on it.

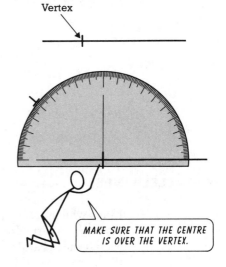

We place the protractor on the arm we have drawn as shown in the diagram.

The scale to use starts from 0 on this arm. Go round to 140 on this scale and make a neat mark on the paper.

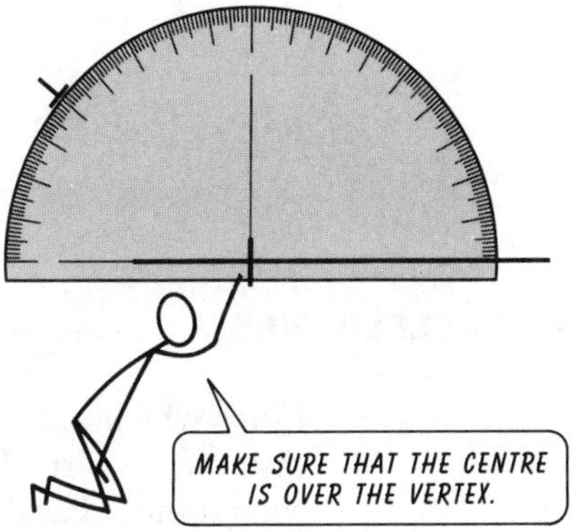

MAKE SURE THAT THE CENTRE IS OVER THE VERTEX.

Remove the protractor and join this mark to the vertex. The angle we have drawn is 140°.

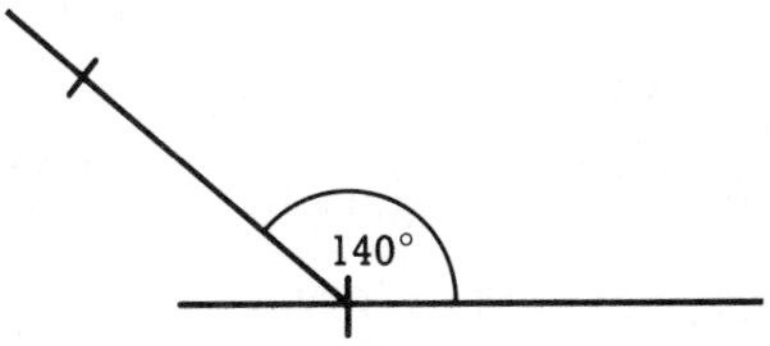

Now we check that the angle *looks* the right size.

EXERCISE 21c For each question, first sketch an angle of about the right size; then use a protractor to draw the angle accurately.

1. 50°	**5.** 100°	**9.** 45°	**13.** 120°
2. 70°	**6.** 30°	**10.** 80°	**14.** 20°
3. 120°	**7.** 60°	**11.** 95°	**15.** 40°
4. 75°	**8.** 150°	**12.** 105°	**16.** 55°

PERPENDICULAR LINES

If the angle between two lines is 90°, i.e. one right angle, the lines are *perpendicular* to each other.

PARALLEL LINES

Lines which are always the same distance apart are *parallel* to each other. Parallel lines go in the same direction.

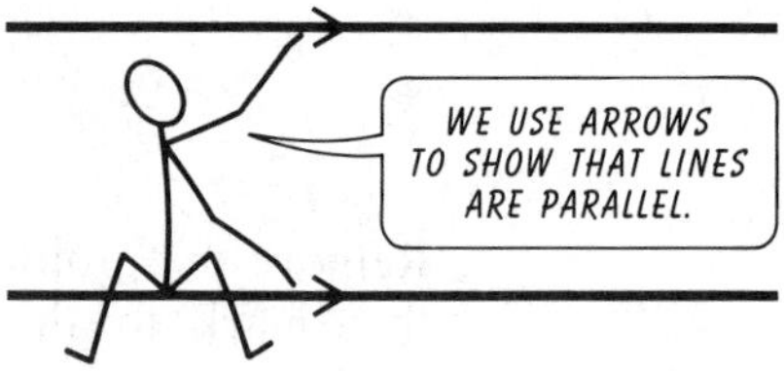

EXERCISE 21d In each question, state whether the two lines are parallel, perpendicular or neither.

1.
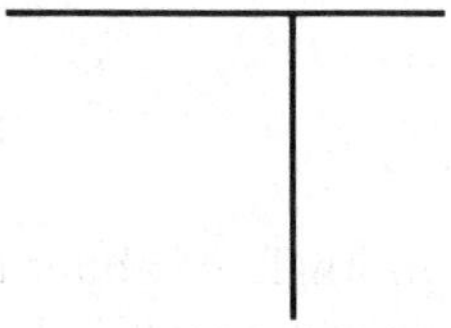

3.
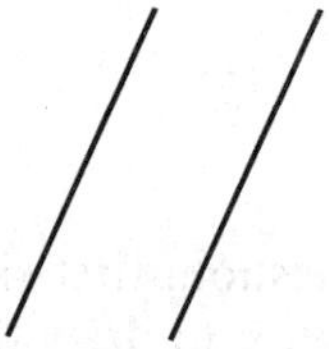

5.
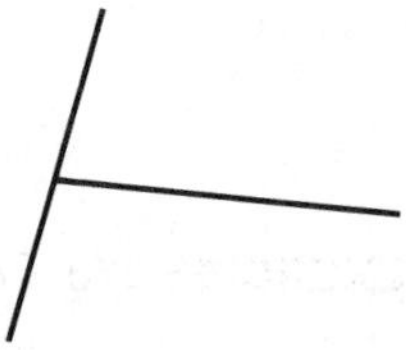

2.
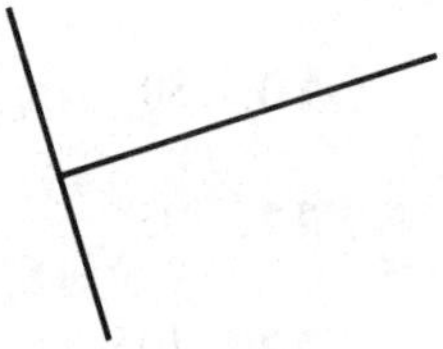

4.

6.
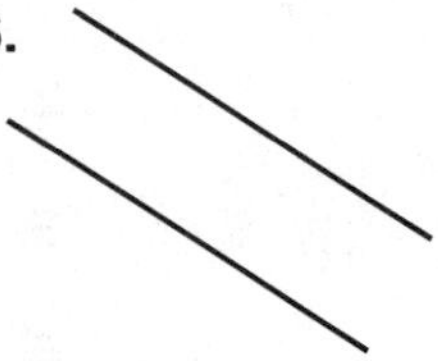

ANGLES ON A STRAIGHT LINE

EXERCISE 21e Draw a straight line at least 12 cm long. From a point on this line, somewhere near the middle, draw another line like the one shown.

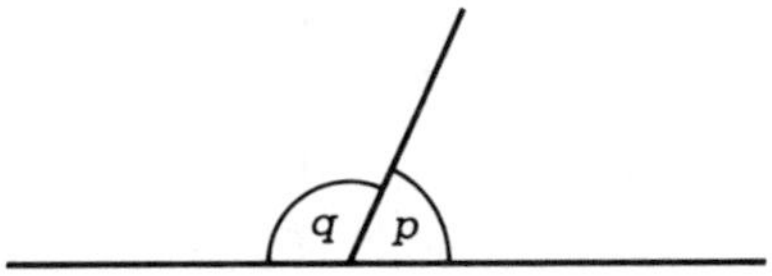
q
p

1. Measure the size of the angle marked p.

ANGLE p IS ACUTE, SO IT IS LESS THAN 90°.

2. Measure the size of the angle marked q.

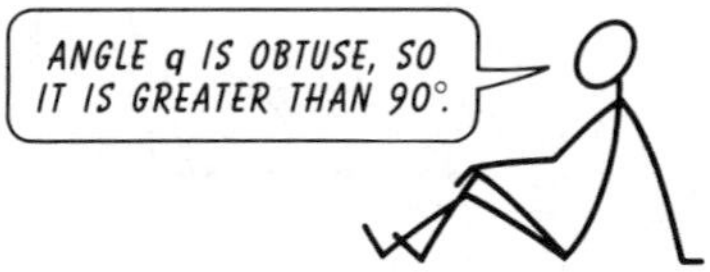
ANGLE q IS OBTUSE, SO IT IS GREATER THAN 90°.

3. Add p and q.

Do this again with some more lines.

4. What do you notice about $p + q$?

You will see that

> angles on a straight line add up to 180°.

EXERCISE 21f

Calculate the size of the angle marked p.

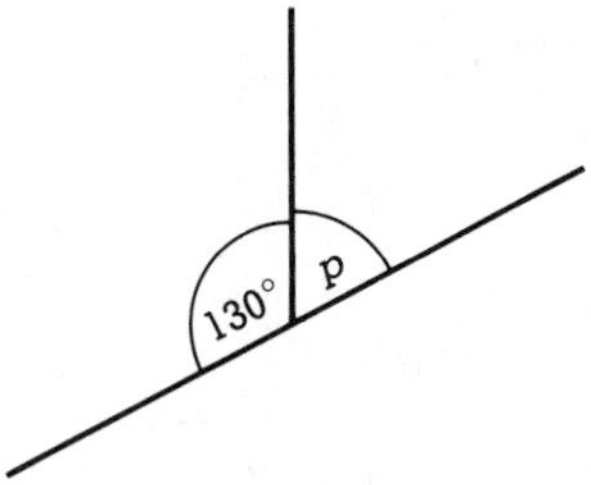
130°
p

$$p + 130° = 180°$$

$$\therefore \quad p = 50°$$

In each question, calculate the size of the angle marked with a letter.

1.

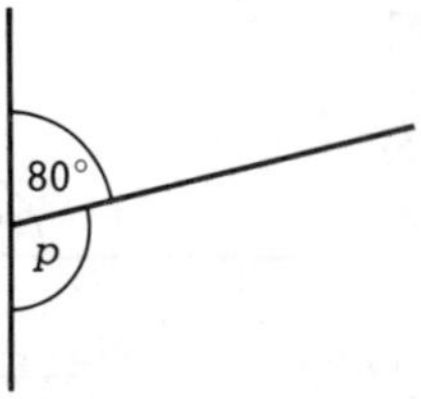

2.

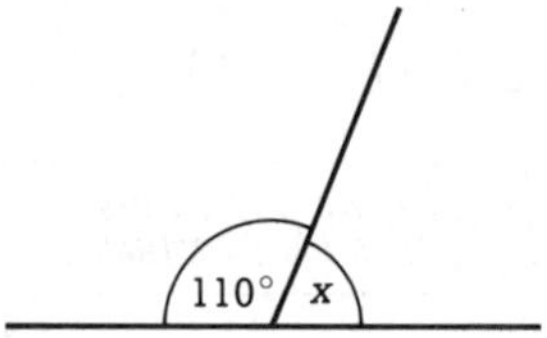

3.

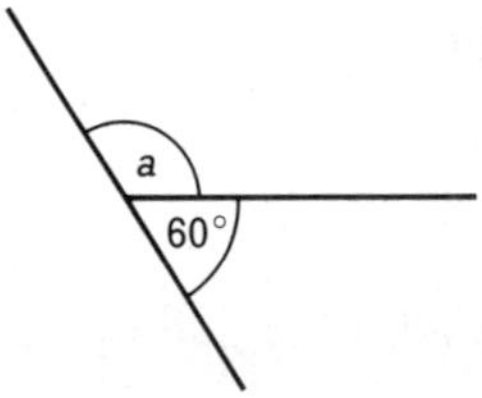

4.

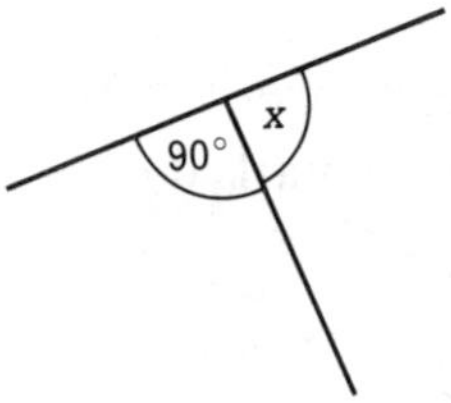

5.

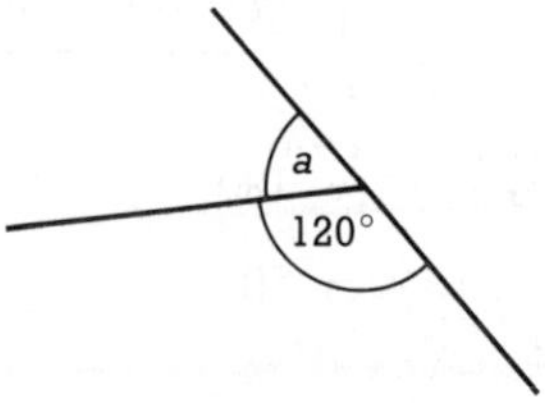

6.

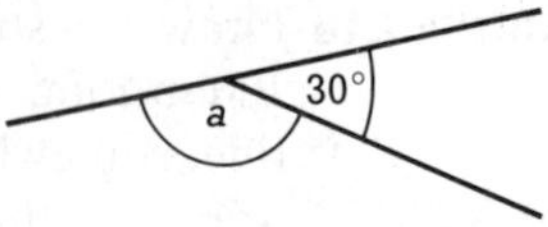

7.

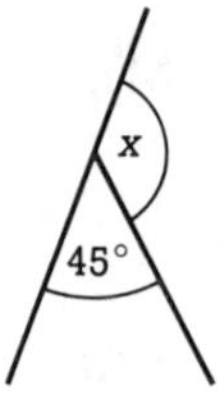

8.

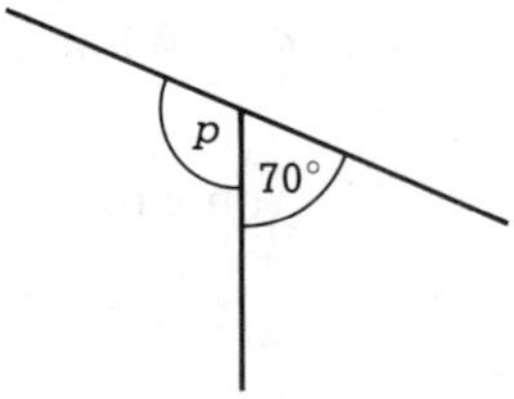

9.

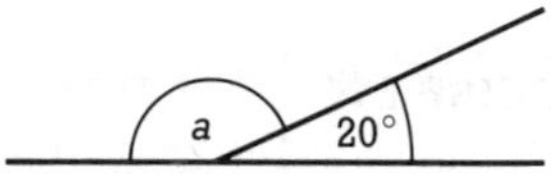

10.

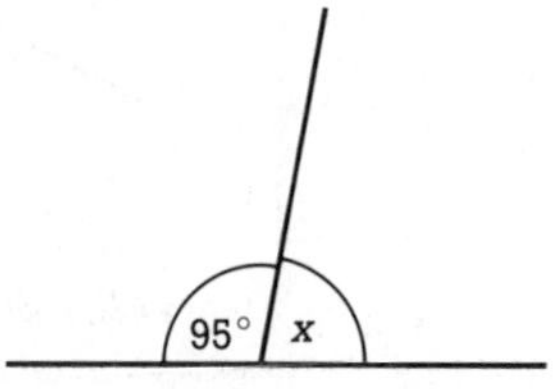

ANGLES AT A POINT

When several angles make a complete revolution they are called *angles at a point*.

There are 360° in one revolution, so

$$a + b + c = 360°.$$

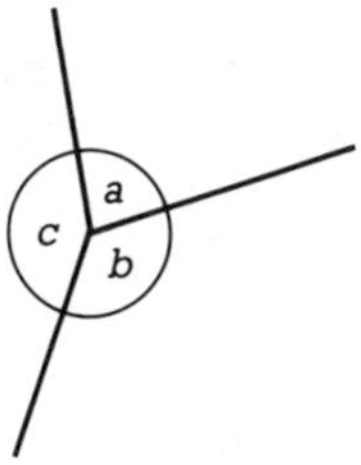

Angles at a point add up to 360°.

EXERCISE 21g

Find the size of the angle marked a.

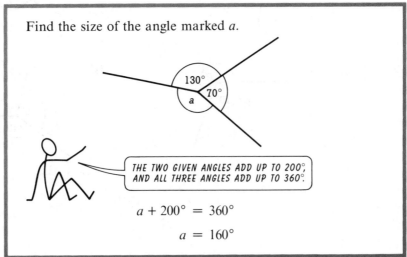

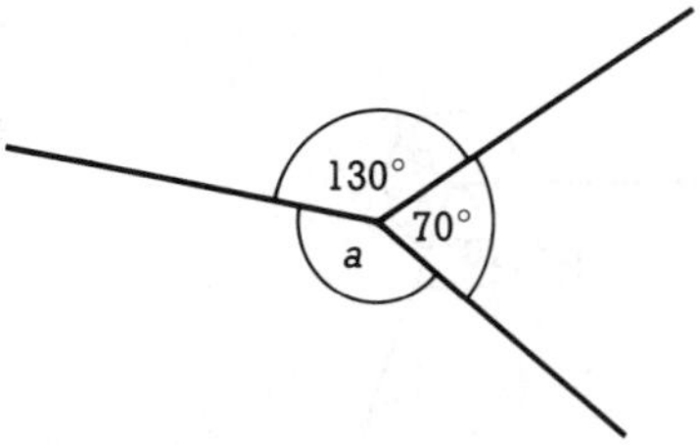

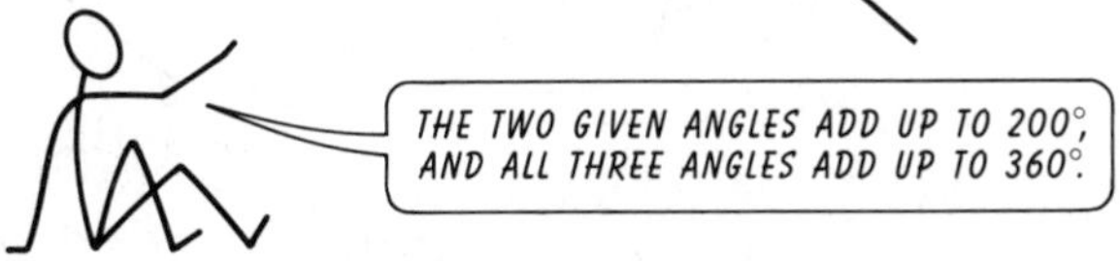

THE TWO GIVEN ANGLES ADD UP TO 200°,
AND ALL THREE ANGLES ADD UP TO 360°.

$$a + 200° = 360°$$
$$a = 160°$$

In each question find the angle marked with a letter.

1.

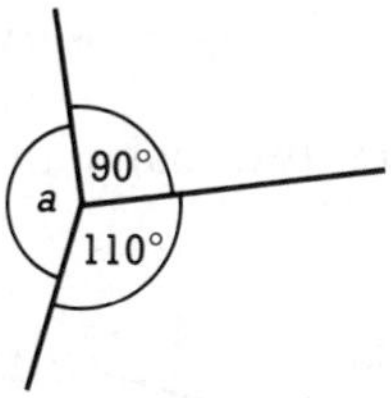

2.

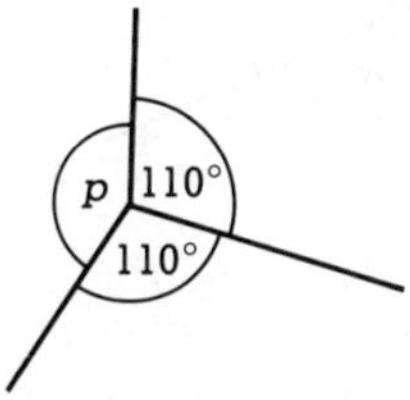

3.

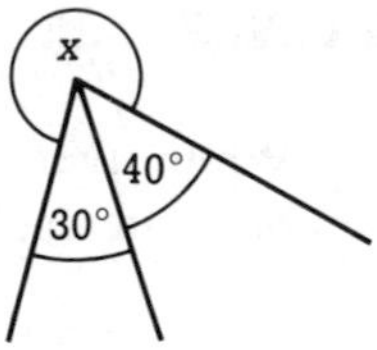

4.

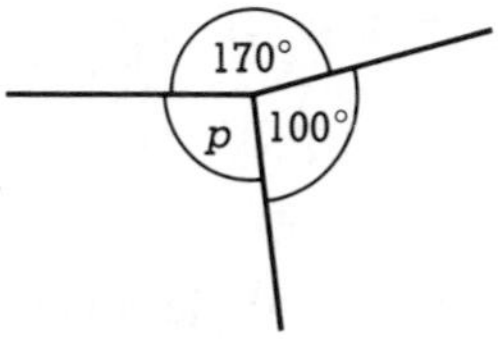

5.

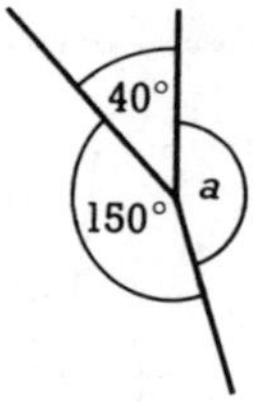

8.

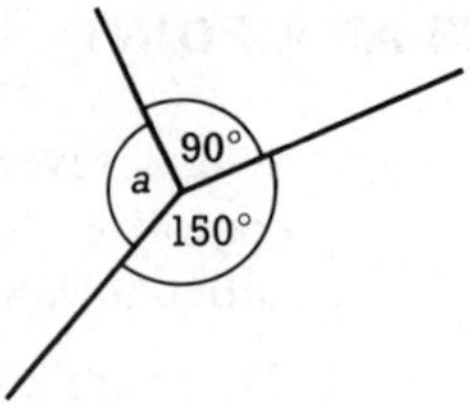

6.

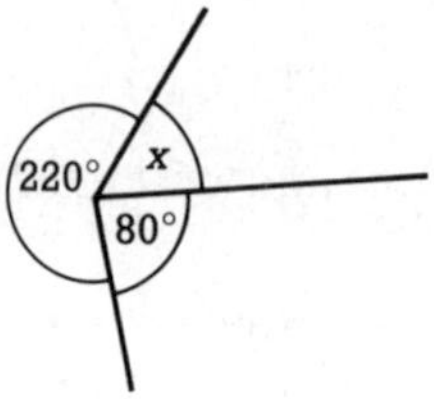

9.

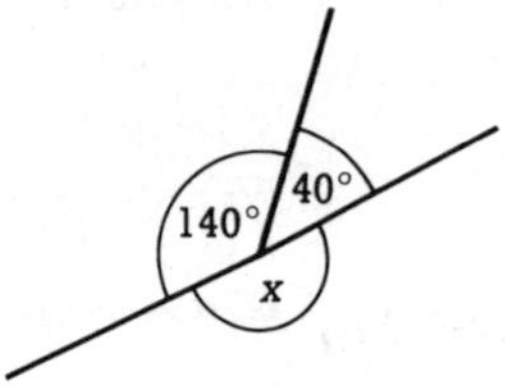

7.

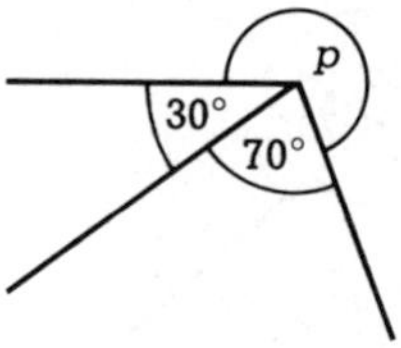

10.

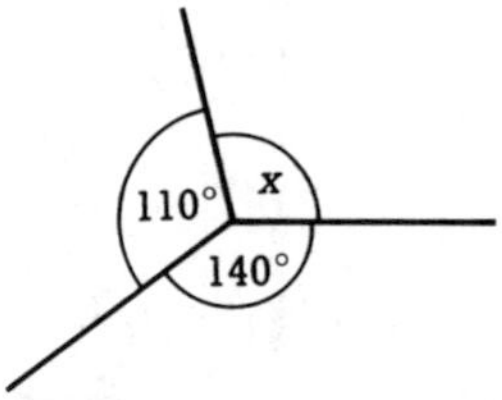

CROSSING LINES

When two lines cross they form two pairs of angles which are opposite each other.

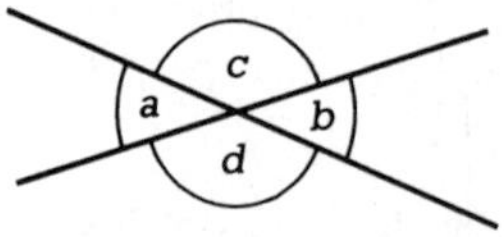

Angle a is opposite angle b.
Angle c is opposite angle d.

EXERCISE 21h Measure and write down the sizes of angles *a* and *b*.

1.

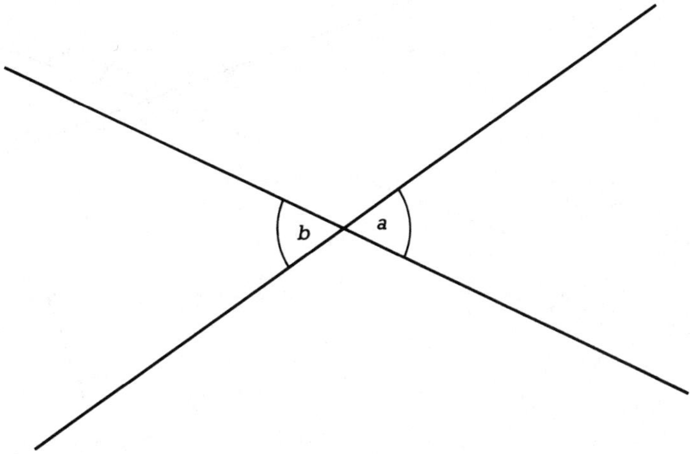

2.

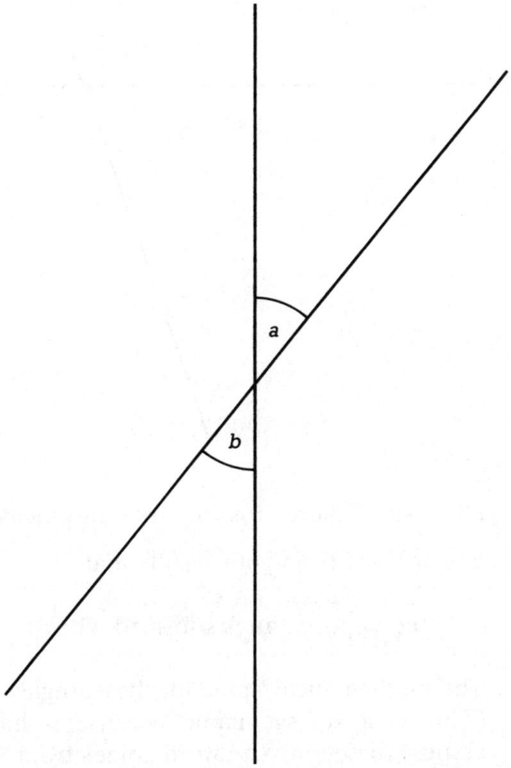

Measure and write down the sizes of *c* and *d*.

3.

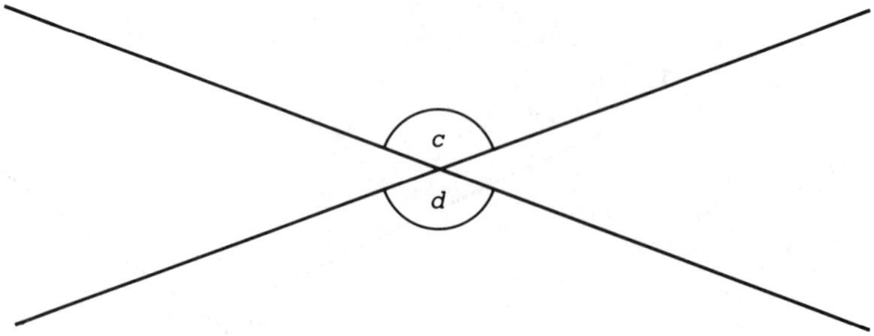

4.

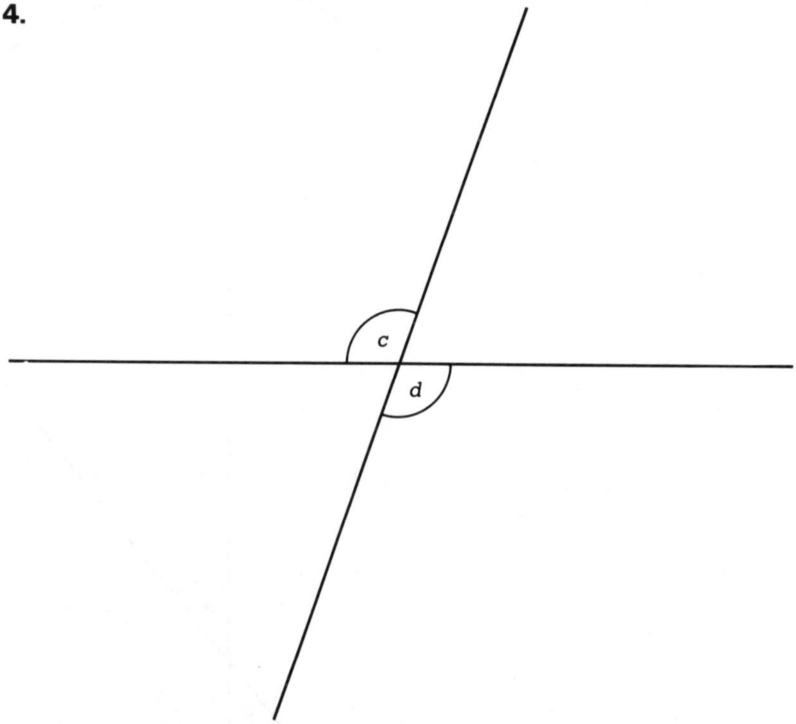

Draw some more crossing lines and measure the opposite angles.

You will see from your results that

> the opposite angles formed when two lines cross are equal.

The mathematical name for these angles is *vertically opposite.*
(This is a strange name because it has nothing to do with the vertical direction! The word comes from "vertex".)

EXERCISE 21i

1. Copy this picture of a deck chair and shade one pair of vertically opposite angles. Shade another pair in a different colour.

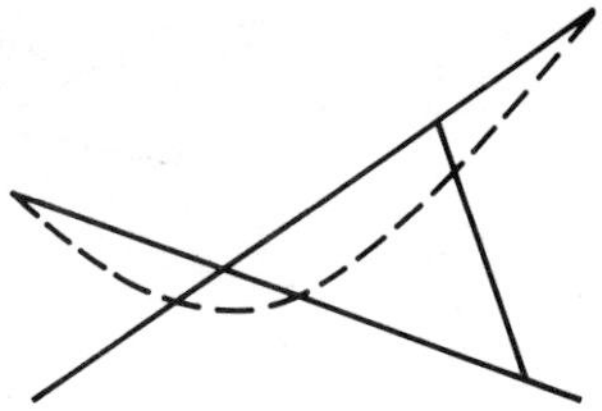

2. This is a picture of part of an electricity pylon.
Write down as many pairs of vertically opposite angles as you can find.
One pair is done for you.

$p = r$

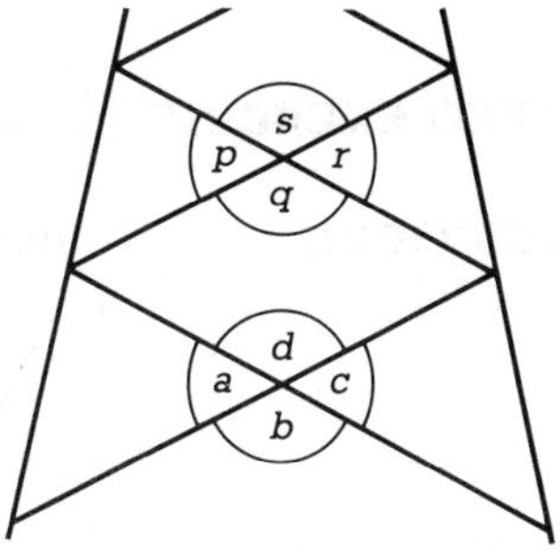

3.

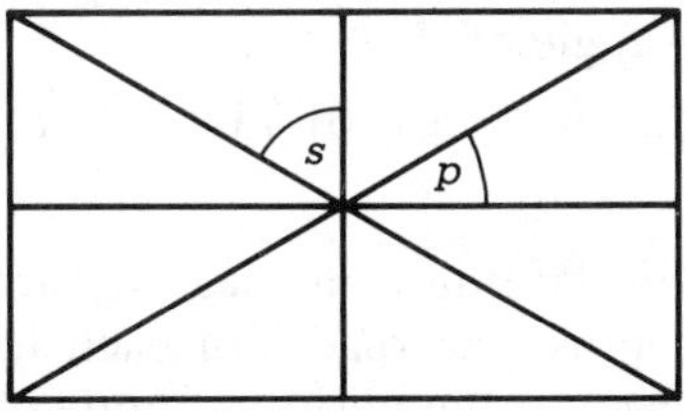

Copy this flag. On your copy

a) mark with q an angle equal to p

b) mark with r an angle equal to s

c) shade another pair of equal angles not using p or s.

Write down the size of the angle marked with a letter.

4.

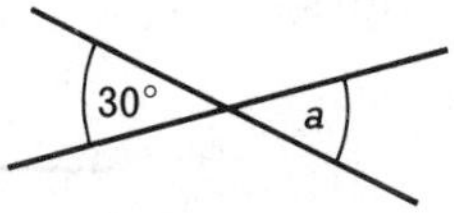

5.

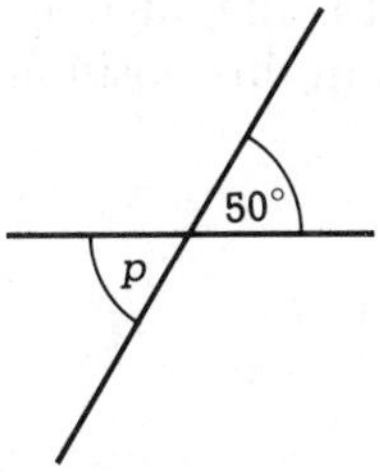

6.

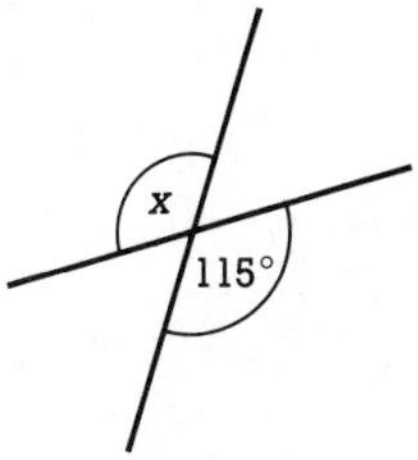

7. 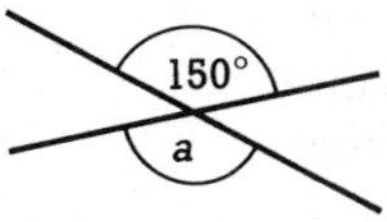

8. 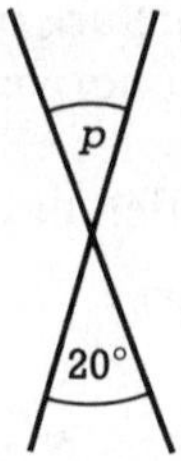

9. 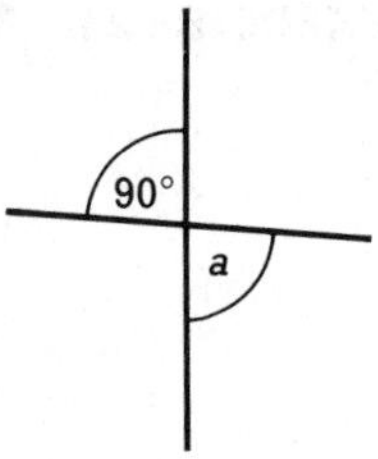

MIXED EXERCISE

EXERCISE 21j

1. Estimate the size of each angle.

a) 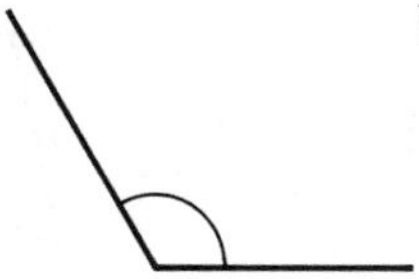

b) 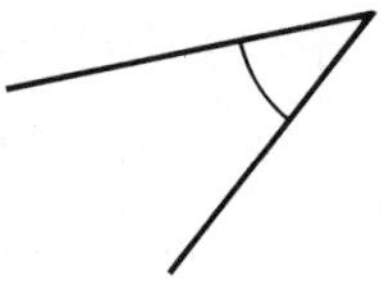

c) 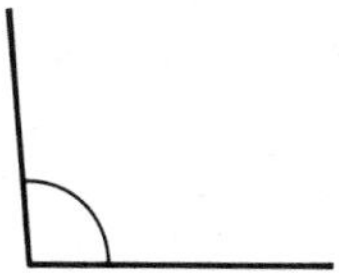

2. First sketch, and then draw accurately with a protractor, an angle of

a) 35° b) 75° c) 22°.

Ann is sending a message by arm signals to her friend Katie who lives across the road. For each letter of the message she must hold each arm in the position of one of the hours on a clock.
(Sending messages this way is called semaphore.)

3. How many degrees are there between Ann's arms in this position?

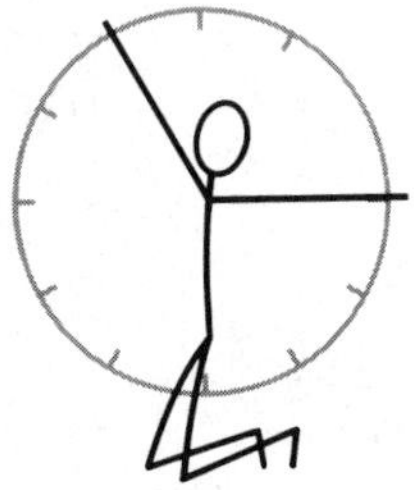

4. What is the angle between Ann's arms in this position?

5. In each case, find the size of the angle marked x.

a)

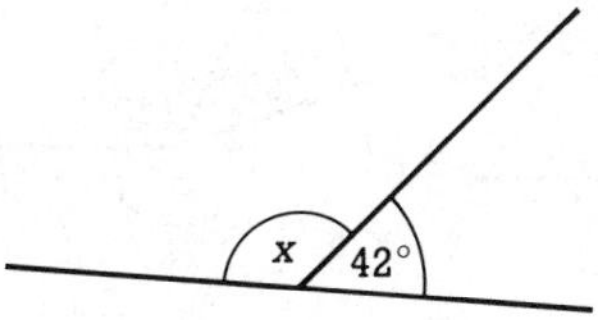

b)

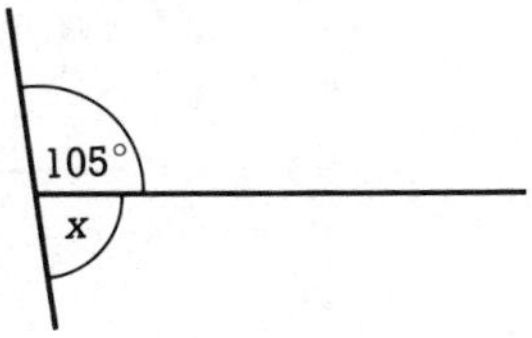

6. Copy each diagram and shade two equal angles.

a)

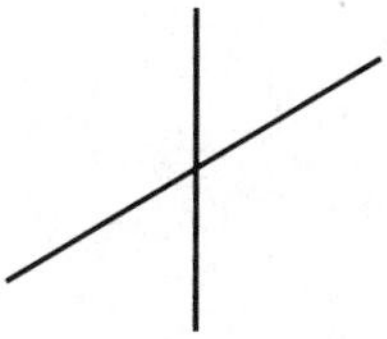

b)

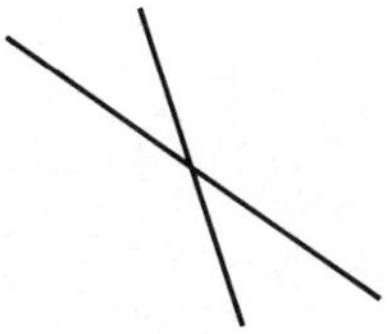

c)

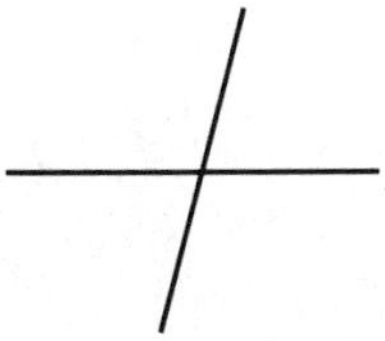

7. In each case, find the size of the angle marked a.

a)

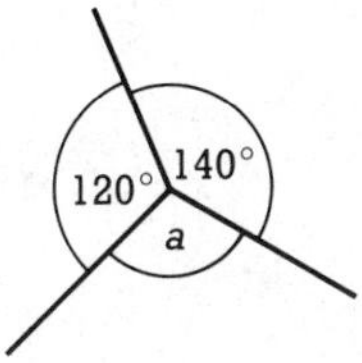

b)

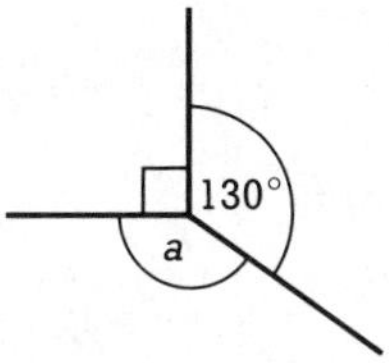

c)

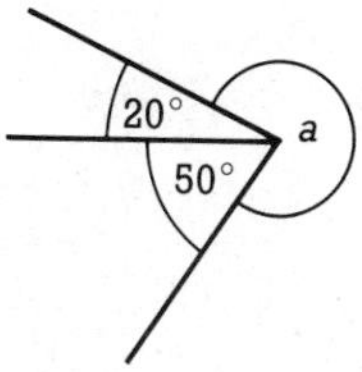

8. Copy each diagram and shade an angle equal to x.

a)

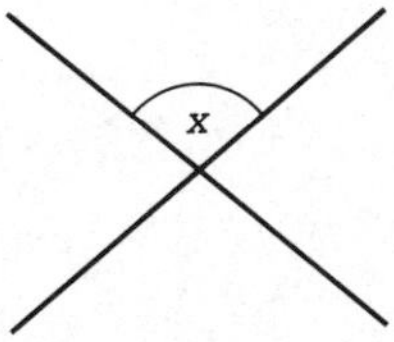

b)

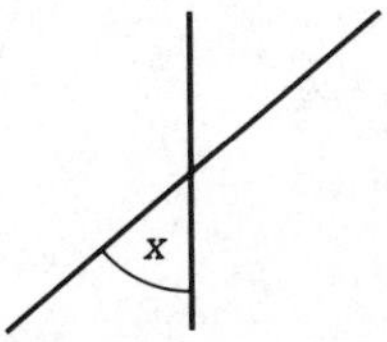

c)

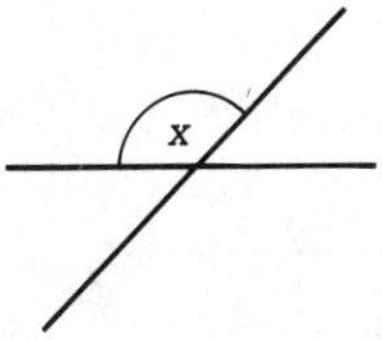

9. In each case, find the size of the angle marked p.

a) 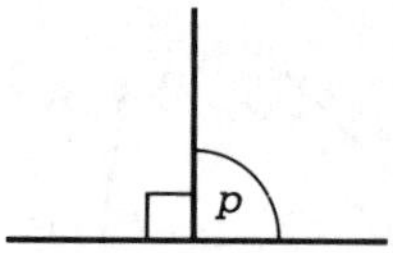

b) 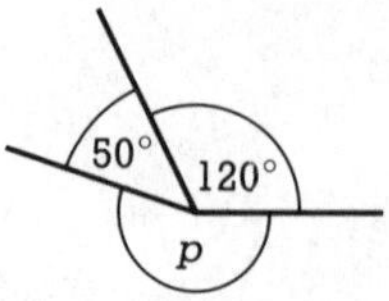

c) 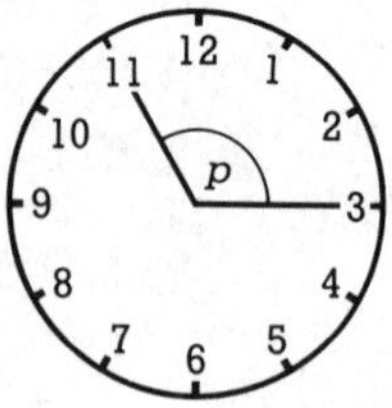

10. State whether each of the following statements is true or false.

a) 180° is equal to 2 right angles.
b) Angles on a straight line add up to 360°.
c) Vertically opposite angles add up to 180°.
d) Angles at a point add up to 4 right angles.

22 COORDINATES

THE COORDINATES OF A POINT

It is easy to locate a point on a grid if we start by drawing two straight lines called the *axes.*

One of these lines is drawn across the grid and the other line is drawn up the grid.

The two axes meet at a point called the *origin* which is labelled O.

The line across the grid is called the x-axis and is labelled Ox.
The line drawn up the grid is called the y-axis and is labelled Oy.

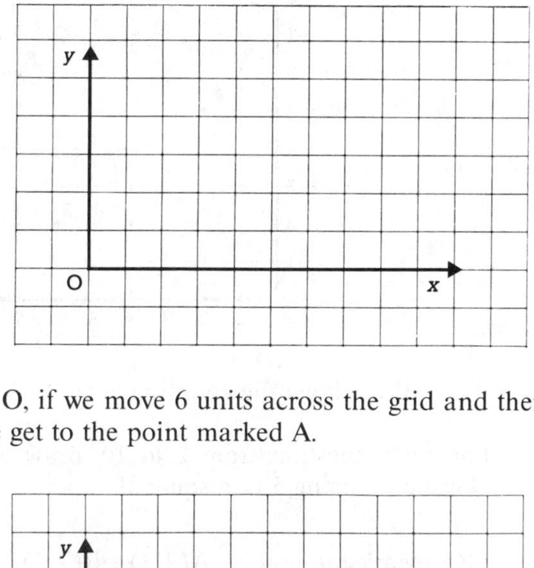

Starting at O, if we move 6 units across the grid and then 3 units up the grid we get to the point marked A.

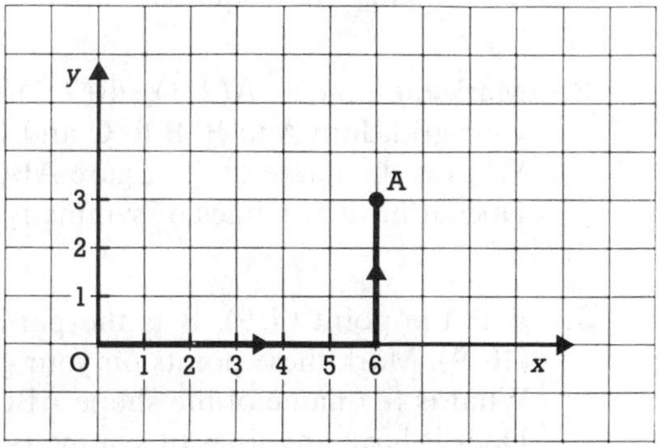

We say that *the coordinates* of A are (6, 3) and we say that A is the point (6, 3).

The *first number*, 6, is the x-coordinate of A, i.e. the number of units across.

The *second number*, 3, is the y-coordinate of A, i.e. the number of units up.

We always give the x-coordinate first.

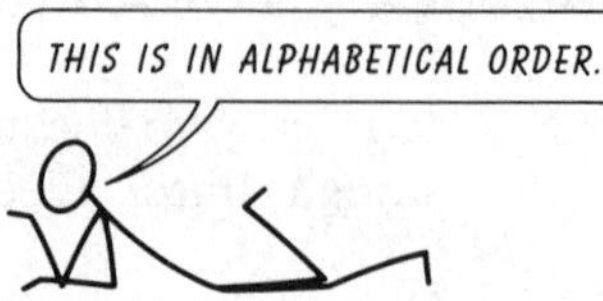

EXERCISE 22a **1.**

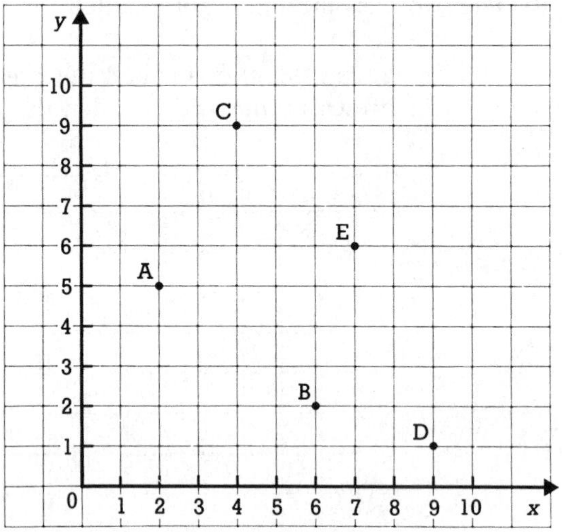

Write down the coordinates of A, B, C, D and E.

For each question from 2 to 10, draw a set of axes like those in Question 1 using 5 mm squared paper.

2. Mark the points A(2, 3), B(7, 3), C(7, 8) and D(2, 8) on your grid. Join A to B, B to C and C to D.
What is the name of the figure ABCD?
Does it have any lines of symmetry?

3. A is the point (4, 9), B is the point (7, 3) and C is the point (10, 9). Mark these points on your grid and join them up.
What is the name of the shape ABC?
Does it have any lines of symmetry?

4. Mark the points A(1, 2), B(1, 8), C(4, 5), D(7, 8), E(7, 2). Join the points in alphabetical order, starting from A and finishing at E.
What letter have you drawn?
This letter has a line of symmetry: draw it on your grid.

5. Repeat Question 4 with these points: A(8, 7), B(2, 7), C(2, 2), D(8, 2).

6. Mark the points A(4, 0), B(4, 3), C(1, 3), D(5, 8), E(9, 3), F(6, 3) and G(6, 0) on your grid. Join the points in alphabetical order.
What does the shape you have drawn look like?

7. The coordinates of three points A, B and C are respectively (2, 7), (2, 1) and (6, 1), ("Respectively" means "in the same order".) Join the points to make a triangle. Find the midpoint of AB and mark it D: find the midpoint of BC and call it E.

a) Measure the length of AC.
b) Measure the length of DE.
c) What do you notice about the answers to (a) and (b)?

8. Mark these points on your grid: A(2, 1), B(8, 1), C(8, 5), and D(2, 5). Join the points to make the figure ABCD.
What is the name of ABCD?

9. Three corners of a square are the points (1, 2), (1, 6) and (5, 6). Mark these points on your grid and join them in order. Find the position of the fourth corner and complete the drawing of the square.

10. Draw a simple pattern of your own on squared paper without letting anyone see it. Write down the coordinates of each point and give the set of coordinates to your partner.
See if your partner can use them to draw your diagram.

Write down the x-coordinate of the point (5, 7).

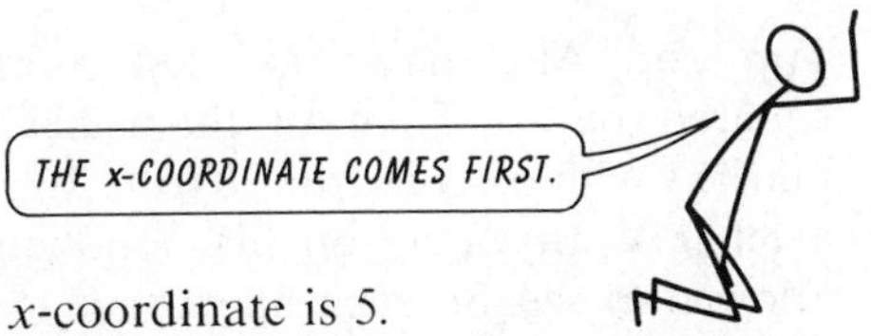
THE x-COORDINATE COMES FIRST.

The x-coordinate is 5.

In Questions 11 to 16, A is the point $(5, 1)$, B is the point $(2, 6)$ and C is the point $(9, 3)$.

11. Write down the x-coordinate of A.

12. Write down the y-coordinate of B.

13. Write down the x-coordinate of C.

14. Write down the y-coordinate of A.

15. Write down the y-coordinate of C.

16. Write down the x-coordinate of B.

Use this diagram to answer Questions 17 to 22.

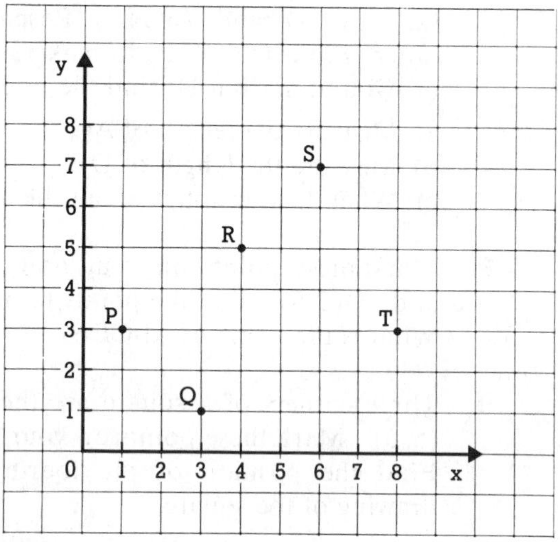

17. Write down the x-coordinate of P.

18. Write down the y-coordinate of S.

19. Write down the y-coordinate of Q.

20. Write down the x-coordinate of R.

21. Write down the y-coordinate of T.

22. Tim and Alec have invented a memory game played on squared paper. Each of them has an x-axis and a y-axis marked with a scale from 0 to 8. Each player is to try to draw a letter V anywhere on his opponent's grid, which he is not allowed to see. So each player has to *remember* what points he has chosen.

The rules are:

Player 1 chooses a point but *does not mark it on his grid.* He tells its coordinates to Player 2 who *does* mark it on his grid.

Player 2 then chooses a point and tells it to Player 1 who marks it on his grid.

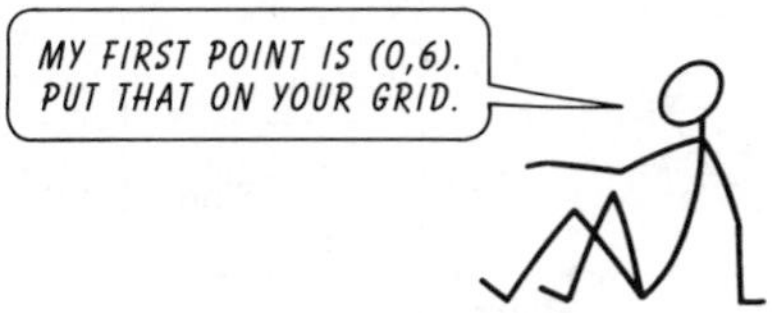

Then Player 1 gives the coordinates of the next point for his letter V and so on.

Try this game with your partner. See which V is the best shape.

If you have a really good memory you can try other letters, such as N or W, which have more points to remember.

MAP GRIDS

When a map is drawn on a grid, places can be located by the values on the horizontal and the vertical scales. These values are similar to coordinates and are called the *grid reference* of the place.

The axes are not marked x and y but the 'across' reference is given first just as it is with x and y coordinates.

EXERCISE 22b

This is a map of a treasure island, drawn on 1 cm squared paper. The exact position of each named place is indicated by a dot.

a) Write down the grid reference of Rocky Cove.
b) Write down the grid reference of High Pines.
c) How many squares are there on the map between Rocky Cove and High Pines?

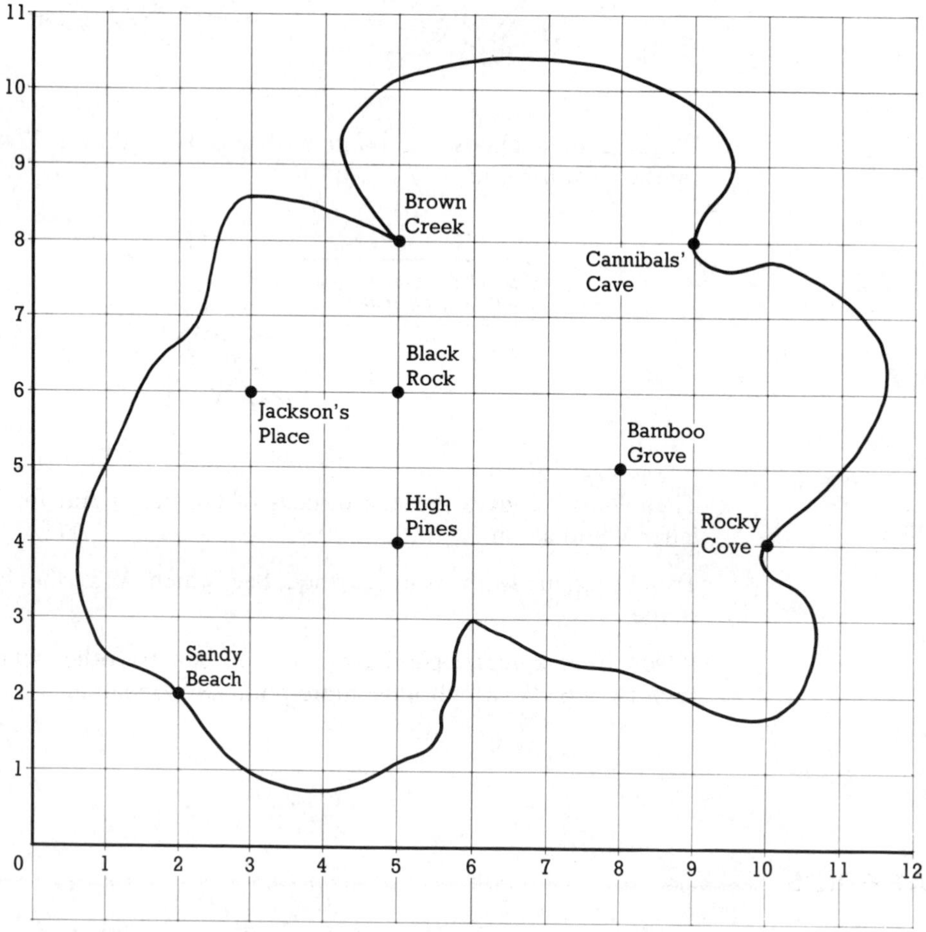

a) Rocky Cove is at (10, 4).
b) High Pines is at (5, 4).
c) There are 5 squares between Rocky Cove and High Pines.

Use the map in the worked example to answer the following questions.

In Questions 1 to 6 write down the grid reference of the given place.

1. Brown Creek

2. Cannibals' Cave

3. Black Rock

4. Sandy Beach

5. Jackson's Place

6. Bamboo Grove

7. Find, by measuring, the distance on the map between Sandy Beach and Black Rock.

8. Find the distance on the map between Brown Creek and Bamboo Grove.

9. There is a water-hole exactly halfway between Jackson's Place and Brown Creek.
What is its grid reference?

10. Halfway between Sandy Beach and Rocky Cove there is an inlet where a boat can be tied up.
What is the grid reference of the inlet?

11. The treasure is hidden halfway between Cannibals' Cave and High Pines.
Write down the grid reference of the spot where the treasure is hidden.

12. Which place on the map are you nearest to if you are at

a) the grid reference (6, 9)
b) the grid reference (4, 4)
c) the grid reference (7, 6)
d) the grid reference (11, 6)?

13. Which is the nearest place on the map to

a) Cannibals' Cave
b) Jackson's Place?

14. There is an area of dangerous swamp within the grid references (7, 6), (7, 7), (9, 6) and (9, 7).
Is it safe to walk in a direct line from Cannibals' Cave to

a) Black Rock
b) High Pines
c) Bamboo Grove
d) Rocky Cove?

MAPS OF LARGE REGIONS

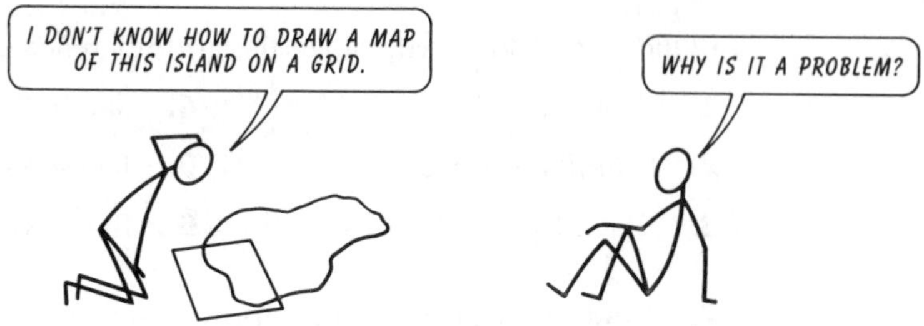

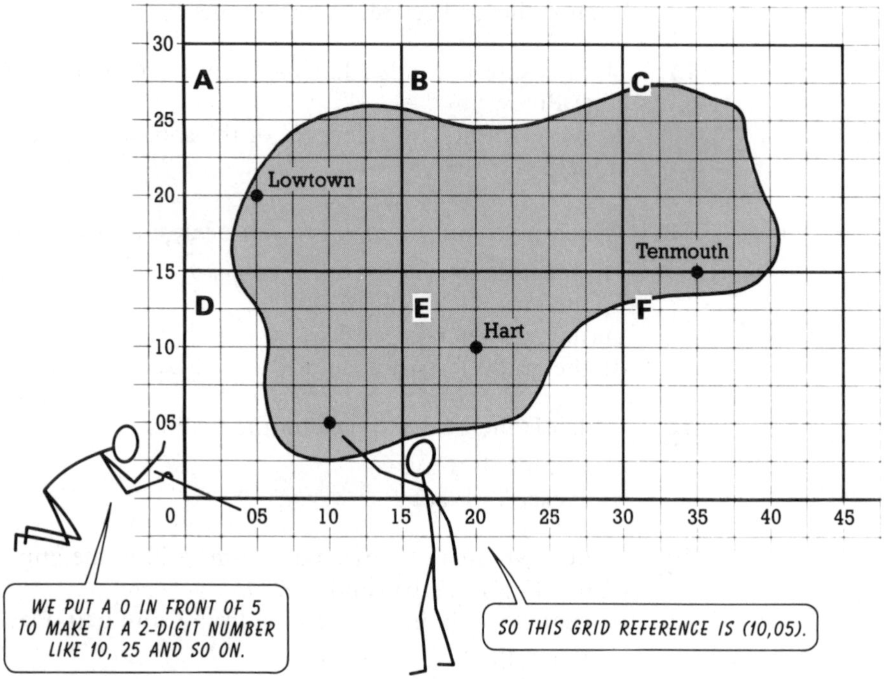

Now each section can be drawn on a grid but *the grid references on most sections do not start from O.*

EXERCISE 22c **1.** Copy and complete the sections of the map and shade the land in each section. **A** and **B** have been done for you.

A

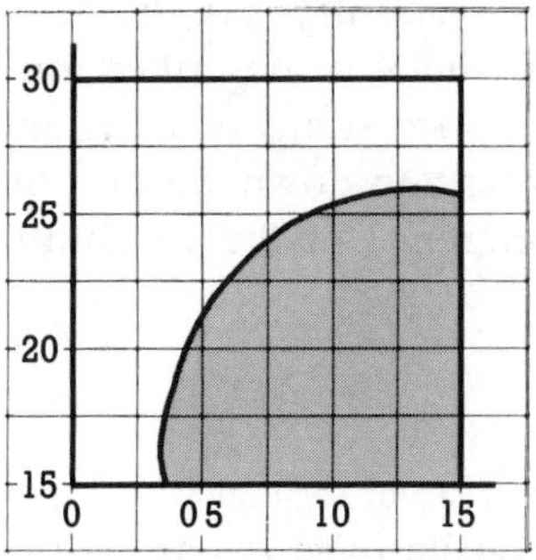

B

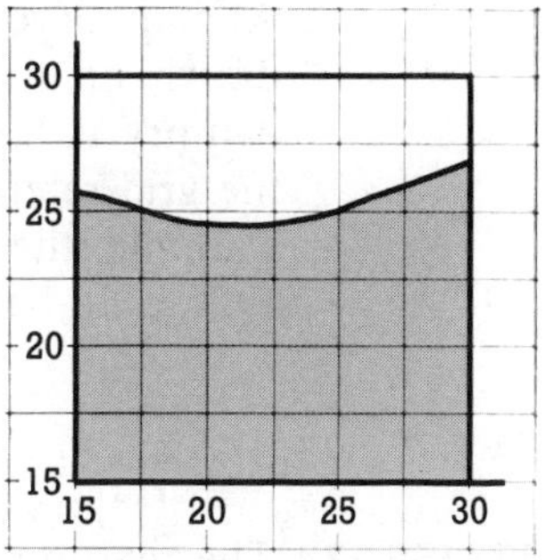

C

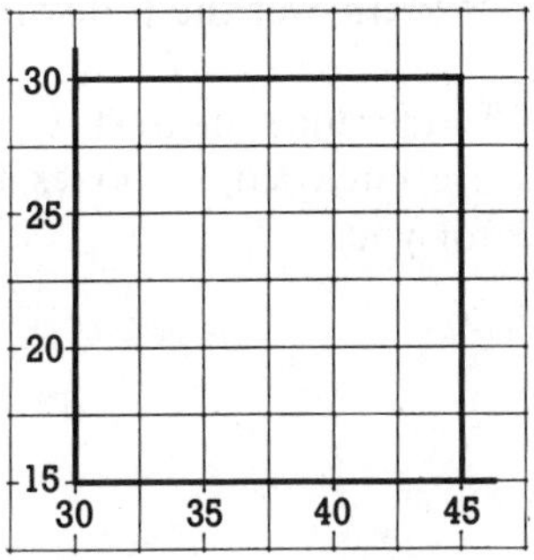

D

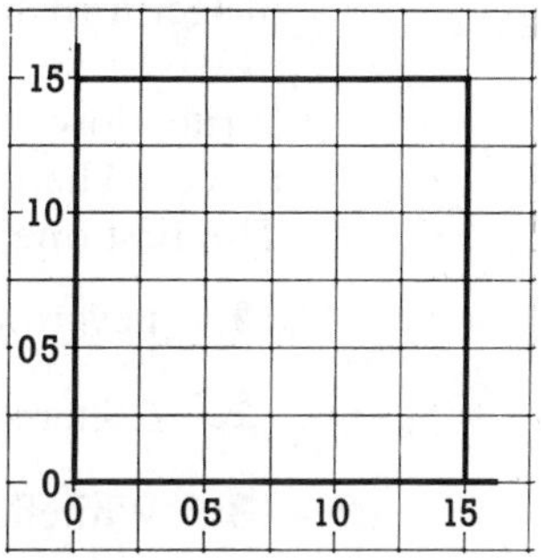

E

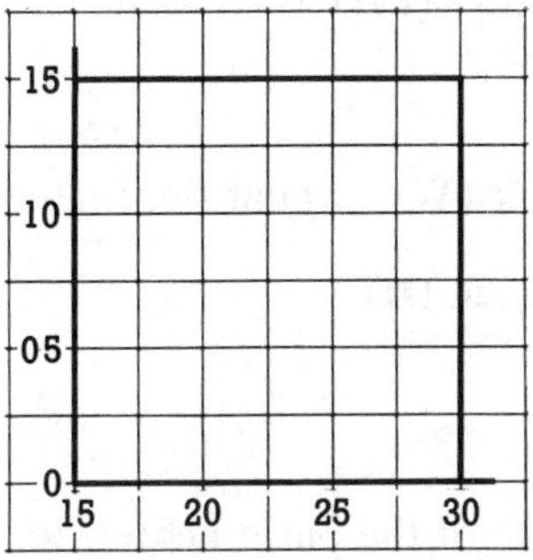

F

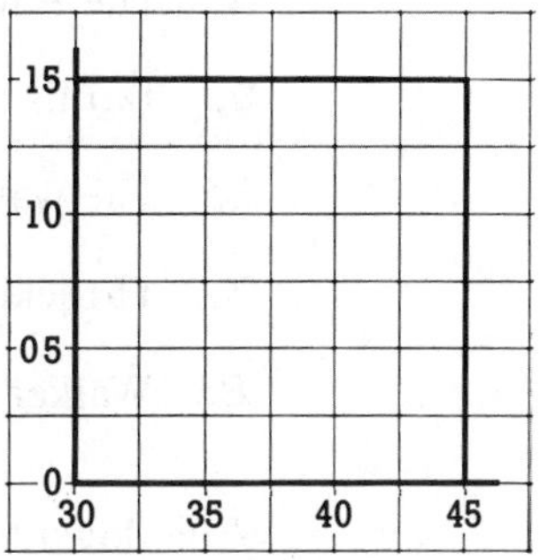

2. What is the grid reference of Lowtown?

3. What is the grid reference of Tenmouth?

4. What is at the grid reference (20, 10)?

5. There is a lighthouse at (40, 25).
a) Which section is it in?
b) Mark it on your section with the symbol 

6. There is a windmill at (20, 20). Mark it as  on the correct section.

ORDNANCE SURVEY MAPS

A map of our whole country can be split up into sections and drawn on a grid in the way described on page 194. Because the country is large, there are some very big numbers on the scales so the grid reference is written down without brackets or a comma. For example, the grid reference of the windmill in Question 6 on page 195 would be written 20 20.

EXERCISE 22d The map on the opposite page is part of the Ordnance Survey Map of Hertfordshire. Use it to answer the following questions.

Write down the grid reference nearest to each of the following places. Their names are enclosed in boxes to help you find them. The first one is done for you.

1. Leycroft 33 26

2. Cottered

3. Whitehall

4. The Public House (PH) at Ardeley

5. Tannis Court

6. The water tower (Wr Twr) at Benington

7. Throcking church (⛪)

8. Walkern Hall

Write down the name of the place nearest to the given grid reference.

9. 30 32

10. 34 26

11. 30 27

12. 35 32

13. 34 27

14. 32 30

15. Midway between 30 28 and 30 29

16. Midway between 32 27 and 32 26

17. Between 32 25 and 32 26

18. Between 33 29 and 34 30

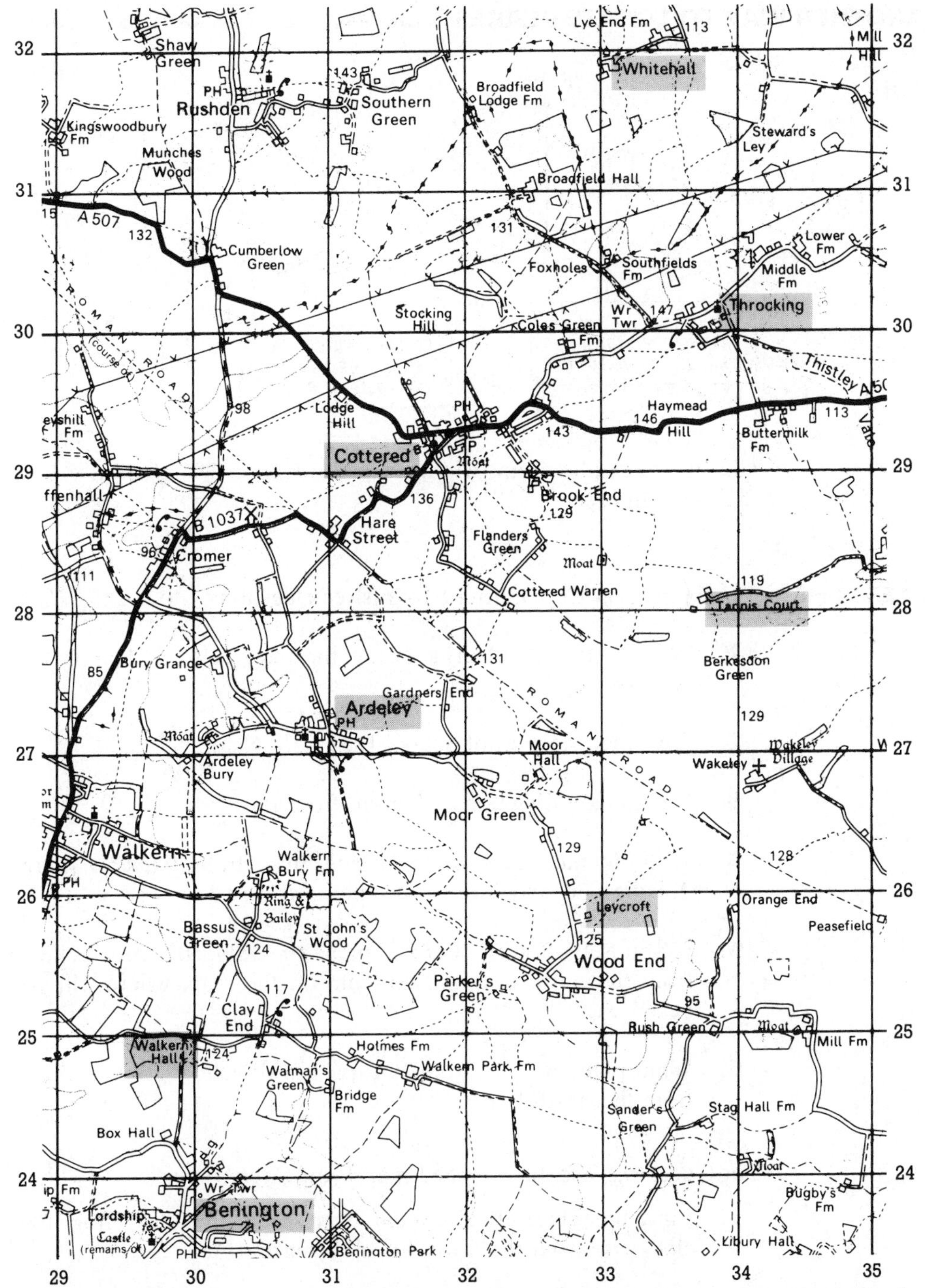

Reproduced from the 1988 Ordnance Survey 1 : 50 000 Landranger map 166 with the permission of the Controller of Her Majesty's Stationery Office, © Crown Copyright.

ANOTHER WAY TO LOCATE PLACES

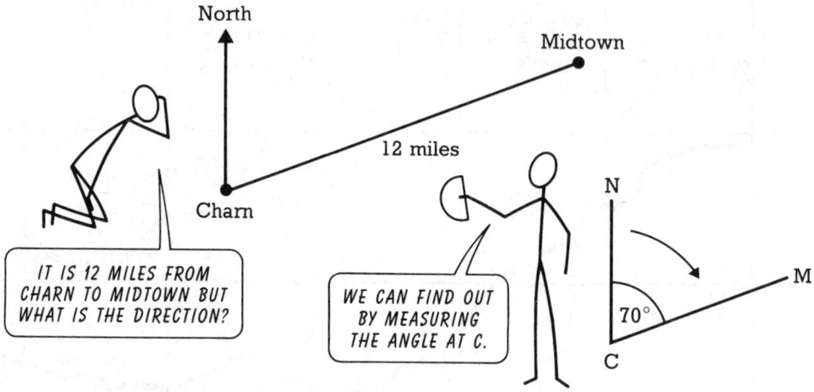

Charn is 12 miles from Midtown in a direction 70° clockwise from the north line.

EXERCISE 22e Use Map A on Copymaster 8 to answer Questions 1 to 6.

1. What is the direct distance on the map between Rinton and Astown?

2. Give the direction of School End from Nean.

3. What is the direction of Lenton from Bardin?

4. What is the name of the place 6 cm from Corston in the direction 30° clockwise from the north line?

5. If you set off from Lenton in a direction 60° anticlockwise from the north line and go 8 cm on the map, where will you be?

6. What place is 3 cm from Bardin in a direction 130° clockwise from the north line?

For Questions 7 to 10 you need map B on Copymaster 8.

7. Find the place that is 8 cm from Karn in a direction 100° clockwise from the north line and mark it A.

8. Mark with B the place that is 5 cm from Nortan in a direction 40° anticlockwise from the north line.

9. Start from Forsham and go 4 cm in the direction 120° anti-clockwise from the north line. Mark as C the place you arrive at.

10. Mark the place D which is 6 cm from Westpoint in a direction 50° clockwise from the north line.

MIXED EXERCISE

EXERCISE 22f On squared paper draw an x-axis and a y-axis and mark a scale from 0 to 10 on each axis.

1. Mark the following points on your grid.
A(3, 2), B(5, 4), C(5, 9), D(1, 9) and E(9, 3).

2. Find the midpoint of AB and mark it P.

3. Write down the coordinates of P.

4. Find the midpoint of CD and mark it Q.

5. Write down the coordinates of Q.

6. If B, C, D are three corners of a rectangle, find the position of the fourth corner and mark it F.

7. Write down the coordinates of F.

8.

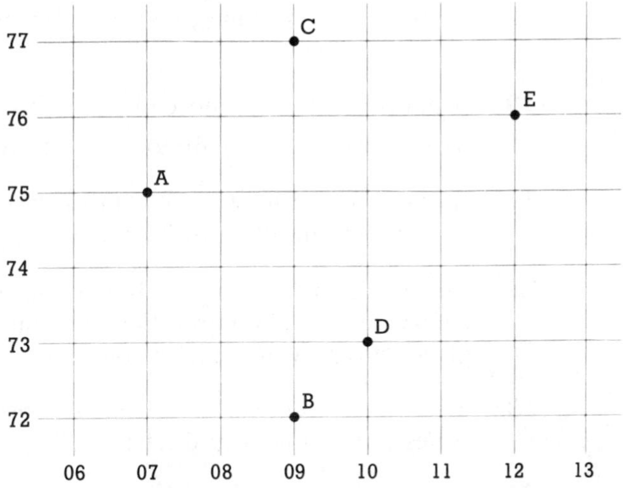

Write down the grid reference of

a) A b) B c) C d) D e) E

On 1 cm squared paper make a copy of this map; the outline need not be accurate but the towns should be marked carefully. Use your map to answer Questions 9 to 14.

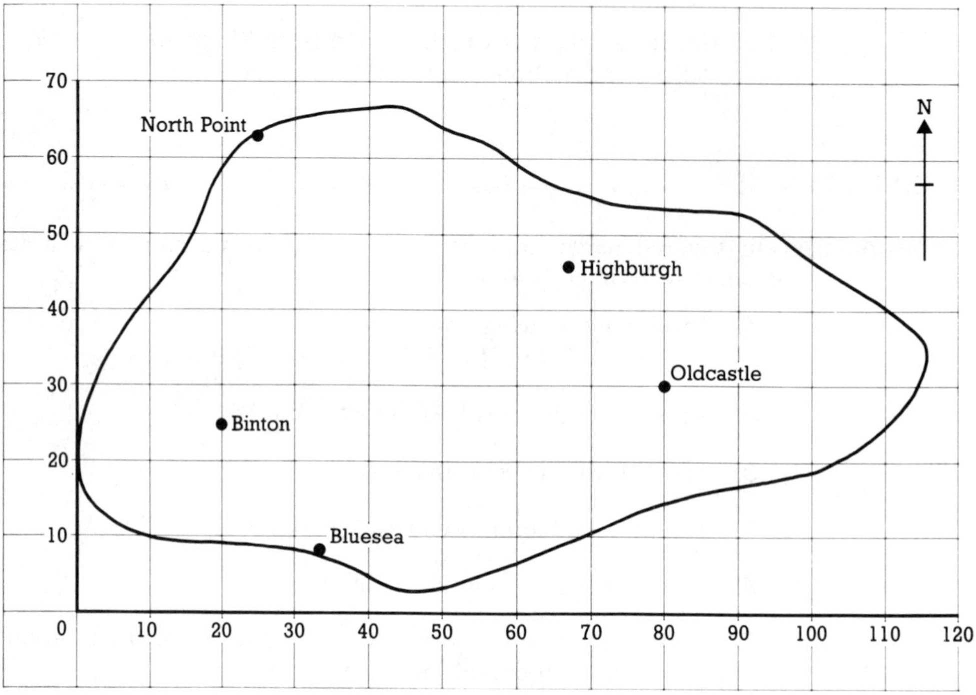

9. What is

a) the direction of Highburgh from Binton

b) the direct distance on the map between Oldcastle and North Point?

10. What is the grid reference of

a) Oldcastle b) Binton c) Bluesea?

11. Starting from Bluesea, go 5 cm in the direction 45° clockwise from the north. What is the name of the place you arrive at?

12. Three centimetres from Highburgh, in the direction 100° clockwise from the north, there is a quarry. Mark the position of the quarry with a dot on your map.

13. There is a caravan park halfway between Highburgh and Bluesea. What is its grid reference?

14. Clarke's Farm is about halfway between Bluesea and North Point.
Give the grid reference of the farm.

23 ACCURATE DRAWING

Sometimes we need to draw shapes on plain paper. Because there are no grid lines to help us draw right angles, we must use a protractor or a set-square.

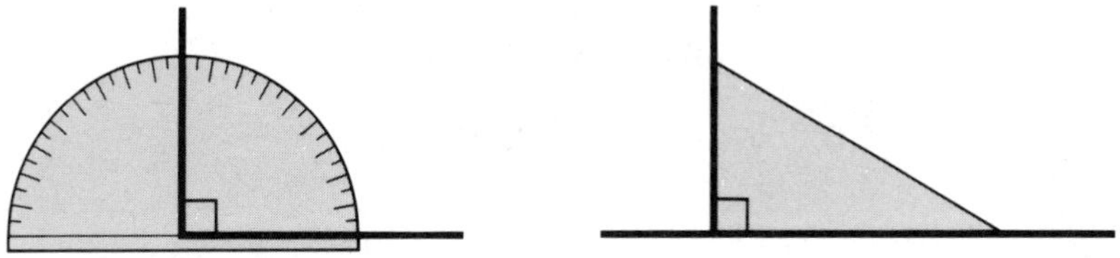

EXERCISE 23a

Draw a square of side 6 cm. Measure the length of each diagonal. (A diagonal is a line joining opposite corners.)

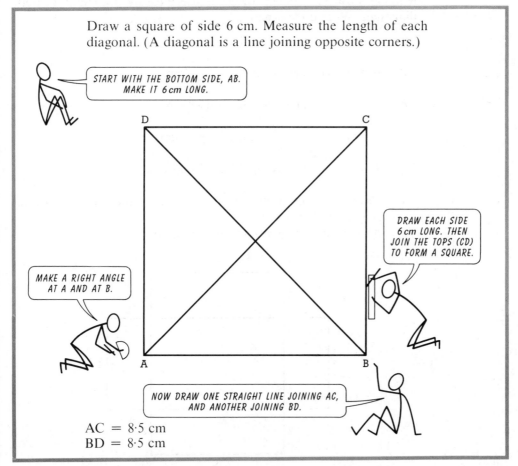

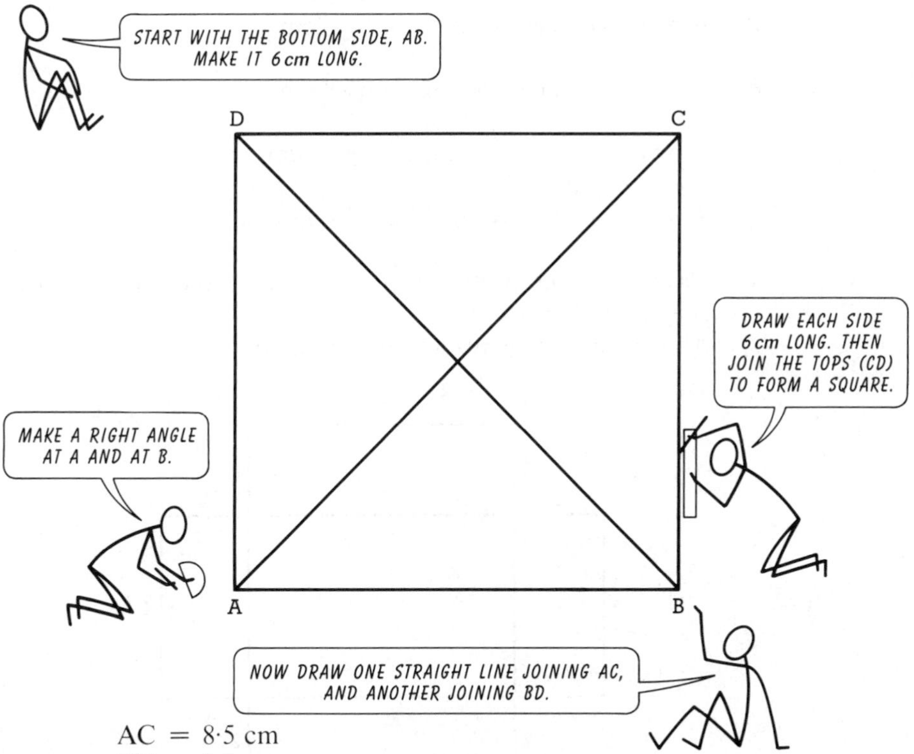

START WITH THE BOTTOM SIDE, AB. MAKE IT 6 cm LONG.
D
C
DRAW EACH SIDE 6 cm LONG. THEN JOIN THE TOPS (CD) TO FORM A SQUARE.
MAKE A RIGHT ANGLE AT A AND AT B.
A
B
NOW DRAW ONE STRAIGHT LINE JOINING AC, AND ANOTHER JOINING BD.

AC = 8·5 cm
BD = 8·5 cm

Use a ruler and protractor (or set square) to draw the following squares on plain paper. In each case record the length of one diagonal.

1. A square of side 5 cm.

2. A square of side 7 cm.

3. A square of side 6·5 cm.

4. A square of side 8 cm.

5. A square of side 10 cm.

Use a ruler and protractor (or set square) to draw the following rectangles on plain paper. In each case measure the length of both diagonals. What do you notice?

6. A rectangle measuring 4 cm by 3 cm.

7. A rectangle measuring 5 cm by 6 cm.

8. A rectangle measuring 6 cm by 8 cm.

9. A rectangle measuring 5 cm by 10 cm.

10. A rectangle measuring 7·5 cm by 12 cm.

11. Use a ruler and protractor (or set square) to draw the following shape on plain paper.
All the measurements are in centimetres.

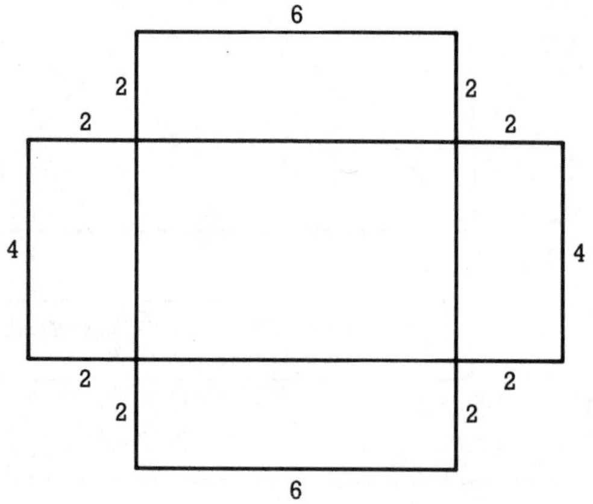

TRIANGLES

EXERCISE 23b

Draw this triangle full size.
60°
60°
8 cm
START WITH THIS SIDE. DRAW IT 8 cm LONG.
NOW USE A PROTRACTOR TO MEASURE AN ANGLE OF 60° AT A. THEN DO THE SAME AT B.
EXTEND THE LINES FORMING THE ANGLES UNTIL THEY MEET.
A
B

Use a ruler and protractor to draw the following triangles on plain paper.

1.

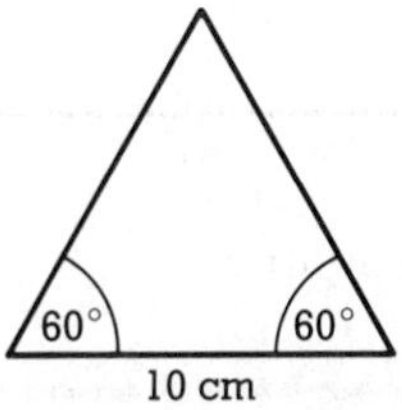

2.

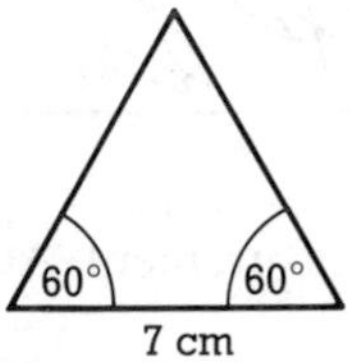

3.

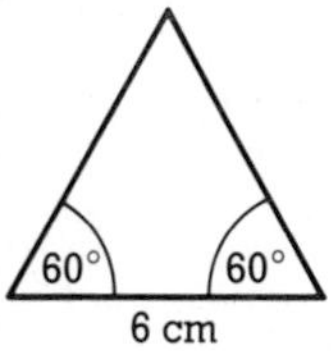

4. a) Measure each side of the triangle that you drew for Question 1. What do you notice?
b) Now do the same for the triangles in Questions 2 and 3. Does the same thing happen?

5. Draw this pattern. All the triangles are the same.

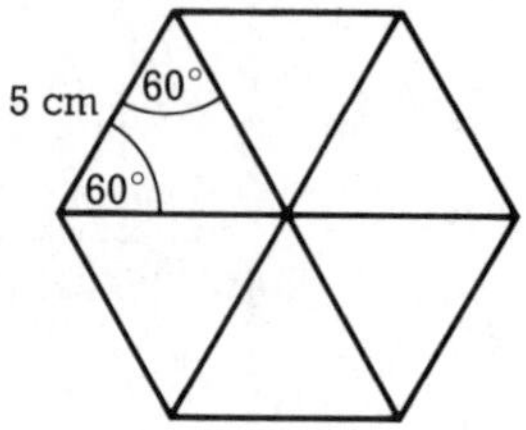

6. Make another pattern using the same basic triangle as given in Question 5. Draw at least six triangles.

a) Draw this triangle full size.
b) Measure the length of AC.

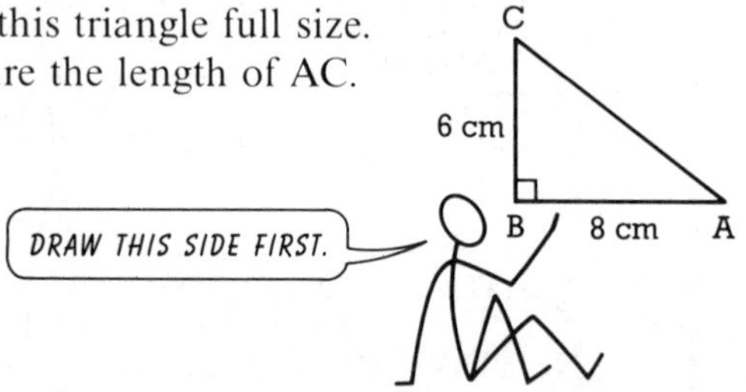

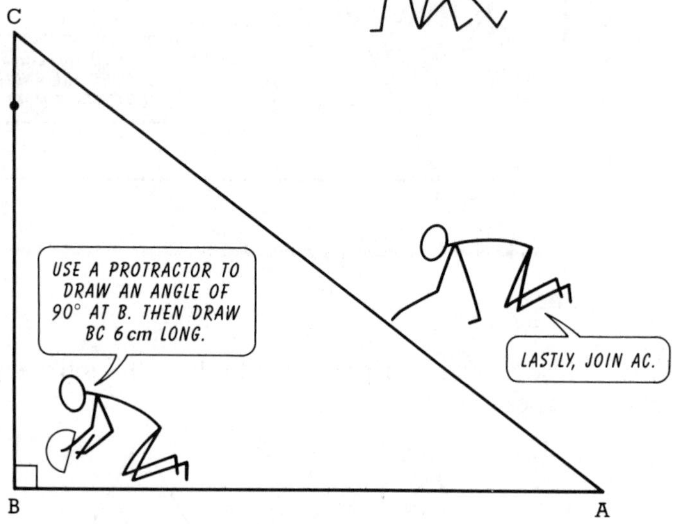
C
USE A PROTRACTOR TO DRAW AN ANGLE OF 90° AT B. THEN DRAW BC 6 cm LONG.
LASTLY, JOIN AC.
B
A

By measurement, AC is 10 cm long.

Draw the following triangles. In each case write down the length of the third side.

7.

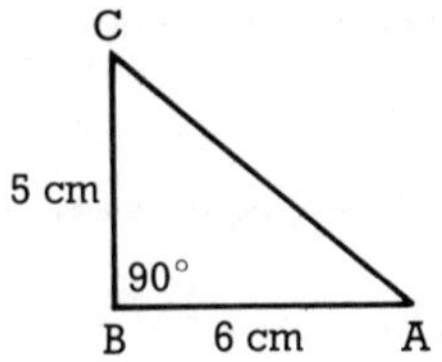

8.

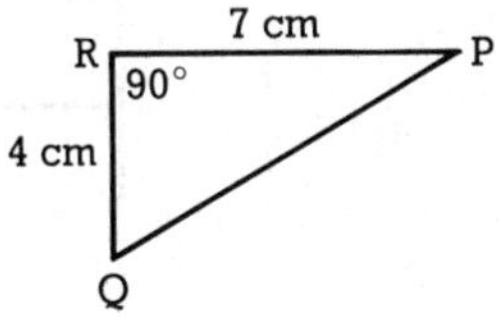

9.

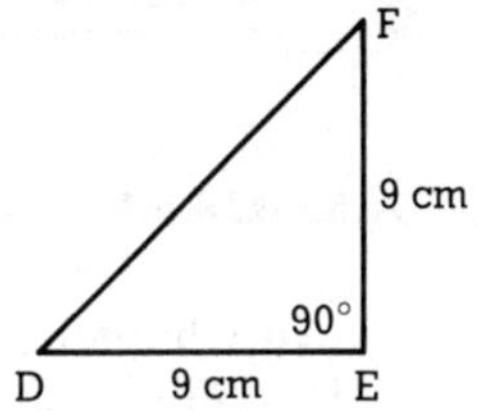

10.

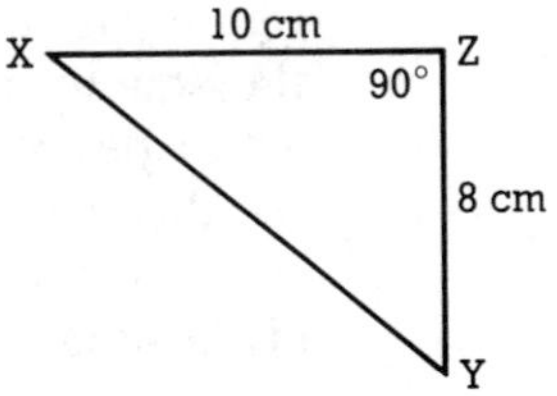

11. Draw this shape. Measure the length of AD.

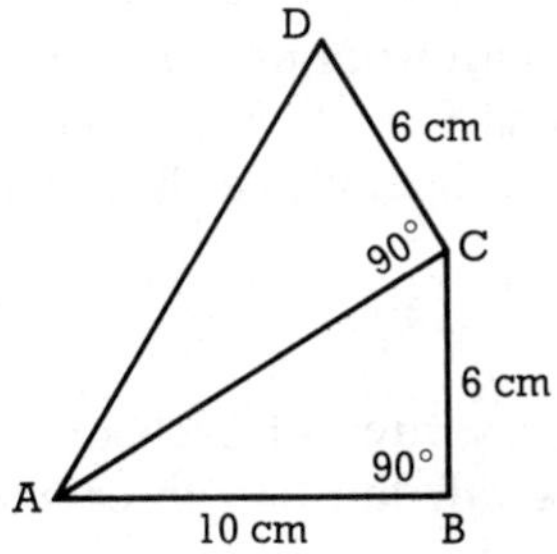

24 AREAS 2

AREA OF A SQUARE

In Chapter 14 we found areas by counting squares. Some areas can be calculated. The simplest figure where this can be done is the square. If we have a square with sides 3 cm long, it is easy to see that we must have 9 squares, each of side 1 cm, to cover the given square.

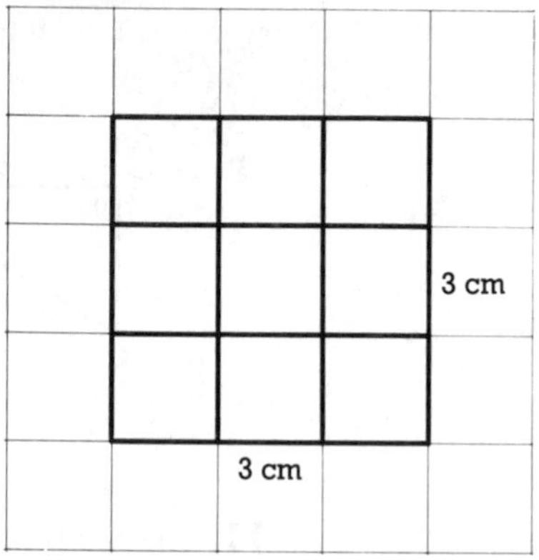

i.e. the area of a square of side 3 cm is 3×3 square centimetres

$= 9$ square centimetres

Now we can work out *without counting squares* the area of any square whose side is known. e.g. the area of a square of side 7 cm is 7×7 square centimetres, i.e. 49 square centimetres.

EXERCISE 24a What is the area of each of the following squares? State the units clearly. Draw the first three squares full size so that you can check your answer.

1. A square of side 2 cm.

2. A square of side 4 cm.

3. A square of side 5 cm.

4. A square of side 8 cm.

5. A square of side 6 m.

6. A square of side 10 mm.

7. A square of side 9 m.

8. A square of side 7 mm.

9. A square of side 2·5 cm.

10. A square of side 4·5 m.

11. A square of side 5·5 m.

12. A square of side 3·4 cm.

ABBREVIATIONS FOR UNITS OF AREA

To avoid writing out 'square centimetres' we use the short form 'cm^2'.

In the same way, 'm^2' means 'square metres'.

AREA OF A RECTANGLE

If we have a rectangle measuring 4 cm by 3 cm we need 3 rows, each containing 4 squares of side 1 cm, to cover it.

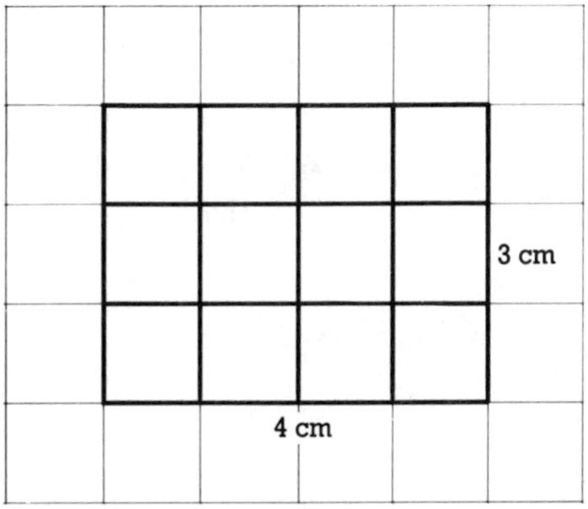

i.e. the area of the rectangle is $4 \times 3\ \text{cm}^2$

$$= 12\ \text{cm}^2$$

Draw other rectangles and find the area of each. All your results should indicate the fact that

Area = Length × Breadth

EXERCISE 24b

What is the area of this table mat?

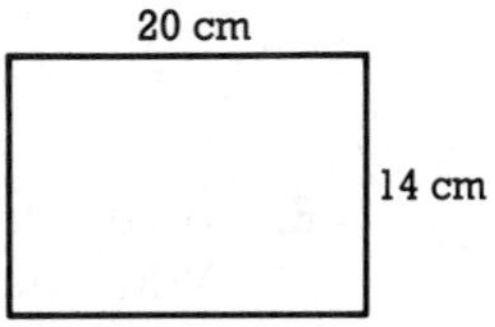

$$\text{Area} = 20 \times 14\ \text{cm}^2$$
$$= 280\ \text{cm}^2$$

1. What is the area of this photograph ?

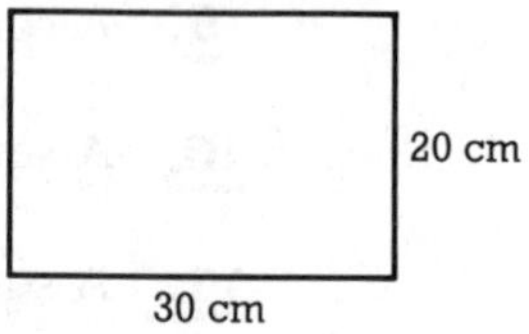

2. What is the area of this table top ?

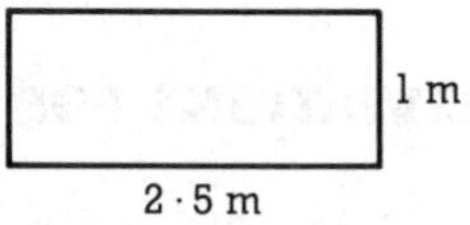

3. What is the area of the floor of this room ?

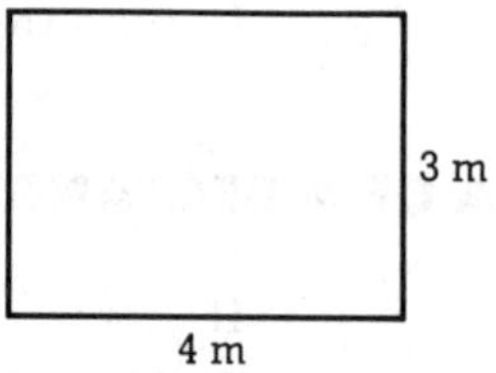

4. What is the area of this playing field ?

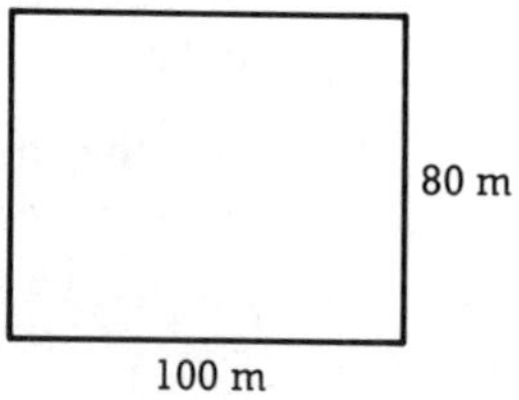

5. What is the area of this page from a book ?

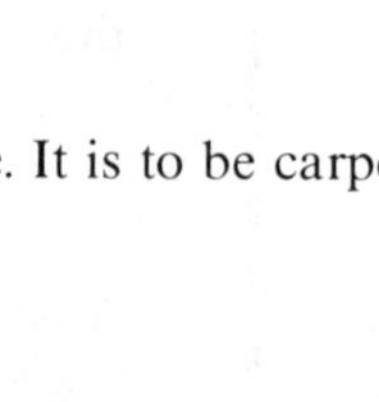

6. A corridor is 25 m long and 3 m wide. It is to be carpeted. What area of carpet is needed ?

7. An oil painting measures 30 cm by 24 cm. What area of canvas has been painted ?

8. A door measures 200 cm by 80 cm.
What is the area of one face?

9. A swimming pool is 50 m long and 20 m wide.
What is the area of the surface of the water?

10. Each playing card in a pack measures 9 cm by 6 cm.
What is the total area of card in a pack of 52 playing cards?

FINDING THE SIDE OF A SQUARE OF KNOWN AREA

The area of a square side 5 cm is 25 cm^2. Therefore the length of the side of a square whose area is 25 cm^2 is 5 cm.

EXERCISE 24c

The area of a square is 64 cm^2
What is the length of a side?

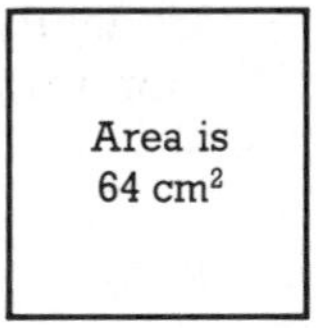

Since $64 = 8 \times 8$ the length of a side is 8 cm.

1. The area of a square piece of paper is 9 cm^2.
What is the length of one side?

2. The area of a square piece of land is 16 km^2.

a) What is the length of one side?
b) What is the perimeter of this square?

3. A square piece of piastic has an area of 100 mm^2.
What is the length of one side?

4. The area of a square paving slab is 1600 cm^2.
What is the length of one side?

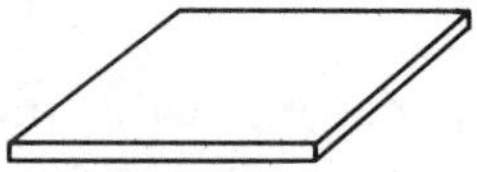

5. The area of a square table top is 1 m^2.

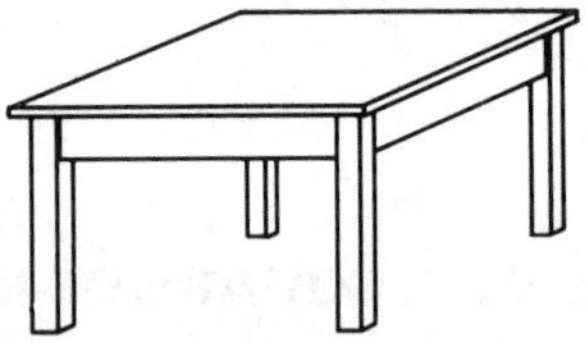

a) What is the length of one side?
b) What is the perimeter of the table top?

Sometimes the area of a square is such that the length of a side is not a whole number.

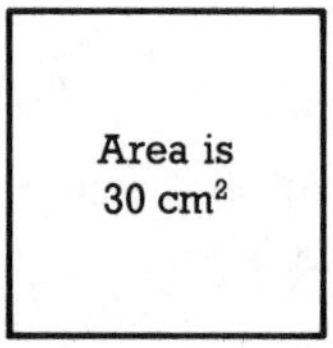

We know that a square of side 5 cm has an area of 25 cm^2 and a square of side 6 cm has an area of 36 cm^2. If the area is 30 cm^2 the length of a side is greater than 5 cm but less than 6 cm.

Use a calculator to find the whole number values between which the length of a side must lie.

Using a calculator,

$$6^2 = 36$$
$$7^2 = 49$$
$$8^2 = 64$$
$$9^2 = 81$$

75 is between 64 and 81.

Therefore the length of a side lies between 8 cm and 9 cm.

Use a calculator to answer Questions 6 to 9.

6. The area of a square table top is 120 sq cm.

a) Is each side more than 10 cm?

b) Is each side less than 11 cm?

7. The area of a square patio is 40 m^2.

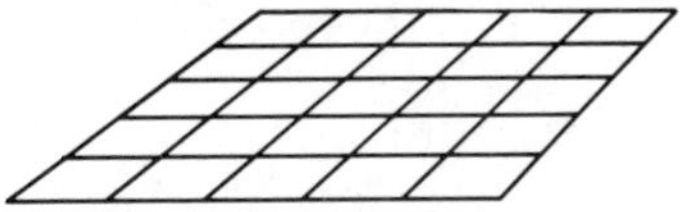

a) Is the length of a side more than 6 m?

b) Is the length of a side less than 7 m?

8. The area of a square floor tile is 500 cm^2.

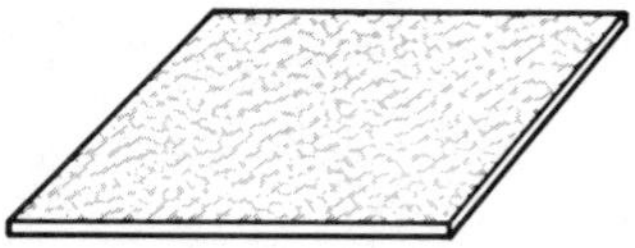

a) Is the length of a side more than 22 cm?

b) Is the length of a side less than 23 cm?

9. Hassan wants to find the side of a square that has an area of 200 m^2. Copy and complete this table.

Side of square (m)	Area (m^2)	Too small	Too big
10	100	√	
11			
12			
13			
14			
15			
16	256		√

Copy the two sentences given below and then fill in the blanks with two consecutive whole numbers.
The length of the side is greater than _____ m.
The length of the side is smaller than _____ m.

25 USING ARITHMETIC

USING A CALENDAR

A calendar gives the date of each day in the year.

Each year has 12 months.

The months of April, June, September and November have 30 days. February has 28 days except in leap years when it has 29 days. The other months of the year have 31 days.

Some people remember the number of days in each month by saying

Thirty days hath September
April, June and November
All the rest have thirty-one
Except for February alone
Which has twenty-eight days clear
And twenty-nine days each leap year

To give the date, we write (day number), (month), (year).

When we see the date 12 Feb 1990 it means the 12th day of February in the year 1990.

Sometimes the month number is given instead of its name. As February is the second month in the year, the date could be written 12.2.1990.

On many forms, the space given to fill in the date allows just two numbers each for (day), (month), (year). In this case, 12 Feb 1990 would be written as 12.02.90. Notice that when the day number or the month number is less than ten, a zero is put in the first space. The year number is reduced to two figures by missing out the century numbers.

If you ever receive letters from, or send letters to, the United States of America, you need to know that the convention there is to write the month first, followed by the day, then the year. A document from the USA dated 6.12.90 could mean 12th June 1990, or, if they have changed it around for our benefit, it would mean 6th December 1990! The way in which dates are written varies from country to country so it is sensible always to spell out the month and then there can be no misunderstanding.

EXERCISE 25a Use this calendar for 1990 to answer the questions.

	January	February	March	April
Sunday	7 14 21 28	4 11 18 25	4 11 18 25	1 8 15 22 29
Monday	1 8 15 22 29	5 12 19 26	5 12 19 26	2 9 16 23 30
Tuesday	2 9 16 23 30	6 13 20 27	6 13 20 27	3 10 17 24
Wednesday	3 10 17 24 31	7 14 21 28	7 14 21 28	4 11 18 25
Thursday	4 11 18 25	1 8 15 22	1 8 15 22 29	5 12 19 26
Friday	5 12 19 26	2 9 16 23	2 9 16 23 30	6 13 20 27
Saturday	6 13 20 27	3 10 17 24	3 10 17 24 31	7 14 21 28

	May	June	July	August
Sunday	6 13 20 27	3 10 17 24	1 8 15 22 29	5 12 19 26
Monday	7 14 21 28	4 11 18 25	2 9 16 23 30	6 13 20 27
Tuesday	1 8 15 22 29	5 12 19 26	3 10 17 24 31	7 14 21 28
Wednesday	2 9 16 23 30	6 13 20 27	4 11 18 25	1 8 15 22 29
Thursday	3 10 17 24 31	7 14 21 28	5 12 19 26	2 9 16 23 30
Friday	4 11 18 25	1 8 15 22 29	6 13 20 27	3 10 17 24 31
Saturday	5 12 19 26	2 9 16 23 30	7 14 21 28	4 11 18 25

	September	October	November	December
Sunday	2 9 16 23 30	7 14 21 28	4 11 18 25	2 9 16 23 30
Monday	3 10 17 24	1 8 15 22 29	5 12 19 26	3 10 17 24 31
Tuesday	4 11 18 25	2 9 16 23 30	6 13 20 27	4 11 18 25
Wednesday	5 12 19 26	3 10 17 24 31	7 14 21 28	5 12 19 26
Thursday	6 13 20 27	4 11 18 25	1 8 15 22 29	6 13 20 27
Friday	7 14 21 28	5 12 19 26	2 9 16 23 30	7 14 21 28
Saturday	1 8 15 22 29	6 13 20 27	3 10 17 24	1 8 15 22 29

What is the date of the last Wednesday in October?

FIRST FIND OCTOBER.

THEN GO ALONG THE WEDNESDAY LINE.

	September	October
Su	2 9 16 23 30	7 14 21 28
M	3 10 17 24	1 8 15 22 29
T	4 11 18 25	2 9 16 23 30
W	5 12 19 26	3 10 17 24 31
Th	6 13 20 27	4 11 18 25
F	7 14 21 28	5 12 19 26
S	1 8 15 22 29	6 13 20 27

The last Wednesday in October is the 31st day of October.

1. Is this the calendar for a leap year?

2. How many Saturdays are there in March?

3. What day of the week is

a) September 20th b) 3.5.1990 c) 04.12.90?

4. What is the date of the first Saturday in November?

5. How many Fridays are there in June?

6. What is the date of the last Friday in December?

7. What day of the week is

a) May 22nd b) 12.10.1990?

8. Peter goes on holiday on 4th August. He is spending 6 nights away.
What is the date of the day he comes home?

9. Which day of the week is

a) Christmas Day b) New Year's Eve?

10. Ruth's summer term ends on 25th July and the autumn term starts on 3rd September.

a) What day of the week is the first day of the autumn term?
b) How many Saturdays are there in the summer holiday?
c) How many complete weeks are there in the summer holiday?

11. Dean's spring term starts on 3rd January and ends on 6th April. He has a half-term holiday of one week. How many school days are there in this term? (School is open for five days a week.)

12. The application form for membership of a club has this line on it.

DATE OF BIRTH [ ][ ].[ ][ ].[ ][ ]
DAY MONTH YEAR

Write down the figures to be filled in for each of these dates of birth.

a) June 16th, 1965
b) 20 March, 1979
c) September 1st, 1956

THE TIME OF DAY

There are 24 hours in 1 day
60 minutes in 1 hour
60 seconds in one minute

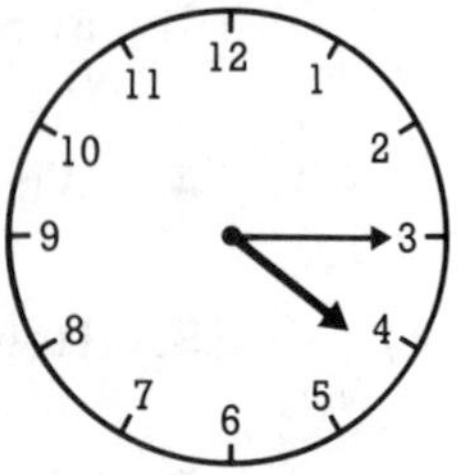

The day starts at midnight.

The twelve hours from midnight to noon (12 midday) are a.m. times.
For example, you may leave home at 8 a.m.

The twelve hours from noon to midnight are p.m. times.
For example, you may get home at 5 p.m.

Minutes are written after the hour. To write "five past eight in the morning" in figures, we write 8.05 a.m.

0 GOES IN HERE TO GIVE TWO FIGURES FOR THE MINUTES.

Notice that the figures after the point give the number of minutes; they are *not* decimal places.

EXERCISE 25b

Peter leaves home at 8.30 a.m. and returns at 4 p.m. For how long is he out of the house?

The time from 8.30 a.m. to 9 a.m. is 30 minutes.

12
6
FIRST FIND THE NUMBER OF MINUTES TO THE NEXT HOUR.

The time from 9 a.m. to noon is 3 hours.

The time from noon to 4 p.m. is 4 hours.

THEN COUNT THE WHOLE HOURS.

So Peter is out for (3 + 4) hours and 30 minutes,

i.e. for $7\frac{1}{2}$ hours.

1. A television programme starts at 7.50 p.m. and ends at 8.30 p.m. How long is the programme?

2. Sandra leaves home at 8 a.m. and returns at 3.30 p.m. For how long is she out of the house?

3. John goes to sleep at 9.30 p.m. and wakes up at 6.30 a.m. How many hours sleep does he have?

4. BBC 1 showed the following programmes on the evening of 17th July.

6.00 p.m.	*News*	8.00 p.m.	*The Lenny Henry Show*
6.30 p.m.	*Local Magazines*	8.30 p.m.	*Bread*
7.00 p.m.	*Wogan*	9.00 p.m.	*News*
7.35 p.m.	*Perfect Strangers*		

a) How long did *Wogan* last?

b) Anthea watched the six o'clock *News* and then did homework until the *Lenny Henry Show*. How long did she spend on homework?

c) How long does *Perfect Strangers* last?

d) Barry switched on the television for *Wogan* and turned it off halfway through *Bread*. How long was the television on for?

5. ITV showed the following programmes one Tuesday afternoon.

1.30 p.m.	*Santa Barbara*
2.00 p.m.	*TV Weekly*
2.30 p.m.	*Take the High Road*
3.00 p.m.	*Sounds Like Music*
3.25 p.m.	*News*
3.30 p.m.	*Sons and Daughters*
4.00 p.m.	*Oh! Mr Toad*
4.20 p.m.	*Phoenix Hall*
4.50 p.m.	*Scooby Doo*
5.10 p.m.	*Blockbusters*
5.40 p.m.	*News*

a) How long did *Phoenix Hall* last?

b) How long was it from the end of *TV Weekly* to the beginning of *Sons and Daughters*?

c) Sara watched *Scooby Doo* and *Blockbusters*. For how long was this?

d) Tim went out at the beginning of *Sons and Daughters* and got back at the end of *Oh! Mr Toad*. For how long was he out?

6. Here is part of a bus timetable showing the times of buses running from Apley to Newtown.

	a.m.	a.m.	a.m.	p.m.	p.m.
Apley	8.15	9.30	10.45	noon	2.30
Lock	8.45	10.15	11.30	12.45	3.20
Newtown	9.20	10.55	noon	1.30	4.08

Amy lives in Apley. She wants to get to Newtown by 11 a.m. Which bus should she catch?

LOOK ALONG THE NEWTOWN ROW. FIND THE ARRIVAL TIME CLOSEST TO 11 BUT BEFORE 11.
NOW LOOK UP THE COLUMN TO FIND THE TIME THAT THIS BUS LEAVES APLEY.

	a.m.	a.m.	a.m.	p.m.	p.m.
Apley	8.15	9.30	10.45	noon	2.30
Lock	8.45	10.15	11.30	12.45	3.20
Newtown	9.20	10.55	noon	1.30	4.08

Amy should catch the 9.30 a.m. bus.

a) At what time does the 8.15 a.m. bus from Apley arrive at Newtown?
b) How long does the 8.15 a.m. bus take to get to Newtown?
c) Raj catches the 10.15 a.m. bus from Lock. At what time does he arrive in Newtown?
d) How long does Raj's journey take?
e) Anne just missed the 11.30 a.m. from Lock. How long does she have to wait for the next bus?

7. The programme times at the local cinema are

1.55 p.m., 4.15 p.m., 6.25 p.m., 8.35 p.m.

a) Dawn went to the 4.15 p.m. programme and stayed until the start of the next programme. How long was she there?
b) About what time should the last programme end?

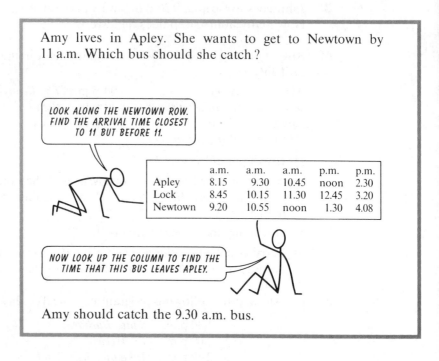

SPENDING MONEY

Most places where an entrance fee is charged, such as cinemas and swimming pools, show the admission charges clearly on a notice.

EXERCISE 25c

These are the admission charges at the local cinema. How much does Mr. Evans pay for himself, his two children and his mother who is over 60?

Adult:	£2·50
Over 60s:	£1·00
Child:	£1·50

Mr. Evans has to pay £2·50 for himself, £1·00 for his mother and 2 × £1·50 for his children.

He pays £2·50 + £1·00 + (2 × £1·50)
= £2·50 + £1·00 + £3·0
= £6·50

1. The admission charges at the swimming pool are

Adult: £2·00 Child: 75 p Spectator: 20 p

a) How much will it cost for one adult and two children to swim?

b) Mother, Father, John (who is six) and Grandmother to go to the swimming pool. Mother watches but everyone else swims. What do they have to pay to go in?

2. The charges at the ice-rink are

ADMISSION Adult: £1·50 Child: £1·00
SKATE HIRE: 80 p

a) How much does it cost two adults to go skating if they both take their own skates?

b) How much does it cost two children to go skating if they both hire skates?

c) What does Mrs Brown have to pay when she takes her two children skating if they all hire skates?

3. Three ten-year-olds go to an adventure playground.
How much do they have to pay to get in?

Adults: £1·00
Under 12: 75 p
Under 5: free

4. The admission charges for a concert are:

Adult: £12.00 Child: £6.00 OAP: £8.00

a) How much does it cost for two adults and their two children to go to the concert?
b) How much does it cost an Old Age Pensioner to take her three grandchildren to the concert?

TRAIN FARES

This is a train line in Newtown.

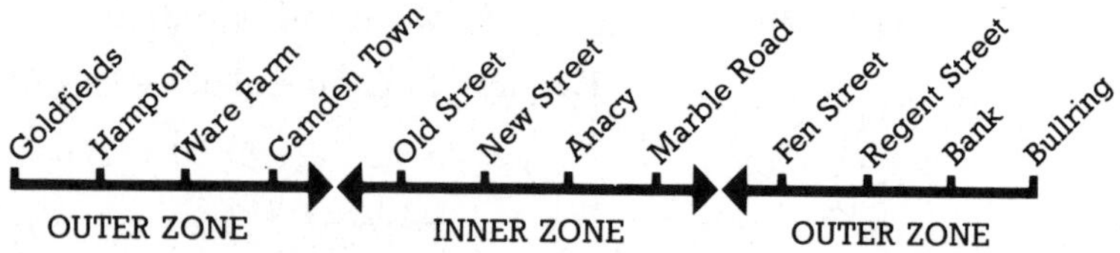

The fare is Adult £1·50 Child 50 p for each zone used.

If a zone is entered twice, it counts as two zones.

EXERCISE 25d

How much does it cost Peter, who is an adult, to travel from Hampton to Fen Street?

Peter starts in the outer zone, goes through the inner zone and gets off in the outer zone. He uses three zones, so his fare is $3 \times £1{\cdot}50 = £4{\cdot}50$.

1. Find the cost for an adult to travel from

a) Anacy to Marble Road
b) Bank to Camden Town
c) Ware Farm to Goldfields.

2. Find the cost for a child to travel from

a) Hampton to Marble Road
b) Bullring to Regent Street
c) Fen Street to Ware Farm.

3. Mr and Mrs Smith and their three children travel from Marble Road to Bank.
How much does it cost them?

4. Jane, who is an adult, goes out for the day with her younger sister, who is a child. They travel from their home at Bank to Anacy. On the way back, they travel from Marble Road back to Bank.
How much do their journeys cost?

5. Amjad, who is eleven, has to travel from Camden Town to school at Hampton and back again in the evening.

a) How much does it cost him each day?
b) How much does it cost him each week (five days)?
c) How much does he save if he buys a weekly ticket which costs £4·50?

6. Mr. Major leaves Old Street and travels to Regent Street. There he collects his two young children from the nearby Youth Club. All three of them catch the train at Regent Street and travel to Goldfields.
How much do these journeys cost Mr. Major altogether?

BUS FARES

Bridgetown has two kinds of buses.

One sort of bus is called a CITY HOPPA.
This does short journeys with lots of stops.

CITY HOPPA
ADULT: 50p CHILD: 20p

The other sort of bus is called a CITY LINER.
This does long journeys without many stops.

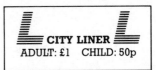

CITY LINER
ADULT: £1 CHILD: 50p

There is only one fare for any journey on a City Hoppa and only one fare for any journey on a City Liner.

EXERCISE 25e **1.** Mrs. Pimm takes her three children to school on a City Hoppa. How much does the journey to school cost her?

2. Stuart Robinson travels to and from work on a City Liner. He works six days each week.

a) What does he have to pay in fares each week?
b) A weekly bus pass would cost him £10·50. How much would he save if he got a weekly pass?

3. Karen, who is eleven, goes into the city centre. First she catches a City Liner, and then she ends her journey on a City Hoppa.
How much does her journey into town cost her?

4. A one-day bus pass costs £2·50 for an adult and it can be used on any kind of bus.
One day Paul, who is an adult, took a City Liner into town. While he was in town he had two rides on a City Hoppa. He then went home on a City Liner.
How much would he have saved if he had bought a one-day bus pass?

5. A one-day bus pass for a child costs 75 p. John, who is ten, travels into town on a City Liner. He then comes home by having four rides on City Hoppas.
How much does he save if he buys a one-day bus pass?